*A Laboratory Guide*

# Human Physiology
## *Concepts And Clinical Applications*

## Stuart Ira Fox, Ph.D.

**Pierce College**

## Fourth Edition

**wcb**
**Wm. C. Brown Publishers**
Dubuque, Iowa

**Book Team**

*Editor*
Edward G. Jaffe

*Developmental Editor*
Lynne M. Meyers

*Production Editor*
Kevin Campbell

*Designer*
Julie E. Anderson

*Permissions Editor*
Carla D. Arnold

*Photo Research Editor*
Shirley Charley

**wcb group**

Wm. C. Brown
*Chairman of the Board*

Mark C. Falb
*President and Chief Executive Officer*

**wcb**

**Wm. C. Brown Publishers, College Division**

G. Franklin Lewis
*Executive Vice-President, General Manager*

George Wm. Bergquist
*Editor in Chief*

Beverly Kolz
*Director of Production*

Chris C. Guzzardo
*Vice-President, Director of Sales and Marketing*

Bob McLaughlin
*National Sales Manager*

Julie A. Kennedy
*Production Editorial Manager*

Marilyn A. Phelps
*Manager of Design*

Faye M. Schilling
*Photo Research Manager*

# Contents

Preface   vii
Laboratory Safety   ix

Section **1** **Introduction: Structure and Physiological Control Systems**
**1**

Exercise **1.1** **Microscopic Examination of Cells   2**
   A.  The Inverted Image   2
   B.  The Metric System; Estimating the Size of Microscopic Objects   4
   C.  Microscopic Examination of Cheek Cells 5
   D.  Cell Structure and Cell Division   6

Exercise **1.2** **Microscopic Examination of Tissues and Organs   11**
   A.  Epithelial Tissue   11
   B.  Connective Tissues   12
   C.  Muscle Tissue   13
   D.  Nervous Tissue   14
   E.  An Organ: The Skin   17

Exercise **1.3** **Homeostasis and Negative Feedback 21**
   A.  Negative Feedback in a Constant-Temperature Water Bath   21
   B.  Resting Pulse Rate; Negative Feedback Control and Normal Range   22

Section **2** **Cell Function and Biochemical Measurements 27**

Exercise **2.1** **Measurements of Plasma Glucose, Protein, and Cholesterol   28**
   A.  Carbohydrates: Measurement of Plasma Glucose Concentration   31
   B.  Lipids: Measurement of Plasma Cholesterol Concentration   33
   C.  Proteins: Measurement of Plasma Protein Concentration   34

Exercise **2.2** **Thin-Layer Chromatography of Amino Acids   43**

Exercise **2.3** **Electrophoresis of Serum Proteins 47**

Exercise **2.4** **Measurements of Enzyme Activity 53**
   A.  Liver Catalase   54
   B.  Assay of Alkaline Phosphatase Activity: Effect of Enzyme Concentration and Incubation Time   54
   C.  Assay of Serum Transaminase Activity 57

Exercise **2.5** **Genetic Control of Metabolism   65**
   A.  Phenylketonuria   67
   B.  Alkaptonuria   67
   C.  Cystinuria   67

Exercise **2.6** **Diffusion, Osmosis, and Tonicity   71**
   A.  Solubility of Compounds in Polar and Nonpolar Solvents   72
   B.  Osmosis across an Artificial Semipermeable Membrane   72
   C.  Concentration and Tonicity   73

Section **3** **The Nervous System and Sensory Physiology 81**

Exercise **3.1 Recording the Action Potential 82**

Exercise **3.2 Electroencephalogram (EEG) 91**

Exercise **3.3 Reflex Arc 97**
 A. Tests for Spinal Nerve Stretch Reflexes 97
 B. A Cutaneous Reflex: The Babinski (Plantar) Reflex 100

Exercise **3.4 Cutaneous Receptors 103**
 A. Mapping the Temperature and Touch Receptors of the Skin 103
 B. The Two-Point Threshold in Touch Perception 104
 C. Adaptation of Temperature Receptors 105

Exercise **3.5 Referred Pain 109**

Exercise **3.6 Eyes and Vision 113**
 A. Refraction: Test for Visual Acuity and Astigmatism 113
 B. Accommodation 115
 C. The Extrinsic Muscles of the Eye and Nystagmus 116
 D. The Pupillary Reflex 117
 E. Examination of the Eye with an Ophthalmoscope 117
 F. The Blind Spot 118
 G. The Afterimage 119

Exercise **3.7 Ears and Hearing 123**
 A. Conduction of Sound Waves through Bone: Rinne and Weber's Tests 123
 B. Binaural Localization of Sound 125

Exercise **3.8 Vestibular Apparatus 129**

Exercise **3.9 Taste Buds 133**

Section **4** **Skeletal Muscles 137**

Exercise **4.1 Neural Control of Muscle Contraction 139**
 A. Frog Muscle Preparation 141
 B. Stimulation of Motor Nerve 142

Exercise **4.2 Summation, Tetanus, and Fatigue 147**
 A. Summation, Tetanus, and Fatigue in Frog Gastrocnemius Muscle 147
 B. Twitch, Summation, and Tetanus in Human Muscle 148

Exercise **4.3 Electromyogram (EMG) 151**
 A. Electromyogram during Arm Flexion and Extension 151
 B. Biofeedback and the Electromyograph 153

Section **5** **The Cardiovascular System 157**

Exercise **5.1 Effects of Drugs on the Frog Heart 158**
 A. Effect of Calcium Ions on the Heart 161
 B. Effect of Digitalis on the Heart 161
 C. Effect of Pilocarpine on the Heart 162
 D. Effect of Atropine on the Heart 162
 E. Effect of Potassium Ions on the Heart 162
 F. Effect of Epinephrine on the Heart 162
 G. Effect of Caffeine on the Heart 163
 H. Effect of Nicotine on the Heart 163

Exercise **5.2 Electrocardiogram 169**

Exercise **5.3 Effects of Exercise on the Electrocardiogram 177**

Exercise **5.4 Mean Electrical Axis of the Ventricles 181**

Exercise **5.5 Heart Sounds 187**
 A. Auscultation of Heart Sounds with the Stethoscope 187
 B. Correlation of the Phonocardiogram with the Electrocardiogram 188

Exercise **5.6 Measurements of Blood Pressure 193**

Exercise **5.7 Cardiovascular System and Physical Fitness 199**

Section **6** **Respiration and Metabolism 203**

Exercise **6.1 Measurements of Pulmonary Function 204**
 A. Measurement of Simple Lung Volumes and Capacities 207
 B. Measurement of Forced Expiratory Volume and Maximum Breathing Capacity 211

Exercise **6.2 Total Minute Volume and Oxygen Consumption: Effect of Exercise 225**

Exercise **6.3 Respiration and Acid-Base Balance 231**
    A.  The Ability of Buffers to Stabilize the pH of Solutions 232
    B.  The Effect of Exercise on the Rate of $CO_2$ Production 233
    C.  The Role of Carbon Dioxide in the Regulation of Ventilation 233

Section **7 Blood: Respiratory, Immune, and Clotting Functions 239**

Exercise **7.1 Hemoglobin and Oxygen Transport 241**
    A.  Red Blood Cell Count 242
    B.  Hematocrit 244
    C.  Hemoglobin Concentration 244
    D.  Calculation of Mean Corpuscular Volume (MCV) and Mean Corpuscular Hemoglobin Concentration (MCHC) 246

Exercise **7.2 Oxyhemoglobin Saturation 249**

Exercise **7.3 Total and Differential White Blood Cell Counts 255**
    A.  Total White Blood Cell Count 256
    B.  Differential White Blood Cell Count 256

Exercise **7.4 Coombs' Test for Antibodies on Red Blood Cells 263**

Exercise **7.5 Autoimmunity and the Test for Rheumatoid Factor 267**

Exercise **7.6 Clotting System 271**
    A.  Test for Prothrombin Time 272
    B.  Test for Activated Partial Thromboplastin Time (APTT) 272

Section **8 Renal Function and Homeostasis 277**

Exercise **8.1 Renal Regulation of Fluid and Electrolyte Balance 279**

Exercise **8.2 Urea Clearance Rate Measurement 285**

Exercise **8.3 Clinical Examination of the Urine 291**
    A.  Test for Proteinuria 292
    B.  Test for Glycosuria 292
    C.  Test for Ketonuria 292
    D.  Test for Hemoglobinuria 293
    E.  Test for Bilirubinuria 293
    F.  Microscopic Examination of Urine Sediment 293

Section **9 The Digestive System 299**

Exercise **9.1 Histology of the Gastrointestinal Tract, Liver, and Pancreas 302**
    A.  The Esophagus and Stomach 302
    B.  The Small and Large Intestines 304
    C.  The Liver 306
    D.  The Pancreas 307

Exercise **9.2 Digestion of Starch by Salivary Amylase 311**

Exercise **9.3 Digestion of Egg Albumin by Pepsin 315**

Exercise **9.4 Digestion of Fat by Pancreatic Juice and Bile 319**

Section **10 The Endocrine System, Reproduction, and Genetics 323**

Exercise **10.1 Histology of the Endocrine Glands 325**
    A.  The Ovary 325
    B.  The Testis 326
    C.  The Islets of Langerhans 327
    D.  The Adrenal Gland 328
    E.  The Thyroid 329
    F.  The Pituitary Gland 330

Exercise **10.2 Thin-Layer Chromatography of Steroid Hormones 335**

Exercise **10.3 Insulin Shock 341**

Exercise **10.4 Ovarian Cycle as Studied by a Vaginal Smear of the Rat 345**

Exercise **10.5 Human Chorionic Gonadotrophin and the Pregnancy Test 351**

Exercise **10.6 Patterns of Heredity 355**
    A.  Inheritance of PTC Taste 356
    B.  Inheritance of the Rh Factor 356
    C.  Inheritance of the ABO Antigen System 357
    D.  Sickle-Cell Anemia 357
    E.  Sex-Linked Traits: Inheritance of Color Blindness 358

Appendix 1 Basic Chemistry 365
Appendix 2 Sources of Equipment and Solutions 369
Credits 372
Index 373

Contents    v

# Preface

This guide provides the laboratory experiences required for a one-semester undergraduate course in human physiology. A wide variety of exercises is presented, which support most areas covered in a human physiology course; this gives instructors the flexibility to choose those exercises that are most appropriate for their courses. Background information that is needed to understand the principles and significance of each exercise is presented in a concise manner, so that little or no support is needed from the lecture text. Thus, although this laboratory guide complements *Human Physiology* by Stuart I. Fox particularly well, it can be used with any lecture text.

The laboratory experiences provided by this guide allow students to become familiar—in an intimate way that cannot be achieved by lecture and text alone—with many fundamental concepts of physiology. In addition to providing hands-on experience with the applications of physiological concepts, the laboratory sessions allow students to focus on specific concepts, to discuss issues related to these concepts, and to answer questions about these concepts in laboratory reports and in weekly quizzes.

Although most of the exercises in this guide are modern and clinically relevant, all can be performed by students who do not have a science background. All of these exercises have been student tested and in use for a number of years in human physiology courses. The equipment and solutions required for these exercises are readily available and can be purchased from national suppliers (appendix 2). Vivarium facilities are not needed, as the only animal experiments in this guide are those requiring the short-term use of pithed frogs. Whenever possible, exercises are provided that use the students themselves as the test subjects.

Each exercise in this guide is organized in the following manner:

1. Each exercise begins with a boxed inset that summarizes the **concepts** illustrated by the exercise in a concise manner. This allows students to understand the significance of the exercise.
2. **Learning objectives** are listed following the statement of concepts, so that students can have a reference to guide their learning during the performance of the exercise.
3. **Materials** required for the laboratory exercise are presented before the exercise to provide ease of setup.
4. An **introduction** to the exercise presents, in a concisely written manner, the information needed to understand the physiological significance of the exercise. This short section eliminates the need to consult the lecture text.
5. A boxed inset of **clinical significance** provides and emphasizes the practical relevance of the information presented.
6. The **procedure** is given in clear, easy-to-follow steps and is set off in a different color from the textual material. This allows students to easily locate the procedural directions during the performance of the exercise.
7. A **laboratory report** follows each exercise. Students enter data here when appropriate and answer questions. The questions in the laboratory report begin with the most simple form (objective questions) in most exercises and progress to essay questions. The essay questions are designed to stimulate conceptual learning and to maximize the educational opportunity provided by the laboratory experience.

I am indebted to my colleagues and students for their suggestions and encouragement in the development of these laboratory exercises. Mr. Edmont Katz was particularly instrumental in the development of some of the procedures that are new to this edition. I am very grateful for the editorial support given by Ed Jaffe and Lynne Meyers at Wm. C. Brown Publishers and for the fine copyediting provided by Elizabeth Blake. A special note of thanks is extended to the review panel, whose critical analysis, suggestions, and encouragement are greatly appreciated. These reviewers were Robert Anthony, Triton College; Michael R. Gilmartin, West Hills College; Charles Z. Leavell, Fullerton College; and Charles W. Porter, San Jose State University.

# Laboratory Safety

Most of the reagents (chemicals) and equipment in a physiology laboratory are potentially dangerous. This danger will not detract from the enjoyment and efficacy of the laboratory learning experience as long as some commonsense rules of laboratory safety are followed. Unfortunately, rules of behavior that seem obvious when read at the beginning of the course may be forgotten in the hustle (and, it is hoped, excitement) of the laboratory exercises. Therefore, the rules of laboratory safety should not simply be memorized but should become a habit.

1. Assume that all reagents are poisonous and act accordingly.

   **Do not** ingest any reagents;
   > eat, drink, or smoke in the laboratory;
   > carry reagent bottles around the room;
   > pipette anything by mouth unless specifically told to do so by your instructor.

   **Do** wash your hands thoroughly before leaving the laboratory;
   > stopper all reagent bottles when they are not in use;
   > thoroughly clean up spills;
   > wash reagents off yourself and your clothing if they spill on you, and immediately inform the instructor;
   > immediately inform the instructor if you accidentally get any reagent in your mouth; rinse your mouth thoroughly.

2. Follow the written instructions on procedure or the instructor's modifications of these instructions completely. **Do not** improvise unless the instructor specifically approves it.

3. Clean glassware at the end of each exercise so that residue from one exercise does not carry over to the next exercise.

4. Keep your work area clean, neat, and organized. This will reduce the chances of error and help make your work safer and more accurate.

5. Study the theory and procedures for the laboratory exercises before coming to the laboratory. This will increase your understanding, enjoyment, and safety during exercises. Confusion is dangerous.

6. **Do not** operate any equipment until you are instructed in its proper use. If you are unsure of the procedures, ask the instructor.

7. Be careful about open flames in the laboratory. **Do not** leave a flame unattended, **do not** light a Bunsen burner near any gas tank or cylinder, and **do not** move a lit Bunsen burner around on the desk. If you have long hair, be sure that it is well out of the way of the flame.

8. Always make sure that gas jets are off when you are not operating the Bunsen burner.

9. Handle hot glassware with a test-tube clamp or tongs.

10. Note the location of an emergency first aid kit, eyewash bottle, and fire extinguisher in the room. Report all accidents to the instructor immediately.

11. Wear safety glasses during those exercises in which glassware and solutions are heated with a Bunsen burner.

# Introduction: Structure and Physiological Control Systems

The **cell** is the basic unit of structure and function in the body. Each cell is surrounded by a *cell* (or *plasma*) *membrane* and contains specialized structures called *organelles* within the cell fluid, or *cytoplasm.* The structure and functions of a cell are largely determined by genetic information contained within the membrane-bound *nucleus.* This genetic information is coded by the chemical structure of *DNA,* which forms the major component of structures called *chromosomes* in the nucleus. Through genetic control of RNA and protein synthesis (described in section 2), DNA within the cell nucleus directs the functions of the cell and ultimately of the entire body.

Cells with similar specializations are grouped together to form **tissues,** and tissues are grouped together to form larger units of structure and function known as **organs.** Organs that are located in different parts of the body but that cooperate in the service of a common function are called **organ systems** (e.g., the cardiovascular system). Activities of cells, tissues, organs, and systems are coordinated by a great variety of regulatory mechanisms that act to maintain **homeostasis**—a state of dynamic constancy in the internal environment. Physiology is largely the study of the control mechanisms that participate in maintaining homeostasis.

# 1.1 Microscopic Examination of Cells

The microscope and the metric system are important tools in the study of cells. Cells contain numerous organelles with specific functions and are capable of reproducing themselves by mitosis. A special type of cell division called meiosis is used in the gonads to produce sperm or ova.

## Objectives

1. Identify the major parts of a microscope, and demonstrate proper technique in the care and handling of this instrument.
2. Define and interconvert different metric units.
3. Describe the general structure of a cell, and list the major organelles and their functions.
4. Explain the process and significance of mitosis and meiosis.

## Materials

1. Compound microscopes
2. Prepared microscope slides, clean slides, and cover slips (Note: slides with dots and lines can be prepared with dry transfer patterns used in art work.)
3. Lens paper
4. Methylene blue stain
5. Cotton-tipped applicator sticks

The microscope is undoubtedly the most basic and universally used instrument in the life science laboratory. The average microscope for student use includes the following parts (fig. 1.1):

1. Eyepiece with ocular lenses
2. Stage
3. Mechanical stage controls and mechanical stage
4. Substage condenser lens and iris diaphragm
5. Coarse and fine focus controls
6. Objective lenses on revolving nosepiece

## Care and Cleaning

Despite its rugged and simple appearance, the microscope is an expensive, delicate instrument. To maintain it in good condition, always follow these few simple rules.

1. Carry the microscope with two hands.
2. When using the coarse focus, always move the objective lens *away from the slide,* never toward the slide.
3. Clean the ocular and objective lenses with lens paper moistened with distilled *water or alcohol* before and after use. (Use alcohol if oil has been used with the oil-immersion lens. Use water at other times.)
4. Always leave the lowest power objective lens (usually 10×) facing the stage before putting the microscope away.

## A. The Inverted Image

Obtain a slide with the letter *e* mounted on it. Place the slide on the microscope stage, and rotate the nosepiece until the 10× objective clicks into the down position. Using the coarse adjustment, carefully lower the objective lens until it almost touches the slide. Now, looking through the ocular lens, slowly raise the objective lens until the letter *e* comes into focus.

### Procedure

1. If the visual field is dark, increase the light by adjusting the iris diaphragm. If there is still not enough light, move the condenser closer to the slide by rotating its control knob. Now bring the image into sharp focus using the fine focus control. Draw the letter *e* as it appears in the microscope.

2. While looking through the ocular lens, rotate the mechanical stage controls so that the mechanical stage moves to the right. In which direction does the *e* move?

**Figure 1.1.** The parts of a compound microscope.

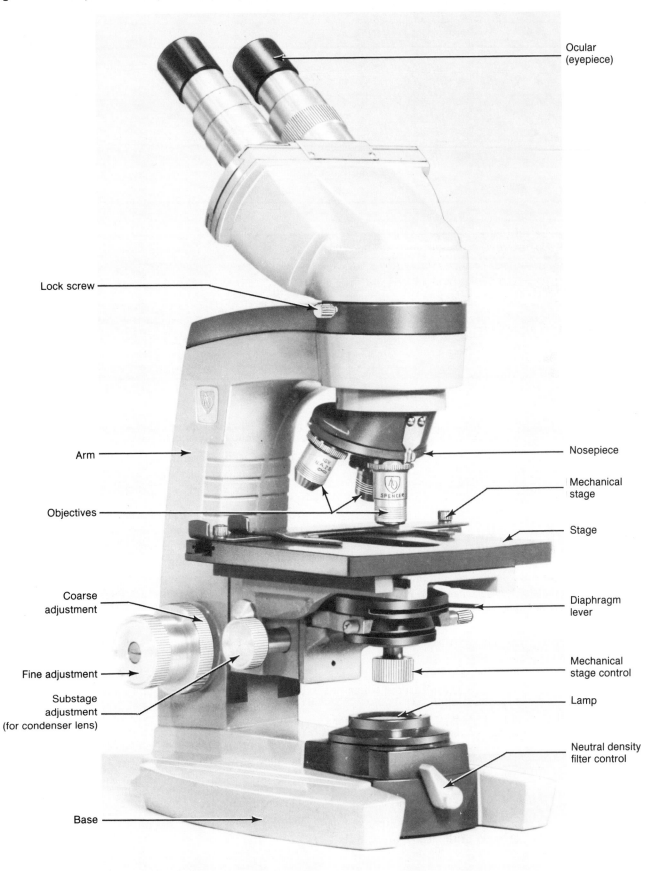

Ocular (eyepiece)

Lock screw

Arm

Objectives

Coarse adjustment

Fine adjustment

Substage adjustment (for condenser lens)

Base

Nosepiece

Mechanical stage

Stage

Diaphragm lever

Mechanical stage control

Lamp

Neutral density filter control

**Table 1.1**  SI unit prefixes.

| Multiplication Factor | | Prefix | Symbol | Term |
|---|---|---|---|---|
| 1,000,000 | = $10^6$ | Mega | M | One million |
| 1,000 | = $10^3$ | Kilo | k | One thousand |
| 100 | = $10^2$ | Hecto | h | One hundred |
| 10 | = $10^1$ | Deka | da | Ten |
| 0.1 | = $10^{-1}$ | Deci | d | One-tenth |
| 0.01 | = $10^{-2}$ | Centi | c | One-hundredth |
| 0.001 | = $10^{-3}$ | Milli | m | One-thousandth |
| 0.000001 | = $10^{-6}$ | Micro | $\mu$ | One-millionth |
| 0.000000001 | = $10^{-9}$ | Nano | n | One-billionth |
| 0.000000000001 | = $10^{-12}$ | Pico | p | One-trillionth |
| 0.000000000000001 | = $10^{-15}$ | Femto | f | One-quadrillionth |

**Table 1.2**  Sample metric conversions.

| To Convert From | To | Factor | Move Decimal Point |
|---|---|---|---|
| Meter (liter, gram) | Milli- | $\times$ 1000 ($10^3$) | 3 places to right |
| Meter (liter, gram) | Micro- | $\times$ 1,000,000 ($10^6$) | 6 places to right |
| Milli- | Meter (liter, gram) | $\div$ 1000 ($10^{-3}$) | 3 places to left |
| Micro- | Meter (liter, gram) | $\div$ 1,000,000 ($10^{-6}$) | 6 places to left |
| Milli- | Micro- | $\times$ 1000 ($10^3$) | 3 places to right |
| Micro- | Milli- | $\div$ 1000 ($10^{-3}$) | 3 places to left |

3. While looking through the ocular lens, rotate the mechanical stage controls so that the mechanical stage moves toward you. In which direction does the *e* move?

---

## B. The Metric System; Estimating the Size of Microscopic Objects

It is important in microscopy—as in other fields of science—to have units of measurement that are easy to use and easily interconverted. This is best accomplished using the **metric system** (from the Greek word *metrikos,* meaning "measure"), which was first developed in late eighteenth-century France. The modern definitions of the units used in the metric system are those adopted by the General Conference on Weights and Measures, which in 1960 established *Le Système international d'unités* (the International System of Units, or *SI*). The definitions for the metric units of length, mass, volume, and temperature are as follows:

**meter (m)**—unit of length equal to 1,650,763.73 wavelengths in a vacuum of the orange-red line of the spectrum of krypton-86

**gram (g)**—unit of mass based on the mass of 1 cubic centimeter ($cm^3$) of water at the temperature of its maximum density

**liter (L)**—unit of volume equal to 1 cubic decimeter ($dm^3$) or 0.001 cubic meter ($m^3$)

**Celsius (C)**—temperature scale in which 0° is the freezing point of water and 100° is the boiling point of water, which is equivalent to the centigrade scale

Conversions between different orders of magnitude in the metric system are based on powers of ten (table 1.1). You can thus convert from one order of magnitude to another simply by moving the decimal point the correct number of places to the right (for multiplying by whole numbers) or to the left (for multiplying by decimal fractions). This is illustrated in table 1.2.

### Dimensional Analysis

If you are unsure about the proper factor to use in making a metric conversion, a technique called dimensional analysis can be used. This technique is based on two principles:

1. Multiplying a number by 1 does not change the number.
2. A number divided by itself is equal to 1.

These principles can be used to change the units of any measurement.

## Example

Since 1 m is equivalent to 1,000 millimeters (mm),

$$\frac{1\text{m}}{1000\text{ mm}} = 1 \text{ and } \frac{1000\text{ mm}}{1\text{ m}} = 1$$

Suppose you want to convert 0.032 m to millimeters:

$$0.032\text{ m} \times \frac{1000\text{ mm}}{1\text{ m}} = 32.0\text{ mm}$$

Notice that in dimensional analysis the problem is set up so that the unwanted units cancel each other. This technique is particularly useful when the conversion is more complex or when some of the conversion factors are unknown.

## Example

Suppose you want to convert 0.1 milliliter (ml) to microliter ($\mu$l) units. If you remember that 1 ml = 1,000 $\mu$l, you can set up the problem as follows:

$$0.1\text{ ml} \times \frac{1000\text{ }\mu\text{l}}{1\text{ ml}} = 100\text{ }\mu\text{l}$$

If you only remember that a milliliter is one-thousandth of a liter and that a microliter is one-millionth of a liter, you can set up the problem in this way:

$$0.1\text{ ml} \times \frac{1.0\text{ L}}{1000\text{ ml}} \times \frac{1000000\text{ }\mu\text{l}}{1.0\text{ L}} = 100\text{ }\mu\text{l}$$

## Visual Field and the Estimation of Microscopic Size

If the magnification power of your ocular lens is 10$\times$ and you use the 10$\times$ objective lens, the total magnification of the visual field is 100$\times$. At this magnification, the diameter of the visual field is approximately 1,600 micrometers ($\mu$m).

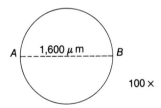

You can estimate the size of an object in the visual field by comparing it with the total diameter of the visual field.

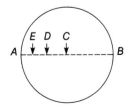

How long is line *AC* in micrometers? _____
How long is line *AD* in micrometers? _____
How long is line *AE* in micrometers? _____

The diameter of the field of vision using the 45$\times$ objective lens (total magnification 450$\times$) is approximately 356 micrometers. Using the same diagram and procedure that you used for the 100$\times$ power, answer the following questions.

How long is line *AC* in micrometers? _____
How long is line *AD* in nanometers (nm)? _____

---

### Procedure

Obtain from the instructor a slide that contains a pattern of small dots and a pattern of thin lines.

1. Using the 10$\times$ objective lens,
   a) estimate the diameter of one dot: _____ $\mu$m;
   b) estimate the distance between the edges of two adjacent dots: _____ $\mu$m.
2. Using the 45$\times$ objective lens,
   a) estimate the width of one line: _____ $\mu$m;
   b) estimate the distance between the edges of two adjacent lines: _____ $\mu$m.

## C. Microscopic Examination of Cheek Cells

The surfaces of the body are covered and lined with epithelial membranes (one of the primary tissues described in exercise 1.2). In membranes that are several cell layers thick, such as the membrane lining of the cheeks, the cells are continuously lost from the surface and replaced through cell division in deeper layers. The cells in the outer layer of epithelial tissue in the cheeks are still alive; this differs from the cells in the outer layer of the epidermis of the skin, which die before they are lost. You can therefore easily collect and observe living human cells by simply rubbing the inside of the cheeks.

Most living cells are difficult to observe under the microscope unless they are stained. In this exercise, the stain methylene blue will be used. This stain is positively charged and combines with negative charges in the chromosomes to stain the nucleus blue. The cytoplasm contains a lower concentration of negatively charged organic molecules and thus appears almost clear.

---

### Procedure

1. Rub the inside of one cheek with the cotton tip of an applicator stick.
2. Press the cotton tip of the applicator stick against a clean glass slide. Maintaining pressure, rotate the cotton tip against the slide, and then push the cheek smear across the slide for about ½ inch.

**Figure 1.2.** The cell.

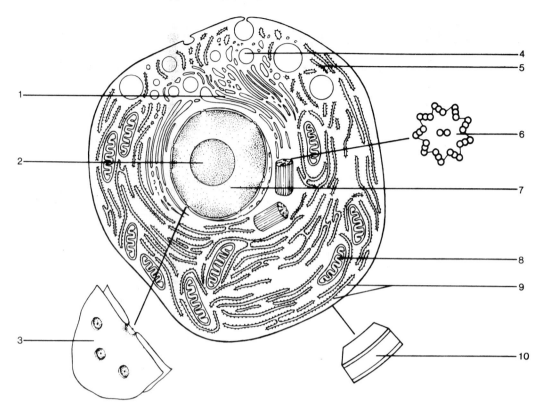

1. Golgi apparatus
2. Nucleolus
3. Nuclear envelope
4. Lysosome
5. Endoplasmic reticulum

6. Centriole
7. Nucleus
8. Mitochondria
9. Ribosomes
10. Plasma membrane

3. Observe the unstained cells under 100× and 450× power.
4. Remove the slide from the microscope, and over a sink or special receptacle, place a drop of methylene blue stain on the smear.
5. Place a cover slip over the stained smear, and again observe the cheek cells at 100× and 450× power.

## D. Cell Structure and Cell Division

Cells vary greatly in size and shape. The largest cell, an ovum (egg cell), is barely visible to the unaided eye; other cells can only be observed through a microscope. Each cell has an outer *plasma membrane* (or cell membrane) and generally one *nucleus,* surrounded by *cytoplasm.* Within the nucleus and cytoplasm are a variety of subcellular structures, called **organelles** (fig. 1.2). The major organelles and their principal functions are listed in table 1.3.

The process of cell division, or replication, is called **mitosis** (fig. 1.3). This process allows new cells to be formed to replace those that are dying and also permits body growth.

Mitosis consists of a sequence of stages (table 1.4) in which both the nucleus and cytoplasm of a cell split to form two identical *daughter cells.* In the process of mitotic cell division the chromosomes (containing the genes) duplicate, and each of the duplicate sets go to each of the daughter cells. The daughter cells therefore have the same number of chromosomes as the parent cell (forty-six in humans).

The forty-six chromosomes in most human cells actually represent twenty-three pairs of chromosomes; one set of twenty-three was inherited from the mother and the other set of twenty-three from the father. A cell with forty-six chromosomes is said to be *diploid,* or *2N.* In the process of gamete (sperm and ova) production in the gonads (the testes and ovaries), cells undergo a type of division

**Table 1.3** Structure and function of cellular components.

| Component | Structure | Function |
|---|---|---|
| Plasma membrane | Membrane composed of phospholipid and protein molecules | Gives form to cell and controls passage of materials in and out of cell |
| Cytoplasm | Jellylike substance in which organelles are suspended | Serves as matrix substance in which chemical reactions occur |
| Endoplasmic reticulum | System of interconnected membrane-forming canals and tubules | Supporting framework within cytoplasm; transports materials and provides attachment for ribosomes |
| Ribosomes | Granular particles composed of protein and RNA | Synthesize proteins |
| Golgi apparatus | Cluster of flattened, membranous sacs | Synthesizes carbohydrates and packages molecules for secretion; secretes lipids and glycoproteins |
| Mitochondria | Membranous sacs with folded inner partitions | Release energy from food molecules and transform energy into usable ATP |
| Lysosomes | Membranous sacs | Digest foreign molecules and worn and damaged cells |
| Peroxisomes | Spherical membranous vesicles | Contain certain enzymes; form hydrogen peroxide |
| Centrosome | Nonmembranous mass of two rodlike centrioles | Helps to organize spindle fibers and distribute chromosomes during mitosis |
| Vacuoles | Membranous sacs | Store and excrete various substances within cytoplasm |
| Fibrils and microtubules | Thin, hollow tubes | Support cytoplasm and transport materials within cytoplasm |
| Cilia and flagella | Minute cytoplasmic extensions from the cell | Move particles along surface of cell or move cell |
| Nuclear membrane | Membrane surrounding nucleus, composed of protein and lipid molecules | Supports nucleus and controls passage of materials between nucleus and cytoplasm |
| Nucleolus | Dense, nonmembranous mass composed of protein and RNA molecules | Forms ribosomes |
| Chromatin | Fibrous strands composed of protein and DNA molecules | Controls cellular activity for carrying on life processes |

**Table 1.4** Major events in mitosis.

| Stage | Major Events |
|---|---|
| Prophase | Chromosomes form from the chromatin material, centrioles migrate to opposite sides of the nucleus, the nucleolus and nuclear membrane disappear, and spindles appear and become associated with centrioles and centromeres. |
| Metaphase | Duplicated chromosomes align themselves on the equatorial plane of the cell between the centrioles, and spindle fibers become attached to duplicate parts of chromosomes. |
| Anaphase | Duplicated chromosomes separate, and spindles shorten and pull individual chromosomes toward the centrioles. |
| Telophase | Chromosomes elongate and form chromatin threads, nucleoli and nuclear membranes appear for each chromosome mass, and spindles disappear. |

called **meiosis.** During meiosis each cell divides twice, and the daughter cells (the gametes) get only one set of twenty-three chromosomes; they are said to be *haploid,* or *1N.* In this way the original diploid number of forty-six chromosomes can be restored when the sperm and egg unite in fertilization.

### Procedure

1. Study figure 1.2, and write in the labels for the organelles without looking at the legend below.
2. Examine a slide of a whitefish blastula (early embryo), and observe the different stages of mitosis.

**Figure 1.3.** The sequence of mitosis.

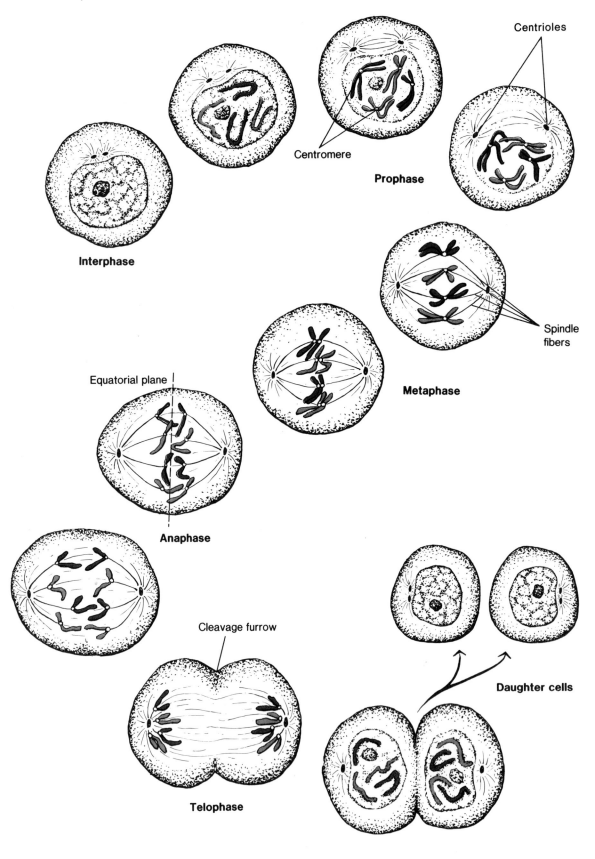

Centrioles

Centromere

**Prophase**

Spindle
fibers

**Interphase**

**Metaphase**

Equatorial plane

**Anaphase**

Daughter cells

Cleavage furrow

**Telophase**

# Laboratory Report 1.1

Name _____

Date _____

Section _____

1. Give the total magnification when you use the

   (a) low-power objective lens _____

   (b) high-dry power objective lens _____

   (c) oil-immersion objective lens _____

2. Give the following metric units for

   (a) the weight of one cubic centimeter of water at its maximum density _____

   (b) the temperature at which water freezes _____

   (c) the unit of volume equal to 0.001 cubic meter _____

3. Match the following equivalent measurements.

   ___ (1) 100 ml                         (a) 100 $\mu$l
   ___ (2) 0.10 ml                       (b) 0.00001 L
   ___ (3) 0.0001 ml                    (c) 1.0 dl
   ___ (4) 0.01 ml                       (d) 100 nl

4. Identify the organelle that has the following function:

   (a) a prominent role in cell division _____

   (b) the major site of energy production in the cell _____

   (c) a system of membranous tubules in the cytoplasm _____

   (d) the location of genetic information _____

   (e) the vesicle that contains digestive enzymes _____

   (f) the site of protein synthesis _____

5. Match the following events of mitosis with the name of the stage.

   ___ (1) the nuclear membrane disappears; spindles      (a) metaphase
           appear                                         (b) telophase
   ___ (2) chromosomes line up at the equator of the       (c) anaphase
           cell                                            (d) prophase
   ___ (3) duplicated chromosomes separate and are
           pulled toward the centrioles
   ___ (4) chromosomes elongate into threads; nuclear
           membranes reappear

6. Compare and contrast mitosis and meiosis in terms of where and when they occur, their end products, and their significance.

# Microscopic Examination of Tissues and Organs

The body is composed of only four primary tissues. An organ consists of different tissues that are specialized to provide services needed for the function of the organ.

## Objectives

1. Define the terms *tissue* and *organ*.
2. Provide the distinguishing characteristics of the four primary tissues.
3. Describe and identify the subcategories of the primary tissues.
4. Correlate the structures of tissues with their functions.

## Materials

1. Compound microscopes
2. Lens paper
3. Prepared microscope slides of tissues

The human body is composed of trillions of cells, each with many common features. Even though all cells have basic similarities, they differ considerably in size, structure, and function. Furthermore, cells neither function in isolated units nor are they haphazardly arranged in the body. An aggregation of cells that are similar in structure and that work together to perform a specialized activity is referred to as a *tissue*. Groups of tissues that occur and function together constitute *organs*.

Tissues are classified into four principal types, or **primary tissues.** The four primary tissues are (1) *epithelial,* (2) *connective,* (3) *muscular,* and (4) *nervous.*

## A. Epithelial Tissue

Epithelial tissue, or *epithelium* (*epi* = upon; *thelium* = to cover), functions to protect, secrete, or absorb. Epithelial membranes cover and line the body cavities; they cover the outer surface of the body (the epidermis of the skin) and the surface of internal organs; they line the lumina (the hollow portion) of ducts, vessels, and tubes. All glands are derived from epithelial tissue. All epithelial tissues share the following characteristics:

1. The cells are closely joined together and have little intercellular substance (matrix) between them.
2. There is an exposed surface either externally or internally.
3. A *basement membrane* is present to anchor the epithelium to underlying connective tissue.

Epithelial tissues may be classified as *simple,* if they are only one layer thick, or *stratified,* if they are two or more layers thick. Epithelial tissues may be further classified by the shape of their surface cells as *squamous* (if the cells are flat), *cuboidal,* or *columnar.* Using these criteria, one can identify the following types of epithelia:

1. **Simple squamous epithelium** (fig. 1.4). This type is found where the diffusion or filtration of molecules and ions is needed, as in parts of the kidney and in the lining, or *endothelium,* of blood vessels.
2. **Stratified squamous epithelium** (fig. 1.4). This is found in areas that receive a lot of wear and tear; the outer cells are sloughed off and replaced by new cells, produced by mitosis in the deeper layers. Stratified squamous epithelium is found in the mouth, esophagus, nasal cavity, and in the opening into the ears, anus, and vagina. A special *keratinized,* or *cornified,* layer of dead surface cells is found in the stratified epithelium of the skin (the epidermis).
3. **Cuboidal epithelium** (fig. 1.4). This type of epithelium is usually simple and lines the surface of many ducts and tubules.
4. **Columnar epithelium** (fig. 1.5). This simple epithelium of columnar cells is found in the lining of the gastrointestinal tract, where it is specialized for absorption of the products of digestion. It also contains mucus-secreting *goblet cells.*

**Figure 1.4.** Epithelial tissues.

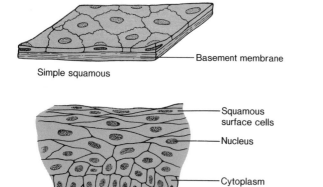

Simple squamous

— Basement membrane

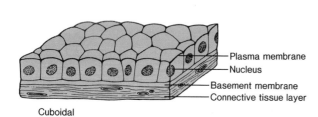

— Squamous surface cells

— Nucleus

— Cytoplasm

— Mitotically active germinal layer

— Basement membrane

Stratified squamous

— Plasma membrane

— Nucleus

— Basement membrane

— Connective tissue layer

Cuboidal

5. **Ciliated columnar epithelium.** These columnar cells contain hairlike *cilia* on the exposed surface. This tissue is found in the uterine tubes of the female and the ductus deferens (vas deferens) of the male.
6. **Pseudostratified columnar epithelium** (fig. 1.5). Found in the respiratory passages of the trachea and bronchial tubes, this epithelium is really simple but appears stratified because the nuclei are at different levels. This type also contains cilia.
7. **Transitional epithelium** (fig. 1.5). It is found in the urinary bladder and is uniquely stratified to allow periodic distension.

## Procedure

1. Observe slides of the mesentery, esophagus, skin, pancreas, ductus deferens or uterine tube, trachea, and urinary bladder.
2. Identify the type of epithelium in each of the slides.

## B. Connective Tissues

Connective tissue is characterized by abundant amounts of extracellular material, or *matrix.* Unlike epithelial tissue, therefore, the cells of connective tissue (which may be of many types) are spread out from each other. The large extracellular spaces in connective tissue provide room for blood vessels and nerves to enter and leave organs.

**Figure 1.5.** Epithelial tissues: columnar and transitional.

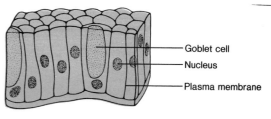

— Goblet cell

— Nucleus

— Plasma membrane

Simple columnar

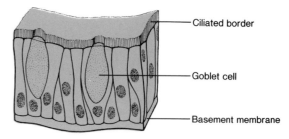

— Ciliated border

— Goblet cell

— Basement membrane

Pseudostratified ciliated columnar

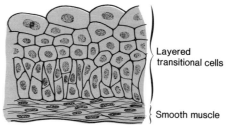

Layered transitional cells

Smooth muscle

Transitional

There are five major types of connective tissues: (1) *mesenchyme,* an undifferentiated tissue found primarily during embryonic development; (2) *connective tissue proper;* (3) *cartilage;* (4) *bone;* and (5) *blood.*

**Connective tissue proper** (fig. 1.6) is a broad category of tissues with a somewhat loose, flexible matrix. This tissue may be *loose (areolar),* which serves as a general packaging material, or *dense,* as is found in tendons and ligaments. The degree of denseness relates to the concentration of protein fibers versus fluid in the matrix. Protein fibers may be made of *collagen,* which provides the tensile strength of tendons and ligaments; they may be *elastic fibers,* which are prominent in large arteries and the lower respiratory system; or they may be *reticular,* giving structural support to the lymph nodes, liver, spleen, and bone marrow. *Adipose tissue* is a type of connective tissue in which the cells are specialized to store fat.

**Cartilage** consists of cells called *chondrocytes* and a semisolid matrix, which imparts strength and elasticity to the tissue. There are three types of cartilage (fig. 1.7): (1) *hyaline cartilage* has a clear matrix that stains a uniform blue; this is the most abundant form of cartilage,

**Figure 1.6.** Connective tissue proper.

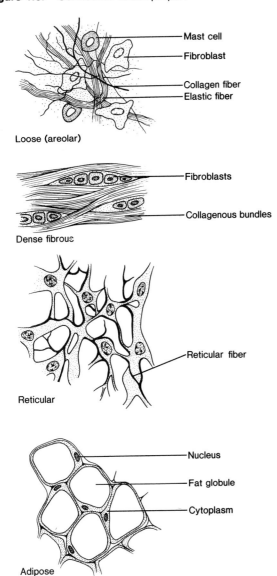

Loose (areolar)
- Mast cell
- Fibroblast
- Collagen fiber
- Elastic fiber

Dense fibrous
- Fibroblasts
- Collagenous bundles

Reticular
- Reticular fiber

Adipose
- Nucleus
- Fat globule
- Cytoplasm

**Figure 1.7.** Cartilage tissue.

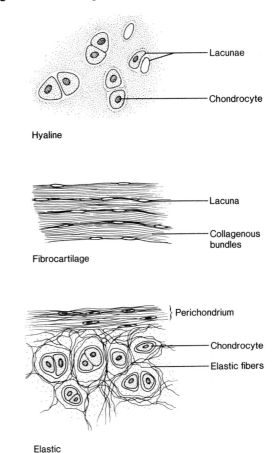

Hyaline
- Lacunae
- Chondrocyte

Fibrocartilage
- Lacuna
- Collagenous bundles

Elastic
- Perichondrium
- Chondrocyte
- Elastic fibers

found in the articular surfaces of bones, the trachea and bronchi, the nose, and the costal cartilages between the ventral ends of the first ten ribs and the sternum; (2) *fibrocartilage* is reinforced with collagen fibers to resist compression; it is found in the symphysis pubis where the two pelvic bones articulate and between the vertebrae where it forms intervertebral discs; and (3) *elastic cartilage* contains abundant elastic fibers for flexibility; it is found in the external ear, portions of the larynx, and in the auditory canal (eustachian tube).

**Bone** (see fig. 1.10*h*) contains cells called *osteocytes,* surrounded by an extremely hard matrix impregnated with calcium phosphate. The osteocytes surround a *central canal,* containing blood vessels, and obtain nourishment via small channels in the matrix, called *canaliculi.*

**Blood** is considered to be a type of connective tissue because it contains abundant extracellular material—the fluid *plasma*—which suspends and transports the blood cells (*erythrocytes, leukocytes,* and *thrombocytes*). The composition of blood will be described in more detail in later exercises.

### Procedure

1. Observe slides of skin, mesentery, a tendon, the spleen, cartilage, and bone.
2. Identify the types of connective tissue in each slide.

## C. Muscle Tissue

Muscles are responsible for the movement of materials through the body, the movement of one part of the body with respect to another, and for locomotion. Muscle tissues, which are contractile, are composed of cells, called *fibers,* that are elongated in the direction of contraction. There are three types of muscle tissues (fig. 1.8): *smooth, cardiac,* and *skeletal.*

**Figure 1.8.** Muscular tissue.

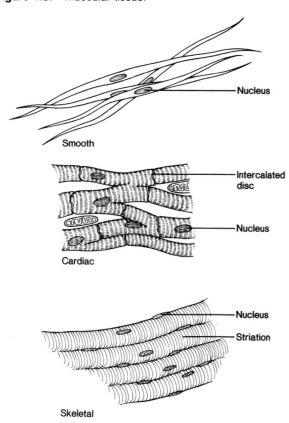

Smooth

Intercalated disc

Nucleus

Cardiac

Nucleus
Striation

Skeletal

**Figure 1.9.** (a) a photomicrograph of neurons in the spinal cord (100×); (b) a diagram of the parts of a neuron.

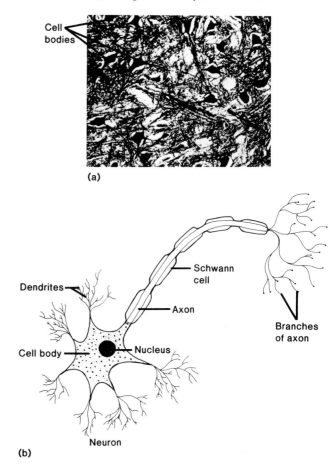

Cell bodies

(a)

Dendrites

Schwann cell

Axon

Branches of axon

Cell body

Nucleus

Neuron

(b)

**Smooth muscle** cells are long and spindle shaped, with a single nucleus near the center. They are found in the digestive tract, blood vessels, respiratory passages, and the walls of the urinary and reproductive ducts. **Cardiac muscle** is found in the heart; its cells are branched and interconnected by *intercalated discs.* **Skeletal muscle,** which is attached to the skeleton, is responsible for voluntary movements. Skeletal muscle fibers are long and thin and contain numerous nuclei. Both skeletal muscle fibers and cardiac muscle cells are included in the category of *striated muscle,* because they contain cross-striations. Skeletal muscle is under voluntary control, whereas cardiac and smooth muscles are classified as involuntary. (These differences relate to the type of innervation and not to the characteristics of the muscles themselves.)

**Procedure**

1. Observe prepared slides of smooth, cardiac, and skeletal muscle.
2. Identify the major distinguishing features of each type of muscle.

## D. Nervous Tissue

Nervous tissue, comprising the nervous system, consists of two major types of cells. The nerve cell, or **neuron** (fig. 1.9), is the functional unit of the nervous system. The typical neuron has a *cell body* with a nucleus, small projections called *dendrites* extending from the cell body, and a single long extension called an *axon,* or *nerve fiber.* The neuron is capable of producing and conducting electrical impulses and of releasing chemicals from the endings of axon branches. A second type of cell found in the nervous system is a **neuroglial cell;** these cells support the neurons both structurally and functionally.

**Procedure**

1. Observe prepared slides of the spinal cord and the brain.
2. Identify the parts of a neuron and the neuroglial cells.

**Figure 1.10.** Histological examples of common types of tissues: (a) simple cuboidal epithelium; (b) simple columnar ciliated epithelium; (c) pseudostratified ciliated columnar epithelium; (d) transitional epithelium; (e) simple columnar epithelium; (f) loose connective tissue; (g) fibrous connective tissue; (h) bone (osseous) tissue. (Continued on next page.)

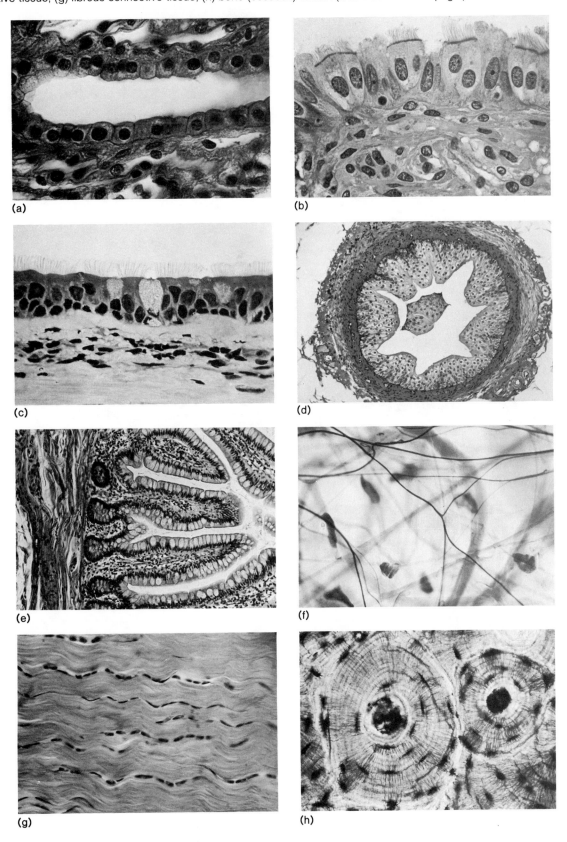

(a)

(b)

(c)

(d)

(e)

(f)

(g)

(h)

**Figure 1.10 (cont.)** Histological examples of common types of tissues: (i) pseudostratified ciliated columnar epithelium; (j) Meissner's corpuscle; (k) scalp; (l) cross section of nerve; (m) bone marrow; (n) cardiac muscle.

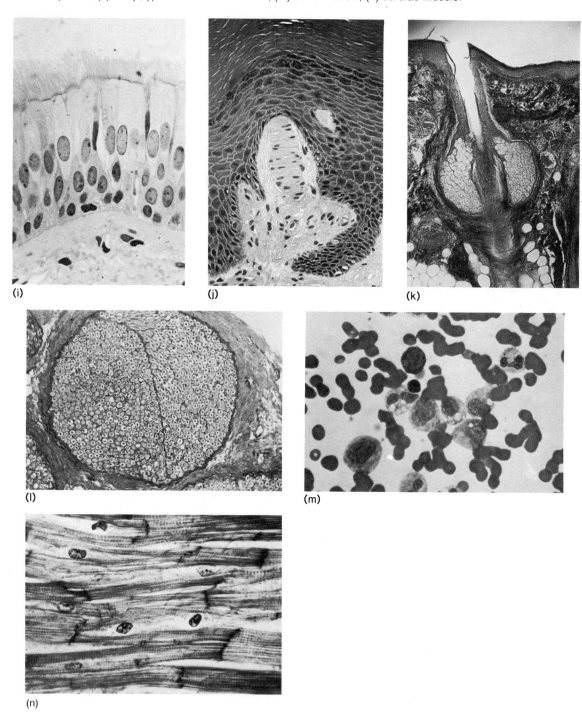

(i)                    (j)                    (k)

(l)                    (m)

(n)

**Figure 1.11.** A diagram of a section of skin.

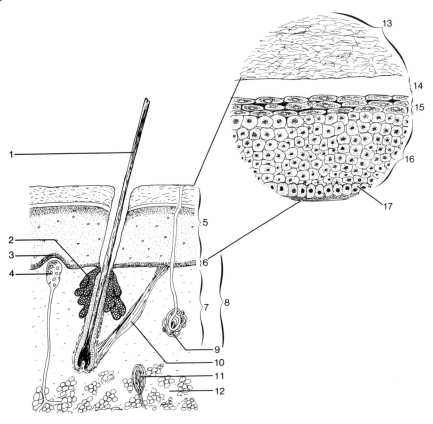

1. Hair
2. Sebaceous gland
3. Papilla
4. Meissner's corpuscle
5. Epidermis
6. Papillary layer
7. Reticular layer
8. Dermis
9. Sweat gland
10. Arrector pili muscle
11. Pacinian corpuscle
12. Hypodermis
13. Stratum corneum
14. Stratum lucidum
15. Stratum granulosum
16. Stratum spinosum
17. Stratum germinativum

## E. An Organ: The Skin

Organs contain more than one type—and usually all four types—of primary tissues. The skin is an excellent example of this. Epithelial tissue is seen as the *epidermis,* the *hair follicles,* and *sebaceous glands,* which extend from the hair follicles (fig. 1.11). One can also see *sweat glands,* which like all glands, are a type of epithelial tissue. The *dermis,* just below the epidermis, is an example of a structure that contains areolar connective tissue. Muscle tissue is seen as the *arrector pili* muscle, a smooth muscle that attaches to the hair follicle and the matrix of the dermis. Nerve tissue may be seen within an onionlike sensory organ, sensitive to pressure, called a *pacinian corpuscle. Meissner's corpuscle* (fig. 1.10*j*) is a similar sensory structure that can be seen in the skin.

## Procedure

1. Observe a prepared slide of the skin or scalp.
2. Identify the structures of the skin, and attempt to see all four types of primary tissue.

# *Laboratory Report* 1.2

Name _____

Date _____

Section _____

1. Define the term *tissue:* _____
   _____

2. Define the term *organ:* _____
   _____

3. Describe and give examples of the following epithelial membranes:

   (a) simple squamous

   (b) stratified squamous

   (c) columnar

   (d) pseudostratified

4. What is the common characteristic of connective tissues? _____
   _____

5. Fill in the blanks.

   (a) Two examples of dense connective tissues are _____
       and _____ .

   (b) The connective tissue of the dermis is classified as _____ .

   (c) Hyaline cartilage is found in the _____
       _____ .

   (d) Fibrocartilage is found in the _____ .

6. Skeletal and cardiac muscles are categorized as _____ muscles.

7. What type of muscle is found in the walls of blood vessels? _____

8. Would you expect the muscle fibers of the tongue to be striated or smooth? Explain your answer.

9. Compare and contrast the structure and function of

    (a) the epithelium of the skin with the epithelium of the intestine;

    (b) the cartilage of the nose with the cartilage of the intervertebral discs;

    (c) cardiac muscle with skeletal muscle.

# Homeostasis and Negative Feedback

The regulatory mechanisms of the body help to maintain a state of dynamic constancy of the internal environment. Homeostasis is made possible by the negative feedback control of effectors.

## Objectives

1. Define the term *homeostasis.*
2. Explain how the negative feedback control of effectors helps to maintain homeostasis.
3. Explain why the internal environment is in a state of dynamic, rather than static, constancy.
4. Explain how a normal range of values for the internal environment is obtained, and explain the significance of these values.

## Materials

1. Watch or clock with a second hand
2. Constant-temperature water bath

Although the structure of the body is functional, the study of body function involves much more than a study of its structure. The extent to which each organ performs the functions endowed by its genetic programming is determined by regulatory mechanisms that coordinate body functions in the service of the entire organism. The primary prerequisite for a healthy organism is the maintenance of **homeostasis,** or constancy of the internal environment.

When homeostasis is disturbed—for example, by an increase or decrease in body temperature or some other parameter—a *sensor* detects the change. The sensor then activates an *effector,* which induces changes opposite to those that activated the sensor. Activation of the effector thus compensates for the initial disturbance, so that the initial change and its compensatory reaction result in only slight deviations from a state of constancy. Homeostasis is therefore a state of dynamic, rather than absolute, constancy.

Since a disturbance in homeostasis initiates events that lead to changes in the opposite direction, the cause-and-effect sequence is described as a **negative feedback** mechanism (or a negative feedback loop). A constant-temperature water bath, for example, uses negative feedback mechanisms to maintain the temperature at which it is set (the *set point*). Deviations from the set point are detected by a sensor, which turns a heating unit on when the temperature drops below the set point and off when the temperature rises above the set point.

## A. Negative Feedback in a Constant-Temperature Water Bath

By means of the negative feedback control of a heating unit (the effector), the water bath temperature is not allowed to rise or fall too far from the set point. The temperature of the water is at the set point only in passing; the set point is in fact only the *average* value within a *range* of fluctuating temperatures. The *sensitivity* of this negative feedback mechanism is measured by the temperature deviation from the set point required to activate the compensatory response (turning the heater on or off).

### Procedure

1. The temperature of the water bath will be set by the instructor somewhere between 40° and 60° C.
2. A red indicator light goes on when the heating unit is activated and goes off when the heater is turned off. In the spaces provided in the laboratory report, record the temperature of the water when the light first goes on and when the light first goes off.
3. Determine the temperature range, the set point, and the sensitivity of the water bath to deviations from the set point.
4. Record your data in the laboratory report.

## B. Resting Pulse Rate; Negative Feedback Control and Normal Range

Homeostasis—the dynamic constancy of the internal environment—is maintained by negative feedback mechanisms that are far more complex than those operating in a constant-temperature water bath. In most cases, several effectors, many with antagonistic effects, are involved in maintaining the homeostasis of a given factor. This is as if, by analogy, the temperature of a water bath were determined by the antagonistic actions of both a heater and a cooling system. The cardiac rate—and thus the pulse rate—for example, is largely determined by the antagonistic effects of two different nerves. One of these (a *sympathetic* nerve, described in section 5) stimulates an increase in cardiac rate. A different nerve (which belongs to the *parasympathetic* system) produces inhibitory effects that slow the cardiac rate.

The resting cardiac and pulse rate, measured in *beats per minute,* is maintained in a state of dynamic constancy by negative feedback loops initiated by sensors in response to changes in blood pressure and other factors. The resting pulse rate is thus not absolutely constant but instead varies about a set point value. In this exercise, you will demonstrate that your pulse rate is in a state of dynamic constancy (implying negative feedback controls), and you will determine your pulse rate set point as the average value of the measurements.

### Procedure

1. Gently press the index and middle fingers (not the thumb) against the radial artery in the wrist until you feel a pulse. Alternatively, the carotid pulse in the neck may be used for these measurements.
2. The pulse rate is usually expressed as pulses per minute. However, only the number of pulses per 15 seconds need be measured; multiplying this by 4 gives the number of pulses per minute. Record the number of pulses per 15-second interval in the data table provided.
3. Pause 15 seconds, and then take the pulse count in the next 15-second interval. Repeat this procedure over a 5-minute period. A total of ten measurements will thus be obtained for a sample of the pulse rate (expressed per minute) once every half-minute for 5 minutes.
4. Graph your results using the grid provided in the laboratory report. Do this by placing a dot at the point corresponding to the pulse rate for each measurement and then connect the dots.

### Normal Values

Questions often asked include, How does my measurement compare with others? and Is my measurement normal? Normal values are those that normal (that is, healthy) people have. Since healthy people may differ to some degree in their particular values, the normal is usually expressed as a range of values that encompasses the measurements of most healthy people. An estimate of the **normal range** is thus a statistical determination that is subject to statistical errors and also subject to questions about what is meant by the term *healthy.*

*Health,* in this context, means the absence of known cardiovascular disease. This definition, however, includes endurance-trained athletes, who usually have lower than average cardiac rates, and more sedentary people, who have higher than average cardiac rates. Determinations of normal ranges can thus vary, depending on the relative proportion of each group in the sample tested. A given class of students may therefore have an average and a range of values that differ somewhat from those of the general population.

### Clinical Significance

The concept of homeostasis is central to medical diagnostic procedures. Through the measurement of body temperature, blood pressure, concentrations of specific substances in the blood, and many others, the clinical examiner samples the internal environment. If a particular measurement deviates significantly from the normal range—if homeostasis is not maintained—the cause of the illness may be traced and proper treatment determined to return the measurement to the normal range.

### Procedure

1. Each student in the class determines his or her own average cardiac rate (pulse rate) from the previous data by either taking an arithmetic average or simply observing the average value of the fluctuations in the previously constructed graph. Record your own average in the laboratory report.
2. Record the number of students in the class with average pulse rates in each of the rate categories shown in the laboratory report. Also, calculate the percentage of students in the class that are within each category, and record this in the laboratory report.
3. Divide the class into two groups: those who exercise on a regular basis (at least three times a week) and those who do not. Determine the average pulse rate and range of values in each of these groups, and enter this information in the given spaces in the laboratory report.

# Laboratory Report 1.3

Name _____

Date _____

Section _____

## Data from Exercise 1.3

### A. Negative Feedback in a Constant-Temperature Water Bath

_____ temperature at which light goes on and heater is activated

_____ temperature at which light and heater go off

_____ temperature range permitted by negative feedback mechanism

_____ set point of constant-temperature water bath

_____ sensitivity of water bath to temperature deviations

### B. Resting Pulse Rate; Negative Feedback Control and Normal Range

1. Pulse rate measurements

| Results | | | | | | | | | | |
|---|---|---|---|---|---|---|---|---|---|---|
| Measurement | 1 | 2 | 3 | 4 | 5 | 6 | 7 | 8 | 9 | 10 |
| Beats per 15 seconds | | | | | | | | | | |
| Beats per minute | | | | | | | | | | |

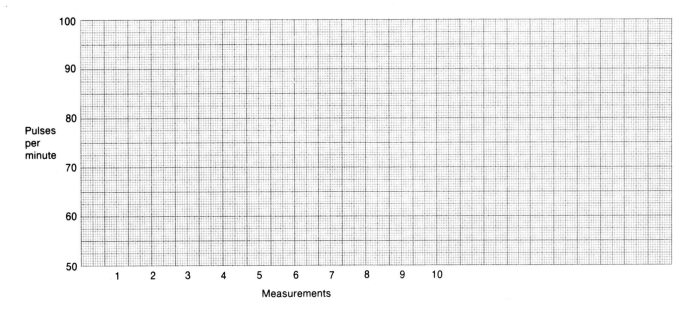

2. Your average pulse rate: _____ beats per minute.

3. Class pulse rate averages

| Pulse rate (beats per minute) | Number of students | Percent of total |
|---|---|---|
| Over 100 | | |
| 90-100 | | |
| 80-90 | | |
| 70-80 | | |
| 60-70 | | |
| 50-60 | | |
| Under 50 | | |

4. Averages for exercise and nonexercise groups

| | Exercise group | Nonexercise group |
|---|---|---|
| Range of pulse rates | | |
| Average of pulse rates | | |

# Questions for Exercise 1.3

1. Define homeostasis, and describe how it is maintained by negative feedback mechanisms. Draw a flow diagram, illustrating cause and effect with arrows, to show how constant temperature is maintained in a water bath.

2. Suppose that a constant-temperature water bath contained two antagonistic effectors: a heater and a cooler. Using a flow diagram, show how this system could operate to maintain a constant temperature.

3. Explain why your graph of pulse rate measurements suggests the presence of negative feedback control mechanisms. Using the earlier description of the effects of sympathetic and parasympathetic nerves on heart rate, draw a flow diagram to show how these antagonistic effectors maintain dynamic constancy of the resting pulse rate.

4. Describe how the normal range for a given measurement is obtained. Explain why published values for normal ranges may differ and why these values must continually be checked and updated.

# Cell Function and Biochemical Measurements

Physiological control systems maintain homeostasis of the internal chemical environment to which the organ systems are exposed. The concentrations of glucose (sugar) and protein in plasma (the fluid portion of the blood), for example, are maintained within certain limits despite the usual changes in diet composition and eating schedule. This is required for health; if plasma glucose levels fall too low, the brain may "starve" and a coma may result; whereas a drop in plasma protein could result in a disturbance in the distribution of fluid between the blood and tissues. An abnormal rise in these values, or other abnormal changes in chemical composition, can endanger a person's health in a variety of ways.

Abnormal changes in the internal chemical environment—which can contribute to disease processes— are usually themselves the result of diseases that affect cell function. Since most plasma proteins are produced by liver cells, for example, diseases of the liver can result in the lowering of plasma protein concentrations. Similarly, abnormal lowering of plasma glucose levels may result from oversecretion of the hormone insulin by certain pancreatic cells. Homeostasis of the internal chemical environment thus depends on proper cell function.

All the molecules found in the internal environment, aside from those obtained from food, are produced within the cells. Some of these remain within the cells, whereas others are secreted into the blood and tissue fluids. Almost all of these molecules are produced by chemical reactions that require catalysis by special proteins known as *enzymes.* All of the enzymes in the body are produced within tissue cells according to information contained in the DNA (genes). The study of organ system physiology is therefore intertwined with the study of cell function and biochemistry, as well as with the study of genetics.

The plasma concentrations of glucose, protein, and cholesterol can be measured by colorimetric techniques. Abnormal concentrations of these molecules give evidence of specific pathological states.

## Objectives

1. Describe how Beer's law can be used to determine the concentration of molecules in solution.
2. Use the formula method and graphic method to determine the concentration of molecules in serum samples.
3. Describe the physiological significance of glucose, protein, and cholesterol in the blood.
4. Explain the pathological significance of abnormal measurements of plasma glucose, protein, and cholesterol.

## Materials

1. Pyrex (or Kimax) test tubes, mechanical 5.0-ml pipettors, 0.10-ml pipettes (fig. 2.1)
2. Constant temperature water bath, set at 37° C
3. Colorimeter and cuvettes
4. Bunsen burners and ring stands
5. Glucose and cholesterol reagents and standards (Harleco), protein standard, and human albumin standards (purchased at concentrations of approximately 2, 4, 6, 8, and 10 g/dl)
6. Glu-cinet reagents (Sclavo Diagnostics, available from Curtin-Matheson Scientific, Inc.) if alternative glucose procedure is used.
7. Biuret reagent: add 45 g of sodium potassium tartrate and 15 g of $CuSO_4 \cdot 5 H_2O$ to a 1.0 liter volumetric flask; fill ¾ full with 0.2N NaOH; shake to dissolve; add 5 g of potassium iodide, and fill to volume with 0.2N NaOH
8. Serum

**Figure 2.1.** (a) devices used to dispense 5.0 ml of reagent automatically, and (b) an automatic microliter pipettor (Eppendorf) for dispensing 100 $\mu$l (0.10 ml) of solutions.

(a)

(b)

| Table 2.1 | Monomers and polymers. |
|---|---|
| **Monomer** | **Polymer** |
| Monosaccharide (e.g., glucose) | Polysaccharide (e.g., starch, glycogen) |
| Amino acids (e.g., glycine) | Protein (e.g., hemoglobin) |
| Fatty acids and glycerol | Triglyceride (i.e., fat) |
| Ribonucleotides and deoxyribonucleotides | Nucleic acid (i.e., DNA, RNA) |

Organic molecules found in the body contain the atoms carbon (C), hydrogen (H), and oxygen (O) in various ratios, and some of these molecules also contain the atoms nitrogen (N), phosphorus (P), and sulfur (S).

Many organic molecules are of enormous size. These large molecules consist of smaller repeating subunits that are chemically bonded to each other. The term **monomer** refers to the individual subunits; the term **polymer** refers to the long chain formed from these repeating subunits.

When two monomers are bonded together, a molecule of water is released. This reaction is called **condensation** or **dehydration synthesis.**

$$A - OH + HO - B \longrightarrow A - B + HOH \text{ (water)}$$

The new molecule ($A - B$) formed from two monomers ($A$ and $B$) is called a *dimer.* This dimer may participate in a condensation reaction with a third monomer to form a *trimer.* The stepwise addition of new monomers to the growing chain by condensation reactions will result in the elongation of the chain and the formation of the full polymer. Table 2.1 gives examples of monomers and polymers.

When the chemical bond between monomers is broken, a molecule of water is consumed. This **hydrolysis** reaction is the reverse of a condensation reaction.

$$A - B + HOH \longrightarrow A - OH + B - OH$$

Ingested foods are usually polymers: mainly proteins, carbohydrates, and triglycerides. In the stomach and small intestine, these polymers are hydrolyzed (in the process of *digestion*) into their respective monomers: amino acids, monosaccharides, fatty acids, and glycerol. These monomers are then moved across the wall of the small intestine into the blood of the capillaries (a process called *absorption*). The vascular system transports these monomers first to the liver and then to all the other tissues of the body.

Once inside the cells of the body, the monomers can be either hydrolyzed into smaller molecules, by a process that yields energy for the cell, or condensed to form new polymers inside the cell. Some of these new polymers are released into the blood (e.g., hormones and the plasma proteins), whereas others remain inside the cell and contribute to its structure and function. Some of the polymers of the cell can eventually be hydrolyzed to form new monomers, which may be used by the cell or released into the blood for use by other cells in the body.

The concentration of the different classes of monomers and polymers in the blood thus reflects the metabolic interactions of the organs, and most concentrations are not greatly influenced by variations in diet. In the healthy person, these concentrations are remarkably constant and vary only within narrow limits. When the concentration of one of these molecules in the blood deviates from the normal range, specific compensatory mechanisms, which bring the concentration back to normal, are activated. By this process, a dynamic state of constancy, or *homeostasis,* is maintained.

When the concentration of any of the monomers or polymers in the blood remains consistently above or below normal, the health of the person may be threatened. Abnormal concentrations of different molecules in the blood are characteristic of different diseases and thus aid in their diagnosis. The disease *diabetes mellitus,* for example, is characterized by a high blood sugar concentration. Accurate measurement of the concentrations of different molecules in the blood is thus of extreme importance in physiology and clinical laboratories.

## The Colorimeter

The colorimeter is a device used in physiology and clinical laboratories to measure the concentration of a substance in solution.[1] This is accomplished by the application of **Beer's law,** which states that the concentration of a substance in solution is directly proportional to the amount of light absorbed by the solution and inversely proportional to the logarithm of the amount of light transmitted by the solution.

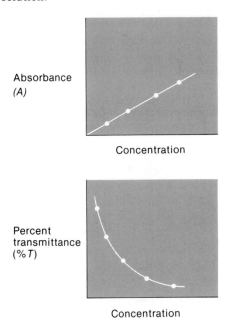

---

1. The colorimeter is a limited type of *spectrophotometer,* and its use (colorimetry) is included under the general category of spectrophotometry.

Beer's law will be followed only if the incident light (the light entering the solution) is monochromatic, that is, light composed of a single wavelength. White light is a mixture of many different wavelengths between 380 and 750 nanometers (nm), or millimicrons (mμ). The rods and cones within the eyes relay the light waves, and the brain interprets these different wavelengths as different colors.

| 380–435 nm | violet |
| 435–480 nm | blue |
| 480–580 nm | green |
| 580–595 nm | yellow |
| 595–610 nm | orange |
| 610–750 nm | red |

By means of a prism or diffraction grating, the colorimeter can separate white light into its component wavelengths. The operator of this device can select incident light of any wavelength by simply turning the appropriate dial to that wavelength. This light enters a tube, the *cuvette*, which contains the test solution. A given fraction of the incident light is absorbed by the solution (the amount absorbed depends on the concentration of the solution), and the remainder of the light, the *transmitted* light, passes through the cuvette. The transmitted light generates an electric current by means of a photoelectric cell, and the amount of this current is registered on a galvanometer scale.

A pointer indicates the **percent transmittance** (% T). Since the amount of light that goes into the solution and the amount of light that leaves the solution are known, a ratio of the two indicates the light **absorbance** (A) of that solution. An absorbance scale is provided in the colorimeter adjacent to the percent transmittance scale. In the following exercises, the absorbance scale rather than the percent transmittance scale will be used, because absorbance and concentration are directly proportional to each other. This relationship can be described in a simple formula:

$$\frac{\text{Concentration}_1}{\text{Absorbance}_1} = \frac{\text{Concentration}_2}{\text{Absorbance}_2}$$

where 1 and 2 are different solutions.

One solution might be a sample of plasma whose concentration (of glucose, for example) is unknown. The second solution might be a *standard*, which contains a known concentration of the test substance (such as glucose). If the absorbance of both solutions are known, the concentration of the substance in plasma (that is, the unknown) can easily be calculated:

$$C_x = C_{std} \times \frac{A_x}{A_{std}}$$

Where: $x$ = the unknown plasma
$std$ = the standard solution
$A$ = the absorbance
$C$ = the concentration

Suppose there are three standards. Standard *1* has a concentration of 1 gram per milliliter (g/ml). Standards *2* and *3* have concentrations of 2 g/ml and 4 g/ml, respectively. Since standard *2* has twice the concentration of standard *1,* it should (according to Beer's law) have twice the absorbance. The second standard, similarly, should have half the absorbance of the third standard, because it has half the concentration. Experimental errors, however, make this very unlikely. It is therefore necessary to average the answers obtained for the unknown concentration when different standards are used. This can be done arithmetically or by means of a graph called a **standard curve.**

| Absorbance | Concentration |
|---|---|
| 0.25 | 30 mg/100 ml |
| 0.38 | 50 mg/100 ml |
| 0.41 | 60 mg/100 ml |
| 0.57 | 70 mg/100 ml |

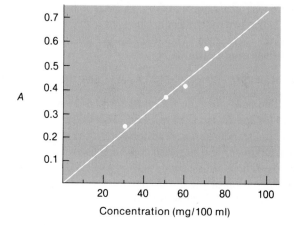

Suppose that a solution of unknown concentration has an absorbance of 0.35. The standard curve previously prepared can be used to determine its concentration.

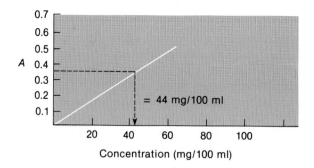

### Standardizing the Colorimeter

The following procedure is intended specifically for the Spectronic 20 (Bausch & Lomb). Although the general procedure is similar for all colorimeters, the specific details may vary between different models.

1. Turn on the colorimeter by rotating knob *b* in figure 2.2 to the right.

**Figure 2.2.** A typical colorimeter (spectrophotometer). (a) the sample holder; (b) the power switch/zero control; (c) the 100% T control; (d) the wavelength control.

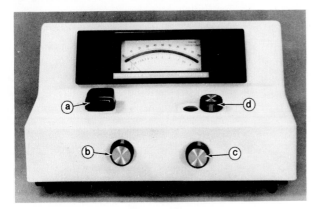

2. Set the monochromator dial (*d* in fig. 2.2) so that the correct wavelength in nanometers—which is provided in each exercise—is lined up with the indicator in the window adjacent to this dial.
3. When there is no cuvette in the cuvette holder (*a* in fig. 2.2), the light source is off. The pointer should thus read zero transmittance or infinite absorbance. This is at the left end of the scale. Turn knob *b* until the pointer is aligned with the left end of the scale.
4. Place in the cuvette holder the cuvette that contains all the reagents in the other tubes except the test solution (such as glucose, for example). This tube is called the **blank** because it has a concentration of test substance equal to zero. It should therefore have an absorbance of zero (or a transmittance of 100%). This is at the right end of the scale. Set the pointer to the right end of the scale using knob *c* (fig. 2.2).
5. Repeat steps 3 and 4 to confirm settings.
6. Place the other cuvettes, which contain the standard solutions and the unknown, in the cuvette chamber. Close the hatch and read the absorbance values of each solution.

Note: *Before placing each cuvette in the chamber, wipe it with a lint-free, soft paper towel. If the cuvette has a white indicator line, place the cuvette so that this line is even with the line in the front of the cuvette holder.*

## A. Carbohydrates: Measurement of Plasma Glucose Concentration

The monomers of the carbohydrates are the **monosaccharides,** or simple sugars. The general formula for these molecules is $C_nH_{2n}O_n$, where *n* can be any number. Glucose, for example, has the formula $C_6H_{12}O_6$. The monosaccharide fructose has the same formula but differs from glucose in the arrangement of the atoms (glucose and fructose are *isomers*).

Two monosaccharides can join together by means of a dehydration synthesis (condensation) reaction to form a **disaccharide.** Sucrose (common table sugar), for example, is a disaccharide of glucose and fructose, whereas maltose is a disaccharide of two glucose subunits.

$$glu\text{—}OH \atop + \atop fru\text{—}O\text{—}H \longrightarrow {glu \atop | \atop O \atop | \atop fru} + H_2O$$

Sucrose

$$glu\text{—}O\,H \atop HO\text{—}glu \atop glu \downarrow glu + H_2O \atop \llcorner O \lrcorner$$

Maltose

The continued addition of glucose subunits to maltose will result in the production of a long chain of repeating glucose subunits, forming the polysaccharide **glycogen** (or animal starch). This polysaccharide is formed inside muscle and liver cells and serves as an efficient storage form of glucose. When the blood glucose level drops below normal, the liver cells can hydrolyze stored glycogen and release glucose into the blood. Conversely, when the blood sugar level rises above normal, the liver cells can take glucose from the blood and store it as glycogen for later use. In this way, the equilibrium between blood glucose and liver glycogen helps to maintain constancy (*homeostasis*) of the blood sugar level. This process is regulated by hormones such as epinephrine (adrenaline), insulin, hydrocortisone, and glucagon.

## Clinical Significance

The most important regulator of the blood sugar level is the hormone **insulin,** produced by the **islets of Langerhans** in the pancreas. This hormone makes the blood sugar more available to the cells of the body; hence, it lowers the blood glucose level. An elevated blood glucose level (*hyperglycemia*) results from insufficient insulin secretion. This disease is called **diabetes mellitus.** Low blood sugar (*hypoglycemia*) can result from the excessive secretion of insulin. There is, in addition, slight hypoglycemia associated with arthritis, renal disease, and the late stages of pregnancy.

**Figure 2.3.** A chart for the colorimetric measurement of glucose concentration.

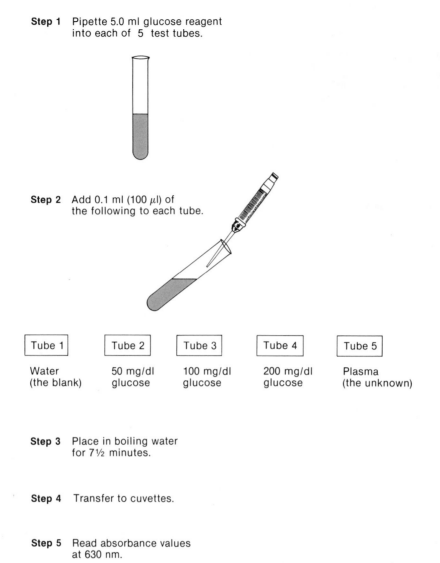

**Step 1** Pipette 5.0 ml glucose reagent into each of 5 test tubes.

**Step 2** Add 0.1 ml (100 µl) of the following to each tube.

| Tube 1 | Tube 2 | Tube 3 | Tube 4 | Tube 5 |
|---|---|---|---|---|
| Water (the blank) | 50 mg/dl glucose | 100 mg/dl glucose | 200 mg/dl glucose | Plasma (the unknown) |

**Step 3** Place in boiling water for 7½ minutes.

**Step 4** Transfer to cuvettes.

**Step 5** Read absorbance values at 630 nm.

## Procedure (see figure 2.3)

*Measurement of Plasma Glucose Concentration*[2]

1. Obtain five Pyrex (or Kimax) test tubes. Number them 1–5.
2. With a small graduated cylinder or mechanical pipettor, accurately measure 5.0 ml *glucose reagent.* Add the measured reagent to each test tube.

**Note:** *The glucose reagent contains orthotoluidine (o-toluidine) in concentrated acetic acid. The o-toluidine can combine with glucose to form a green-colored compound. This solution should be in a fume hood or a well-ventilated area.*

3. Pipette 0.10 ml of the following solutions into each of the tubes indicated; be sure to use a fresh pipette for each solution.

   1—0.10 ml of distilled water (this is the **blank**)
   2—0.10 ml of 50 milligrams per deciliter (mg/dl) glucose standard
   3—0.10 ml of 100 mg/dl glucose standard
   4—0.10 ml of 200 mg/dl glucose standard
   5—0.10 ml of unknown plasma

**Note:** *One deciliter (dl) is equivalent to 100 ml.*

4. Bring a water bath to a rapid boil, and simultaneously immerse all five test tubes into the boiling water.

---

2. For Harleco glucose set.

5. Leave the tubes in the boiling water for exactly 7½ minutes. Carefully and rapidly transfer the tubes (using a test-tube clamp) to a beaker of cold tap water.
6. When the solutions have cooled to room temperature (at least 10 minutes), transfer them to five cuvettes.
7. Set the monochromator dial (see fig. 2.2d) to 630 nm.
8. Standardize the spectrophotometer, using solution 1 as the blank.
9. Record the absorbance values of solutions 2–5 on the chart in the laboratory report.
10. Plot a standard curve, using the absorbances of the standard solutions (2, 3, 4).
11. Determine the concentration of the unknown plasma sample (5) using the graphic method. Enter the value in the laboratory report.

### Alternative Procedure for Plasma Glucose[3]

1. Obtain 5 test tubes, and number them 1–5.
2. Measure 12.5 ml of *Glu-cinet* reagent into each tube.
3. Add distilled water, glucose standards, and unknown plasma (0.10 ml per sample) as described in original step 3.
4. Mix the tubes, and allow them to stand at room temperature for 30 minutes.
5. Set the monochromator (wavelength) dial at 510 nanometers, and follow the procedure for obtaining absorbance readings and analyzing data described in steps 8–11 in the original procedure.

The normal fasting range of glucose in the plasma is 70–100 mg per 100 ml.

## B. Lipids: Measurement of Plasma Cholesterol Concentration

The lipids are an extremely diverse family of molecules that share the common property of being soluble in (can be dissolved in) organic solvents such as benzene, ether, chloroform, and carbon tetrachloride. The lipids found in blood can be divided into the following categories: free fatty acids (FFA, also known as nonesterified fatty acids, NEFA), **triglycerides** (or neutral fats), **phospholipids,** and **steroids.** Carbon, hydrogen, and oxygen form the basic structure of lipids, but these elements are not present in the same ratios as they are in carbohydrates.

Fatty acids are long chains, ranging from sixteen to twenty-four carbons in length. When adjacent carbons are linked by single bonds, the fatty acid is said to be *saturated;* when adjacent carbons are linked by double bonds, the fatty acid is said to be *unsaturated.*

Saturated: $-CH_2-CH_2-CH_2-CH_2-$

Unsaturated: $=CH-CH_2-CH=CH-$

The triglycerides consist of three fatty acids bonded to a molecule of the alcohol glycerol. Triglycerides that are solid at room temperature are called *fats,* and those that are liquid at room temperature are called *oils.* A triglyceride with few sites of unsaturation will be a fat, whereas one with many sites of unsaturation will be an oil.

Like the triglycerides, the phospholipids consist of fatty acids bonded to an alcohol molecule. As their name implies, this complex group of lipids also contains the element phosphorus (in the form of phosphate, $PO_4$) bonded to the alcohol molecule. Phospholipids are important components of cell membranes.

The steroids are characterized by a structure consisting of four rings. One of the most important steroids in the body is cholesterol.

Cholesterol

## Clinical Significance

There is evidence that high blood cholesterol, together with other risk factors, such as hypertension and cigarette smoking, contributes to *atherosclerosis.* In atherosclerosis, deposits of cholesterol and other lipids, calcium salts, and smooth muscle cells build up in the walls of arteries and reduce blood flow. These deposits—called *atheromas*—also serve as sites for the production of *thrombi* (blood clots), which further occlude blood flow. The reduction in blood flow through the artery may result in heart disease or cerebrovascular accident (stroke). It is generally believed that blood cholesterol levels—and thus the risk of atherosclerosis—may be significantly lowered by diets restricted in the amounts of cholesterol and saturated fats.

3. Glu-cinet Glucose Procedure, Sclavo Diagnostics (available from Curtin Matheson Scientific, Inc.).

## Procedure

1. Using a mechanical pipette (do *not* pipette by mouth), add 5.0 ml of cholesterol reagent into each of three test tubes.
2. Pipette 0.10 ml of each of the following into the indicated tube.

    1—0.10 ml of cholesterol standard (200 mg/dl)
    2—0.10 ml of serum
    3—0.10 ml of distilled water

3. Mix the contents of each tube by gentle tapping, and place in a water bath set at 37° C for 10 minutes.
4. Remove the solutions to three cuvettes. Standardize the spectrophotometer at 625 nm, using solution 3 as the blank.
5. Record the absorbance values of solutions 1 and 2 in your laboratory report.
6. Calculate the cholesterol concentration in the unknown plasma sample. Enter this value in your laboratory report.

$$C_{plasma} = \frac{A_{plasma}}{A_{standard}} \times C_{standard}$$

Normal values for plasma cholesterol are 130–250 mg/dl.

## C. Proteins: Measurement of Plasma Protein Concentration

Proteins are long chains of amino acids bonded to one another by condensation reactions. Each amino acid has an amino end ($NH_2$) and a carboxylic acid end (COOH) as shown by the general formula.

When amino acids are bonded together (through a **peptide bond**) to form a protein, one end of the protein will have an amino group and the other end will have a carboxyl group.

Carboxyl end     Peptide bond     Amino end

There are more than twenty-two different amino acids in nature, each amino acid differing from the others in the presence of a different combination of atoms in the *R* group, sometimes known as the *functional group*. The amino acid glycine, for example, has a hydrogen (H) in the *R* position, whereas the amino acid alanine has a methyl group ($CH_3$) in the *R* position.

Glycine                    Alanine

Proteins in the plasma serve a variety of functions: some are enzymes, hormones, and carrier molecules (which transport lipids, iron, and some hormones while they are in blood), and others have an immune function (antibodies). The plasma proteins are divided into classes on the basis of their behavior during biochemical separation procedures. These classes are the *albumins,* the *alpha* and *beta globulins* (synthesized mainly in the liver), and the *gamma globulins* (antibodies produced by the lymphoid tissue).

In addition to the separate functions of the different plasma proteins, the total concentration of proteins in the plasma is physiologically important. The plasma proteins exert an osmotic pressure, the **colloid osmotic** (or **oncotic) pressure,** which pulls fluid from the tissue spaces into the capillary blood. This compensates for the continuous filtration of fluid from the capillaries into the tissue spaces, produced by the hydrostatic pressure of the blood (fig. 2.4).

**Figure 2.4.** The circulation of fluid between the blood plasma in a capillary and the tissues. Arrows pointing away from the capillary indicate the force exerted by the blood pressure, whereas arrows pointing toward the capillary indicate the force exerted by the colloid osmotic pressure of the plasma proteins. The heavy arrow indicates the direction of blood flow along the capillary from arteriole to venule.

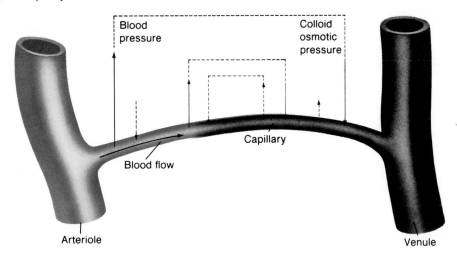

## Clinical Significance

An abnormally low concentration of total blood protein (*hypoproteinemia*) may be due to an inadequate production of protein by the liver caused by liver disease (e.g., cirrhosis or hepatitis) or to the loss of protein in the urine (*albuminuria*) caused by kidney diseases. Hypoproteinemia decreases the colloid osmotic pressure of the blood and may lead to the accumulation of fluid in the tissue spaces (**edema**).

An abnormally high concentration of total plasma protein (*hyperproteinemia*) may be due to dehydration or to an increased production of the plasma proteins. An increased production of gamma globulins (antibodies), for example, is characteristic of many infections (e.g., pneumonia) and parasitic diseases (e.g., malaria).

## Procedure

*Total Plasma Proteins*

1. Obtain seven clean test tubes, and label them 1–7.
2. Using a small graduated cylinder or mechanical pipettor, accurately add 5.0 ml of biuret reagent to all the tubes.
3. Pipette the following solutions into each of the indicated tubes.

   1—0.10 ml of distilled water (this is the blank)
   2—0.10 ml of 2.0 g/dl protein standard
   3—0.10 ml of 4.0 g/dl protein standard
   4—0.10 ml of 6.0 g/dl protein standard
   5—0.10 ml of 8.0 g/dl protein standard
   6—0.10 ml of 10.0 g/dl protein standard
   7—0.10 ml of unknown serum sample

**Note:** *The expression g/dl is equivalent to g per 100 ml or g%.*

4. Let the tubes stand at room temperature for 30 minutes.
5. Transfer the solutions to seven clean cuvettes.
6. Standardize the spectrophotometer using solution 1 as the blank, with the monochromator dial set at 555 nm.
7. Record the absorbance values of the solutions in your laboratory report.
8. Using the absorbances of solutions 2–6, plot a standard curve.
9. Determine the concentration of protein in the unknown serum sample, and enter this value in your laboratory report.

> The normal fasting protein level is 6.0–8.0 g/dl.

# Laboratory Report 2.1

Name _____

Date _____

Section _____

## Data from Exercise 2.1

### A. Carbohydrates: Measurement of Plasma Glucose Concentration

1. Enter your absorbance data in the following table:

| Tube Number | Glucose Concentration (mg/dl) | Absorbance |
|---|---|---|
| 1 | 0 (*blank*) | 0 |
| 2 | 50 | |
| 3 | 100 | |
| 4 | 200 | |
| 5 | Unknown (*serum sample*) | |

2. Plot a standard curve using the graph paper provided at the end of the exercise.

3. Use the standard curve you prepared to determine the glucose concentration of the unknown serum sample. Enter this value in the space below:

   _____ mg/dl

4. Is the glucose concentration of the unknown serum sample normal or abnormal? Explain.

### B. Lipids: Measurement of Plasma Cholesterol Concentration

1. Record the absorbance values of solutions 1 and 2 in the spaces below:

   Absorbance of solution 1: _____

   Absorbance of solution 2: _____

2. Calculate the cholesterol concentration of the unknown serum sample using the formula shown in step 6 of the procedure. Enter this concentration in the space below:

   _____ mg/dl

3. Is the cholesterol concentration of the serum sample normal or abnormal? Explain.

## C. Proteins: Measurement of Plasma Protein Concentration

1. Record your absorbance values in the data table below:

| Tube Number | Protein Concentration (g/dl) | Absorbance |
|---|---|---|
| 1 | 0 (*blank*) | 0 |
| 2 | 2.0 | |
| 3 | 4.0 | |
| 4 | 6.0 | |
| 5 | 8.0 | |
| 6 | 10.0 | |
| 7 | Unknown (*serum sample*) | |

2. Use the graph paper at the end of the exercise to plot a standard curve.

3. Using the graph you prepared, determine the protein concentration of the unknown serum sample, and enter this value in the space below:

_____ g/dl

4. Is the protein concentration of the unknown serum sample normal or abnormal? Explain.

# Questions for Exercise 2.1

1. The concentration of a solution is _____ proportional to its absorbance.

2. The above relationship is described by _____ law.

3. Hyperglycemia is characteristic of the disease _____ .

4. Hyperglycemia may be caused by a deficiency in the hormone _____ .

5. Cholesterol is a (general category) _____
   and a (specific category) _____ .

6. High blood cholesterol is a contributing factor in the disease _____ .

7. Most of the plasma proteins are produced by the _____ .

8. Low plasma protein concentration can produce a physical condition called _____ .

9. The colloid osmotic pressure of the blood is related to the plasma concentration of _____ .

10. "All fats are lipids, but not all lipids are fats." Explain.

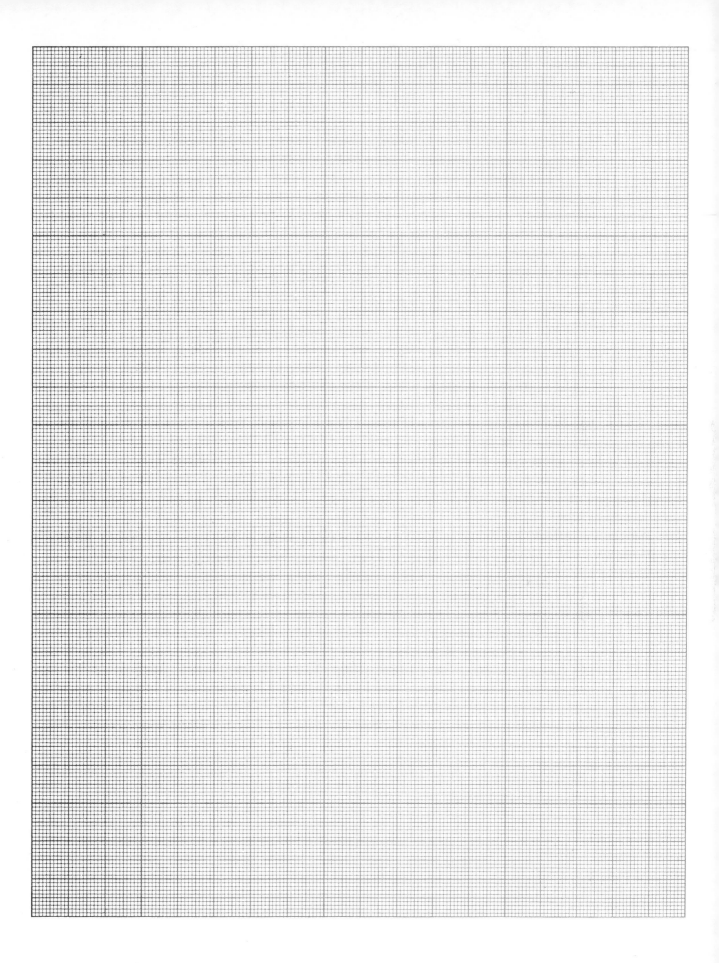

11. Amino acids found in the blood may originate from either the digestive tract or the tissue cells, whereas all the proteins in the blood are secreted by the tissue cells. Explain why this is true.

12. Although the ingestion of carbohydrates fluctuates greatly, the blood glucose levels remain within a fairly narrow range. Using the information in this exercise, explain how this is accomplished.

13. What does the blank tube contain, and what is its function in a colorimetric assay?

14. Why do you always draw a linear standard curve (absorbance vs. concentration) even though your experimental values may deviate slightly from a straight line? Why must the standard curve intersect the origin (zero concentration = zero absorbance)?

# Thin-Layer Chromatography of Amino Acids

The amino acids, which function as the subunits of proteins, are divisible into about twenty types which are each chemically unique. The unique properties of each type of amino acid provide the basis for their separation and identification. This information can be clinically useful in the diagnosis of genetic diseases that involve amino acid metabolism.

## Objectives

1. Explain, using the general formula for amino acids, how one amino acid differs from another.
2. Explain how thin-layer chromatography can separate different amino acids that are present together in a single solution.
3. Define the $R_f$, calculate the $R_f$ value for different spots, and use this information to identify unknown amino acids.

## Materials

1. Silica gel plates (F-254 rapid, adhered to plastic or glass), capillary tubes, chromatography (or hair) driers, rulers
2. Developing chambers, oven set at about 60° C
3. Amino acid solutions: arginine, cysteine, aspartic acid, phenylalanine, 1.0 mg/ml each dissolved in 0.1N HCl:isopropyl alcohol (9:1); "unknown" solution of amino acids, containing two of these amino acids in the same solution
4. Developing solvent: 20 ml of 17% $NH_4OH$ (dilute concentrated $NH_4OH$ with an equal amount of water), 40 ml of ethyl acetate, and 40 ml of methanol per developing chamber
5. Ninhydrin spray

In this exercise, an attempt will be made to identify two unknown amino acids that are present in the same solution. To do this, you must (1) *separate* the two amino acids and (2) *identify* these amino acids by comparing their behavior with that of known amino acids.

Since each amino acid has a different R group, each will have a different *solubility* (ability to be dissolved) in a given solvent. These differences will be used to separate and identify the amino acids on a *thin-layer plate*.

The thin-layer plate consists of a thin layer of porous material (in this procedure, silica gel) that is coated on one side of a plastic, glass, or aluminum plate. The solutions of amino acids are applied on different spots of the plate (a procedure called spotting), and the plate is placed in a solvent bath with the spots above the solvent.

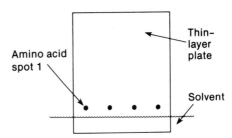

As the solvent creeps up the plate by capillary action, it will wash the amino acids off their original spots (the *origin*) and carry them upward toward the other end of the plate. Since the solubility of each amino acid is different, it takes longer for the solvent to wash and carry some amino acids than to wash and carry others. If the process is halted some time before all the amino acids have been washed off the top of the plate, some amino acids will have migrated farther from the origin than others.

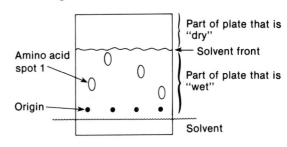

If this chromatography were repeated using the same amino acids and the same solvent, the final pattern *(chromatogram)* would be the same as obtained previously. In other words, the distance that a given amino acid migrates in a given solvent, relative to the *solvent front,* can be used as an identifying characteristic of that amino acid. We can give this identity a numerical value by calculating the distance the amino acid traveled relative to the front (the $R_f$ value) as follows.

$$R_f = \frac{\text{distance from origin to amino acid spot } (D_s)}{\text{distance from origin to solvent front } (D_f)}.$$

We can identify the unknown amino acid by comparing its $R_f$ value in a given solvent with the $R_f$ values of known amino acids in the same solvent.

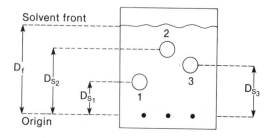

---

## Clinical Significance

An abnormally high concentration of certain amino acids or their metabolites in the blood frequently results in deterioration of the central nervous system and mental retardation. These abnormal concentrations are usually the result of the presence of defective enzymes involved in the degradation of the amino acids.

In the disease **phenylketonuria (PKU)**, for example, the enzyme that converts the amino acid phenylalanine to tyrosine is defective, leaving phenylalanine and its other metabolites to accumulate in the body. This condition, which affects one baby in every 10,000 to 20,000, results in severe mental retardation. Other diseases of similar etiology (cause) include homocystinuria, alkaptonuria, and maple syrup disease (the name refers to a characteristic odor of the urine).

The defective enzymes are synthesized by defective genes; hence, the diseases of amino acid metabolism that have this etiology are referred to as **inborn errors of metabolism** (see exercise 2.5).

## Procedure

1. Fill a capillary tube with amino acid solution 1 (arginine). Gently touch it to a spot on the plate 1½ inches from the bottom and ½ inch from the left-hand edge. Dry the spot with a hair dryer. Repeat the spotting and drying procedure until you have made five applications of the same amino acid to the same spot.

**Note:** *Be careful to (1) apply the amino acid solution to exactly the same spot each time (use a spotting guide, or make Xs lightly with pencil before spotting), (2) dry the spot thoroughly between applications, and (3) spot gently so that you do not gouge out the silica gel.*

2. Repeat the spotting procedure for amino acid 2 (cysteine), using a new capillary tube and applying the spot about ½ inch to the right of the first amino acid.
3. Repeat the spotting procedure for amino acids 3 (aspartic acid) and 4 (phenylalanine), applying them about ½ inch to the right of the preceding spot.
4. Repeat the spotting procedure with the solution containing two unknown amino acids, applying it about ½ inch to the right of amino acid 4.
5. Place the thin-layer plate in a chromatography developing chamber that has been previously filled with solvent. Cover the chamber and allow the solvent to migrate up the plate for 1 hour.
6. Remove the plate from the developing chamber, dry, and spray in a well-ventilated area with ninhydrin.

**Note:** *Since amino acids are colorless, it is necessary to react them with ninhydrin, a reagent that combines with the amino acids to produce a blue-colored complex.*

7. Heat the plates in an oven set at approximately 60°C for 10–15 minutes.
8. Remove the plate and measure the distance, in centimeters, from the origin to the solvent front and from the origin to the center of each amino acid spot. Record these values; calculate $R_f$ values and enter your data in the laboratory report.

# Laboratory Report 2.2

Name ______________________

Date ______________________

Section ______________________

## Data from Exercise 2.2

| Amino Acids | $D_s$ | $D_f$ | $R_f$ |
|---|---|---|---|
| Arginine | | | |
| Cysteine | | | |
| Aspartic acid | | | |
| Phenylalanine | | | |
| Unknown 1 | | | |
| Unknown 2 | | | |

*Note:* $D_f$ is the same for all spots.

The unknown solution contained ______________________

and ______________________.

## Questions for Exercise 2.2

1. Which part of an amino acid grants it chemical specificity?

______________________

2. What is the maximum $R_f$ number a spot can have? ______________________

3. Suppose a spot is 8 cm from its origin, and the solvent front is 12 cm from the origin. What is the $R_f$ of the spot?

______________________

4. What is meant by the symbol $R_f$? Why do different amino acids have different $R_f$ values?

5. What is the purpose of chromatography? How can this technique be used in clinical diagnosis?

# Electrophoresis of Serum Proteins

Plasma contains classes of proteins that differ in structure and function. These classes can be separated from each other and identified by electrophoresis.

## Objectives

1. Describe the amphoteric nature of amino acids and proteins, and explain how this can be used to separate these molecules by electrophoresis.
2. Identify the different bands of serum proteins in an electrophoresis pattern.
3. Describe the origin and the functions of the different classes of plasma proteins.

## Materials

1. Plastic troughs, buffer chamber, sample applicator, power supply, Sepharose strips (the Sepra Tek system, Gelman)
2. Unheparinized capillary tubes and micro rubber bulbs (to expel solutions from the capillary tubes)
3. High-resolution buffer, Ponceau S stain (Gelman), 5% acetic acid (v/v)
4. Sterile lancets, 70% ethanol, and microhematocrit centrifuge (alternatively, test tubes containing previously prepared serum samples may be used)

The unique structure and physiological role of each type of protein is determined by the specific number, type, and sequence of its amino acids. Proteins differ in size, range, and shape from elliptical (globular) to fibrous, and contain different numbers of positive and negative charges because of the functional groups ($R$ groups) of their amino acids.

Under acidic conditions, amino groups gain a $H^+$ and become positively charged, whereas under basic conditions, carboxyl groups lose a $H^+$ and become negatively charged. Since amino acids can have either polarity, depending on the pH, they are said to be *amphoteric*.

$$
\begin{array}{c}
\text{COOH} \\
| \\
H_2N-\overset{\;}{\underset{\;}{C}}-H \\
| \\
CH_3
\end{array}
\quad
\begin{array}{c}
\xrightarrow{\;OH^-\;} \\[2ex]
\xrightarrow{\;H^+\;}
\end{array}
\quad
\begin{array}{c}
\text{COO}^- \\
| \\
H_2N-\overset{\;}{\underset{\;}{C}}-H + H_2O \\
| \\
CH_3 \\[3ex]
\text{COOH} \\
| \\
{}^+H_3N-\overset{\;}{\underset{\;}{C}}-H \\
| \\
CH_3
\end{array}
$$

When an amino acid is electrically neutral, its amphoteric nature can be shown by the *zwitterion* formula, in which neutrality is indicated by a balance between positive and negative charges.

$$
\begin{array}{c}
\text{COO}^- \\
| \\
{}^+H_3N-\overset{\;}{\underset{\;}{C}}-H \\
| \\
CH_3
\end{array}
$$

Zwitterion

In addition to the amino and carboxyl ends of a protein, many amino acids have either an amino-containing functional group (e.g., lysine, arginine) or a carboxylic acid–containing functional group (e.g., aspartic acid, glutamic acid). Since each type of protein has a characteristic ratio of these two types of amino acids, each protein will have a characteristic *net charge* at a given pH.

At a pH of 8.8 (slightly basic), the different types of plasma proteins will have different degrees of net negative charge; and if placed in an electric field, they will migrate away from the negative pole (cathode) and toward the positive pole (anode) at different rates. The rates at which they travel, of course, will also be modified by their size and shape. This technique, known as **electrophoresis,** can be used to separate and identify the different classes of plasma proteins.

**Figure 2.5.** The electrophoresis pattern of normal serum.

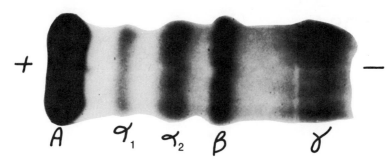

There are two main types of plasma proteins: albumin and globulins. The latter protein is composed of four primary subclasses: *alpha–1* ($\alpha_1$), *alpha–2* ($\alpha_2$), *beta* ($\beta$), and *gamma* ($\gamma$) globulins (fig. 2.5).

The fluid part of the blood as it circulates in the vessels is *plasma.* When blood clots, a soluble protein in the plasma (*fibrinogen*) is converted into an insoluble thread-like protein called *fibrin,* which forms the meshwork of the blood clot. **Serum,** which is the fluid that remains after the clot has formed, does not contain fibrinogen and is thus incapable of further clotting.

*Albumins* are the most abundant of the serum proteins, serving as carrier molecules for hormones, lipids, and bile pigment, and are responsible for most of the colloid osmotic pressure of the blood. The *alpha* and *beta globulins* serve a variety of functions and, like albumin and fibrinogen, are synthesized by the liver. The *gamma globulins* are **antibodies** produced by white blood cells known as lymphocytes.

## Clinical Significance

The diagnosis of a large number of diseases can be aided by an analysis of the electrophoretic pattern of the plasma (or serum) proteins. Although direct observation is useful, more reliable information can be gained by a quantitative measurement of the proteins in each band. These measurements are made by a device (a *densitometer*) that optically scans the electrophoresis pattern and graphically records the absorbance of different regions of the strip.

Diseases whose diagnosis can be aided by electrophoresis include acute inflammations (elevated alpha–2 proteins), viral hepatitis (change in gamma globulin and albumin), cirrhosis of the liver (broad gamma globulin band), as well as many others, including nephrotic syndrome and malignant tumors.

## Procedure

1. Cleanse the tip of the index finger with 70% ethanol, and puncture with a sterile lancet.
2. Quickly fill an unheparinized capillary tube with blood, seal one end, and immediately centrifuge for 3 minutes. Do not use heparinized capillary tubes—the anticoagulant heparin is a protein and will interfere with the test.
3. Float a strip of cellulose acetate in buffer for 1 minute, then immerse it in the buffer for 10 minutes.
4. Using forceps, remove the cellulose acetate strip from the buffer, and blot it with filter paper that has been premoistened with buffer.
5. Raise the tension latch of the frame assembly, placing the movable support bridge in the vertical position (figs. 2.6 and 2.7*a*).[4]
6. Center the cellulose acetate strip on the support bridges, and fasten it with the membrane clamps. Tension the membrane by releasing the latch (fig. 2.7*b* and *c*).
7. Place the membrane frame assembly in the chamber, bringing the strip ends into contact with the buffer, and position the cover on the chamber.
8. Break the capillary tube at the junction of the packed red blood cells and the serum. Place a drop of serum on the sample well of the applicator block by lightly touching it with the capillary tube. A sample of serum from six different students can be placed in each of six wells (fig. 2.7*d*).

---

4. For Gelman Sepra Tek System.

**Figure 2.6.** A membrane frame assembly and buffer chamber for the Gelman Sepra Tek electrophoresis system.

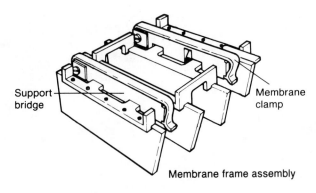

Support bridge

Membrane clamp

Membrane frame assembly

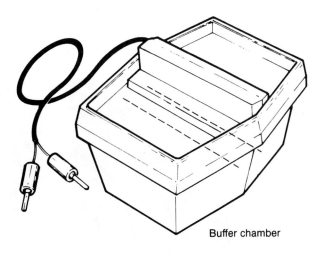

Buffer chamber

9. Fill a capillary tube with the serum provided by the instructor and place it on sample wells 7 and 8.
10. Position the applicator on the applicator block, and load it by depressing the button for 4–5 seconds (fig. 2.7e).
11. Position the loaded applicator on the chamber cover. Depress the button for 4–5 seconds to place the serum on the strip (fig. 2.7f).
12. Connect the chamber to the power supply, and electrophorese for 20 minutes at 200 V (fig. 2.7g and h).

Note: *During this time, clean the applicator by placing it on filter paper moistened with the buffer. Rinse with tap water and distilled water.*

13. When the voltage is off, open the chamber and remove the frame assembly. Raise the tension latch and strip clamps, and remove the strip with forceps.
14. Float the strip on Ponceau S stain for 1 minute; then immerse it in the stain for 10 minutes.
15. Remove the strip with forceps, and rinse it in two successive baths of 5% acetic acid. Tape the cellulose acetate strip in the space provided (or draw a facsimile), and label the bands.

Note: *The albumin band (nearest the anode) is the darkest band, whereas the gamma globulin band (nearest the cathode) is the widest band.*

**Figure 2.7.** (a) through (h), the procedure for performing electrophoresis of serum proteins (see text for description).

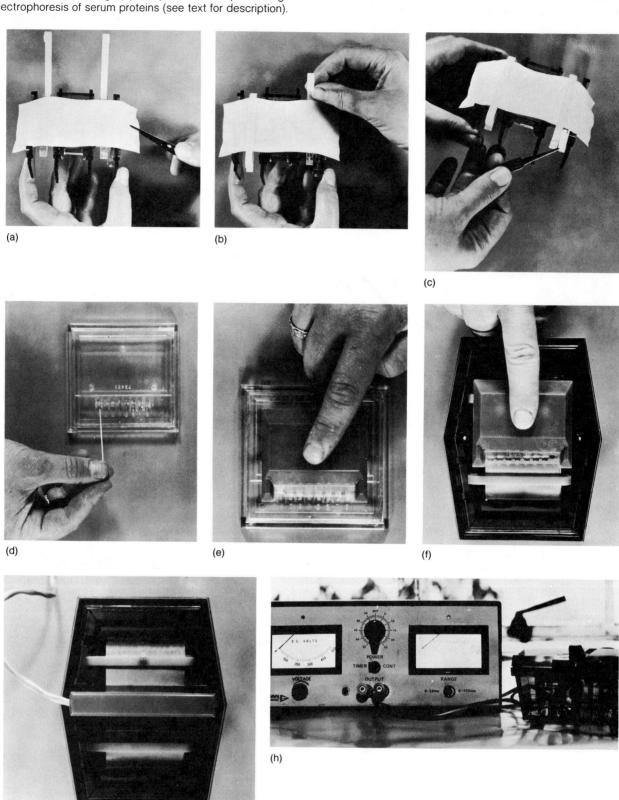

# Laboratory Report 2.3

## Data from Exercise 2.3

1. Tape your electrophoresis strip to (or draw a facsimile in) the space below.

2. Label the protein bands in the above strip.

## Questions for Exercise 2.3

1. Define an amphoteric molecule: _____

_____

2. Name two amino acids that have

   (a) an extra amino group _____ and

   _____

   (b) an extra carboxylic acid group _____

   and _____

3. Proteins have a net _____ charge in acidic solutions

   and a net _____ charge in basic solutions.

4. The most abundant class of plasma proteins is the _____ .

5. Albumins are made by the _____ .

6. The class of plasma proteins containing antibodies is the _____ .

7. What is the difference between serum and plasma?

8. Why is the albumin band dark and relatively narrow, and why is the gamma globulin band wide? **Relate your** answer to the structure and function of these two classes of plasma proteins.

# Measurements of Enzyme Activity

The presence of a specific enzyme can be detected by the reaction it catalyzes, and the enzyme concentration can be measured by the amount of product it forms in a period of time. Enzyme activity is affected by pH, temperature, and the availability of substrates and coenzymes.

## Objectives

1. Describe the lock-and-key model of enzyme activity, and use this model to explain enzyme specificity.
2. Describe the effects of pH and temperature on enzyme activity.
3. Describe how enzyme concentration is measured.

## Materials

1. Beakers, rusty nails, chicken liver
2. Hydrogen peroxide
3. Test tubes, mechanical pipettor, 0.10-ml pipettes
4. Constant temperature water bath set at 37° C
5. Colorimeter
6. Alkaline phosphatase assay reagents (American Monitor)

Enzymes are biological **catalysts;** that is, enzymes are substances that increase the rate of chemical reaction without changing the nature of the reaction and without being altered by the reaction. The catalytic process occurs in two stages: (1) the reactants (hereafter referred to as the *substrates* of the enzyme) attach to the surface of the enzyme, forming an *enzyme-substrate complex;* (2) the enzyme-substrate complex dissociates into free enzyme and *products.*

$$E \quad + \quad S \; \rightleftarrows \; ES \longrightarrow E \quad + \quad P$$

| Enzyme | Substrate | Enzyme-substrate complex | Enzyme | Product |

**Figure 2.8.** The lock-and-key model of enzyme action. The enzyme (E) and substrate (S) combine to form a complex (ES), which can either dissociate to yield the original substrate or combine to form the product (P) of the reaction. In either case, the free enzyme is regenerated at the end of the reaction.

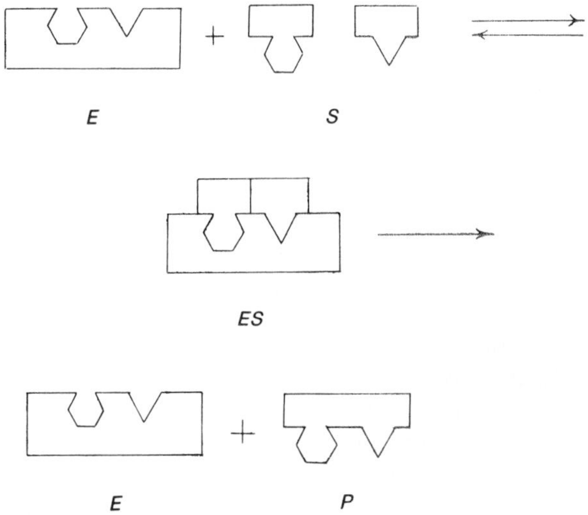

All enzymes are proteins (although not all proteins are enzymes). The polypeptide chain of each enzyme bends and folds in a unique way to produce a characteristic three-dimensional structure. The substrates interact with a specific part of this structure, the **active site,** which is complementary in shape to the substrate molecules. This is most easily visualized by the *lock-and-key* model of enzyme action (fig. 2.8).

The shape of the active site is determined by the amino acid sequence of the protein, and this shape is different for different enzymes. Enzymes are *relatively specific* as to the substrates with which they can interact and as to the reactions they can catalyze.

The relative specificity of an enzyme can often be deduced from its name. Thus, the enzyme lactate dehydrogenase removes a hydrogen from lactic acid (the suffix *-ase* denotes an enzyme), whereas phosphatase enzymes hydrolyze the phosphate group from a wide variety of organic compounds. These rules do not apply to enzymes that were discovered before a systematic terminology was developed, such as the digestive enzymes pepsin and trypsin, which hydrolyze peptide bonds.

Since enzymatic activity is dependent on the delicate bending and folding of polypeptide chains, changes in pH and temperature, which affect the three-dimensional structure of proteins, also affect enzymatic activity. Although most enzymes have their maximum activity at pH 7–8 and at 40°–45° C, the **pH optimum** and **temperature optimum** of one enzyme may be significantly different from those of another. Enzymatic activity diminishes when the pH or temperature increases or decreases from the optimal characteristics for that enzyme.

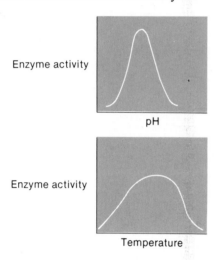

The activity of many enzymes is absolutely dependent on the presence of specific, smaller, nonprotein molecules called *cofactors* or *coenzymes*. Cofactors are specific inorganic ions (e.g., $Mg^{++}$) required for enzyme activity, and coenzymes are organic compounds (derived from the water-soluble vitamins) that play a similar role.

To assay the enzyme activity in an unknown sample, sufficient cofactors (or coenzymes) must be provided, and the pH and temperature must be standardized. In addition, the concentration of substrate should be very large compared with the concentration of enzyme, so that the availability of substrate does not limit the rate of the reaction. Under these conditions, the amount of product doubles when the concentration of enzyme doubles or when the reaction time doubles. If the reaction time is held constant, the amount of product formed is directly proportional to the enzyme concentration.

The concentration of enzyme in a sample is usually measured in **units of activity,** determined under conditions of specified pH, temperature, reaction time, and other controlled factors. For example, the normal concentration of serum alkaline phosphatase is 9–35 units per liter (U/L). The international unit is a measure of the reaction rate and may be determined by either the quantity of substrate consumed or the quantity of product formed in a given time interval.

One **international unit (I.U.)** is defined as *the quantity of enzyme required to convert one micromole of substrate per minute into products,* under specified conditions of pH, temperature, and other controlled factors.

In the following exercises, the activity of three enzymes found in serum will be assayed. These enzymes are not normally active in serum but are cellular enzymes released into the blood by damaged tissues. These enzymatic assays are often valuable in the diagnosis of certain diseases.

## A. Liver Catalase

Catalase is an enzyme that is present in many tissues and that converts hydrogen peroxide to water and oxygen gas.

$$2H_2O_2 \xrightarrow{\text{catalase}} 2H_2O + O_2$$

Substrate  Products

### Procedure

1. Fill two small beakers (100 ml) half-full with hydrogen peroxide.
2. Observe the effect of an inorganic catalyst by immersing a rusty nail or similar object in the solution in one beaker and gently stirring.
3. Mince a fresh chicken liver with scissors, and add it to the hydrogen peroxide in the second beaker. Stir the solution, and record your observations in the laboratory report.

## B. Assay of Alkaline Phosphatase Activity: Effect of Enzyme Concentration and Incubation Time

In this assay, the enzyme alkaline phosphatase hydrolyzes a phosphate group from the artificial substrate thymolphthalein monophosphate. The addition of alkali both stops the reaction and converts the free thymolphthalein to a blue-colored compound.

Thymolphthalein $\xrightarrow{\text{alkaline phosphatase}}$ thymolphthalein
monophosphate + phosphate
**Substrate** **Products**

**Figure 2.9.** A chart for the procedure of measuring alkaline phosphatase activity as a function of enzyme concentration.

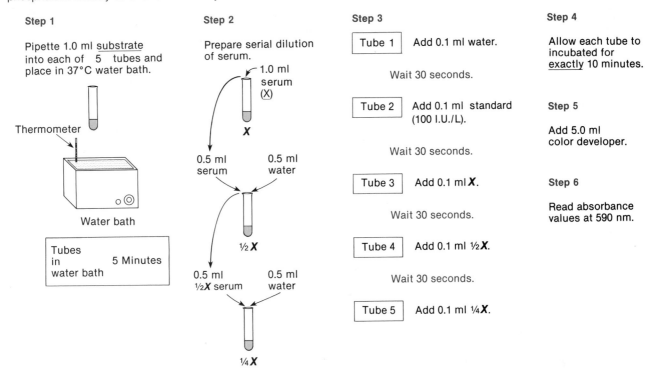

## Clinical Significance

There are two enzymes in serum that have phosphatase activity (remove phosphate from organic compounds). One of these has a pH optimum of 4.9–5.0 (*acid phosphatase*), and the other has a pH optimum of 9.8 (*alkaline phosphatase*). Abnormally high levels of serum acid phosphatase activity may be found in patients with cancer of the prostate, whereas elevated alkaline phosphatase activity is associated with various liver and bone diseases.

## Procedure

*Effect of Enzyme Concentration (fig. 2.9)*

1. Label five test tubes 1–5. Pipette 1.0 ml of substrate into each tube, and let it stand in a 37° C water bath for 5 minutes.[5] (This step is a preincubation.)
2. While the first five tubes are preincubating, prepare a second set of three tubes for **serial dilution** of serum as follows.
   a) Pipette 1.0 ml of serum into the first tube. Label this tube X.
   b) Pipette 0.5 ml of the solution in tube X into a second tube. Then pipette 0.5 ml of distilled water into this tube and mix. Label the tube ½X.
   c) Pipette 0.5 ml of the solution in tube ½X into a third tube. Then pipette 0.5 ml of distilled water into this tube and mix. Label the tube ¼X.
3. At the end of the preincubation period, pipette 0.1 ml of water into tube 1, and 30 seconds later, pipette 0.1 ml of *standard* (100 I.U./L) into tube 2. Quickly return each tube to the 37° C water bath, and record the time.
4. Thirty seconds after the addition of standard to tube 2, pipette 0.1 ml of undiluted serum from tube X into tube 3. Since the serum contains alkaline phosphatase, the addition of serum starts the reaction.
5. Thirty seconds after the addition of undiluted serum to tube 3, pipette 0.1 ml of the solution in tube ½X into tube 4, and 30 seconds later, pipette 0.1 ml of the solution from tube ¼X into tube 5.
6. Terminate the incubations at the end of 10 minutes by pipetting 5.0 ml of *color developer* into each tube.

**Note:** *Since the beginnings of incubation for the five tubes were staggered by 30 seconds, the ends of incubation should be likewise staggered, so that each tube incubates for **exactly** 10 minutes.*

---

5. For Azeurechrome Alkaline Phosphatase, American Monitor.

**Figure 2.10.** A chart of the procedure for measuring alkaline phosphatase activity as a function of incubation time.

**Step 1**

Pipette 1.0 ml substrate into each of 5 tubes and place in 37°C water bath.

**Step 2**

Add 0.1 ml (100 μl) of the following to each tube.

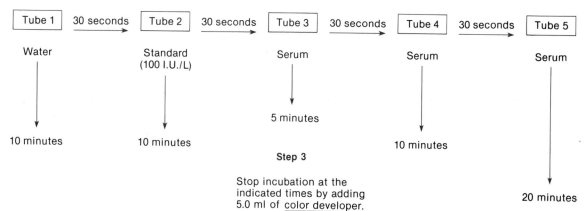

| Tube 1 | 30 seconds | Tube 2 | 30 seconds | Tube 3 | 30 seconds | Tube 4 | 30 seconds | Tube 5 |
|---|---|---|---|---|---|---|---|---|
| Water | | Standard (100 I.U./L) | | Serum | | Serum | | Serum |
| 10 minutes | | 10 minutes | | 5 minutes | | 10 minutes | | 20 minutes |

**Step 3**

Stop incubation at the indicated times by adding 5.0 ml of color developer.

**Step 4**

Read absorbance values at 590 nm.

---

7. Set the colorimeter at 590 nm, and record the absorbance values of the standard (100 I.U./L) and of the unknowns in the laboratory report.
8. Using Beer's law, calculate the alkaline phosphatase concentration (in I.U./L) of the unknown serum $X$. Enter this value in the space provided in the laboratory report.

> The normal range for alkaline phosphatase concentrations in plasma is 9–35 I.U./L.

9. Again using Beer's law, calculate the enzyme concentration for the ½$X$ sample and for the ¼$X$ sample. Record these values in your laboratory report.

**Procedure**

*Effect of Incubation Time (fig. 2.10)*

1. Label five test tubes 1–5. Pipette 1.0 ml of *substrate* into each tube, and let it stand in a 37° C water bath for 5 minutes.[6] (This step is a preincubation.)
2. At the end of the preincubation, pipette 0.1 ml of water into tube 1, and 30 seconds later, pipette 0.1 ml of *standard* (100 I.U./L) into tube 2. Quickly return each tube to the water bath.

---

6. For Azeurechrome Alkaline Phosphatase, American Monitor.

3. Thirty seconds after the addition of standard to tube 2, pipette 0.1 ml of serum into tube 3 to begin the incubation. Pipette 0.1 ml of the same serum into tube 4 and 0.1 ml of serum into tube 5 at 30-second intervals.

4. After tube 3 has incubated for *exactly* 5 minutes, terminate the incubation by pipetting 5.0 ml of *color developer* into tube 3.

5. After tubes 1, 2, and 4 have incubated for *exactly* 10 minutes, terminate the reaction by pipetting 5.0 ml of *color developer* into these tubes.

6. After tube 5 has incubated for *exactly* 20 minutes, terminate the reaction by pipetting 5.0 ml of *color developer* into tube 5.

7. Set the colorimeter at 590 nm, and record the absorbance values of the standard (100 I.U./L) and of the unknowns in your laboratory report.

8. Using the absorbance values of the standard (tube 2—100 I.U./L) and of the unknown under comparable conditions (tube 4), calculate the alkaline phosphatase activity of the unknown serum. Enter this in your laboratory report.

9. Plot a graph of incubation time (*x* axis) versus absorbance values (*y* axis) for tubes 3, 4, and 5.

## C. Assay of Serum Transaminase Activity

**Transaminases** are enzymes that remove the amino group from amino acids and transfer it to *keto acids* (either pyruvic acid or one of the Krebs cycle acids), thus forming new amino acids and new keto acids. If the human diet contains adequate amounts of the eight *essential amino acids* (which cannot be made by transamination because of the lack of the proper transaminases) and adequate amounts of carbohydrates (which are needed for production of the keto acids), the body cells can produce all the other amino acids required for protein synthesis.

The reactions catalyzed by glutamine pyruvate transaminase (GPT) and glutamine oxaloacetate transaminase (GOT) are shown here.

**Glutamic acid** + *pyruvic acid* $\xrightarrow{\text{(GPT)}}$ *a-ketoglutaric acid* + **alanine**

**Glutamic acid** + *oxaloacetic acid* $\xrightarrow{\text{(GOT)}}$ *a-ketoglutaric acid* + **aspartic acid**

## Clinical Significance

There are two enzymes in serum that have phosphatase activity (remove phosphate from organic compounds). One of these has a pH optimum of 4.9–5.0 (*acid phosphatase*), and the other has a pH optimum of 9.8 (*alkaline phosphatase*). Abnormally high levels of serum acid phosphatase activity may be found in patients with cancer of the prostate, while elevated alkaline phosphatase activity is associated with various liver and bone diseases.

While both the enzymes glutamate pyruvate transaminase (GPT) and glutamate oxaloacetate transaminase (GOT) may be elevated in the serum in disease, particular diseases result in the disproportionate increase of one of the pair of enzymes over the other. An increase in SGPT activity is associated with liver disease (e.g., hepatitus) and with infectious mononucleosis. An increase in SGOT activity occurs within 2 days after a myocardial infarction (heart attack). The assay of SGOT activity in serum, together with the measurement of other enzymes—creatine phosphokinase (CPK) and lactate dehydrogenase (LDH)—is thus helpful in the diagnosis of heart disease.

### Procedure (see fig. 2.11)

1. Pipette 1.0 ml of GPT substrate into tube 1 and 1.0 ml of GOT substrate into tube 2. Label a third tube 1b and a fourth tube 2b (these will be the blanks for tubes 1 and 2, respectively). Let all four tubes stand in a 37°C water bath for 5 minutes.

2. Pipette 0.2 ml of the unknown serum into tube 1, wait 30 seconds, pipette 0.2 ml of unknown serum into tube 2, and then add 0.2 ml of distilled water into each of the blank tubes.

3. Thirty minutes after the addition of serum to tube 1, pipette 1.0 ml of color developer into tube 1 and into tube 1b, and remove these two tubes from the water bath.

4. Twenty minutes after the addition of color developer, pipette 10.0 ml of 0.4*N* sodium hydroxide (NaOH) each to tube 1 and tube 1b. Mix the tubes thoroughly and allow them to stand at room temperature for at least 5 minutes.

5. Set the colorimeter at 505 nm, standardize with the blank, and read the absorbance of the unknown.

6. One hour after the addition of serum to tube 2, pipette 1.0 ml of color developer into tubes 2 and 2b and remove them from the water bath.

7. Twenty minutes after the addition of color developer, pipette 10.0 ml of 0.4*N* NaOH each to tube 2 and tube 2b. Mix the tubes thoroughly and allow them to stand at room temperature for at least 5 minutes.

**Figure 2.11**   Chart for the serum transaminase procedure.

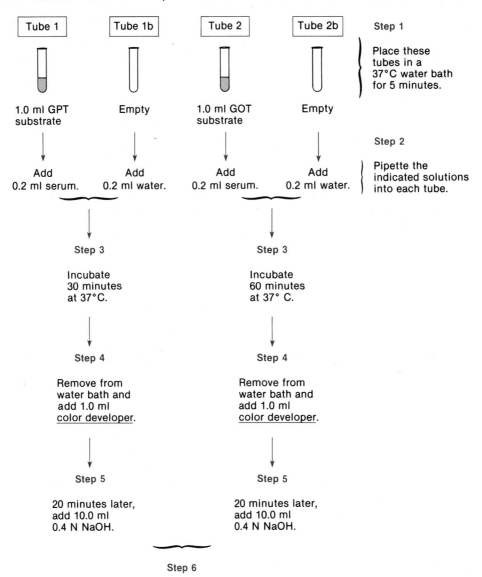

| Tube 1 | Tube 1b | Tube 2 | Tube 2b | **Step 1** |
|---|---|---|---|---|
| 1.0 ml GPT substrate | Empty | 1.0 ml GOT substrate | Empty | Place these tubes in a 37°C water bath for 5 minutes. |

**Step 2**

| Add 0.2 ml serum. | Add 0.2 ml water. | Add 0.2 ml serum. | Add 0.2 ml water. | Pipette the indicated solutions into each tube. |
|---|---|---|---|---|

**Step 3**

Incubate 30 minutes at 37°C.

**Step 3**

Incubate 60 minutes at 37° C.

**Step 4**

Remove from water bath and add 1.0 ml color developer.

**Step 4**

Remove from water bath and add 1.0 ml color developer.

**Step 5**

20 minutes later, add 10.0 ml 0.4 N NaOH.

**Step 5**

20 minutes later, add 10.0 ml 0.4 N NaOH.

**Step 6**

Read absorbance values at 505 nm.

8. Set the colorimeter at 505 nm, standardize with the blank, and read the absorbance of the unknown.

## Procedure
### Standard Curve (SGOT and SGPT)

1. Label four test tubes 1a–4a and pipette the following reagents into their respective tubes.[7]

| Tube | Water | SGOT Substrate | Calibration Standard | SGOT U/ml |
|---|---|---|---|---|
| 1a | 0.2 ml | 1.0 ml | None | 0 |
| 2a | 0.2 ml | 0.9 ml | 0.1 ml | 22 |
| 3a | 0.2 ml | 0.8 ml | 0.2 ml | 55 |
| 4a | 0.2 ml | 0.7 ml | 0.3 ml | 95 |

**Note:** *The S in SGOT and SGPT stands for* serum.

7. For Dade SGOT and SGPT Reagent Kit.

2. Label four test tubes 1b–4b and pipette the following reagents into their respective tubes.

| Tube | Water | SGPT Substrate | Calibration Standard | SGPT U/ml |
|---|---|---|---|---|
| 1b | 0.2 ml | 1.0 ml | None | 0 |
| 2b | 0.2 ml | 0.9 ml | 0.1 ml | 25 |
| 3b | 0.2 ml | 0.8 ml | 0.2 ml | 50 |
| 4b | 0.2 ml | 0.7 ml | 0.3 ml | 83 |

3. Add 1.0 ml of color developer to each tube and let stand at room temperature for 20 minutes.
4. Add 10.0 ml of 0.4N NaOH to each tube and let stand at room temperature for 5 minutes.
5. Standardize the colorimeter at 505 nm with the blank (tube 1a or 1b) and read the absorbance values of the other solutions against their respective blanks. Record these values in your laboratory report.

# Laboratory Report 2.4

## Data from Exercise 2.4

### A. Liver Catalase

1. Describe what occurred when the rusty nail was placed in the beaker of hydrogen peroxide. Write an equation to describe the reaction.

2. Describe what occurred when the chicken liver was placed in the hydrogen peroxide, and explain your observations.

### B. Assay of Alkaline Phosphatase Activity: Effect of Enzyme Concentration and Incubation Time

1. Effect of enzyme concentration

   (a) Record your absorbance values in the spaces below.

| Tube Number | Concentration | Absorbance |
|---|---|---|
| 1 | 0 | 0 |
| 2 | 100 I.U./L | |
| 3 | $X$ | |
| 4 | $\frac{1}{2}X$ | |
| 5 | $\frac{1}{4}X$ | |

   (b) Calculate the alkaline phosphatase concentrations in the unknown samples, and record the values in the spaces below.

   $X$ _____ I.U./L

   $\frac{1}{2}X$ _____ I.U./L

   $\frac{1}{4}X$ _____ I.U./L

   (c) Are your values as predicted? Explain.

2. Effect of incubation time

(a) Enter your absorbance values in the spaces below.

| Tube Number | Incubation Time | Absorbance |
|---|---|---|
| 1 | 0 | 0 |
| 2 | 10 minutes (standard) | |
| 3 | 5 minutes | |
| 4 | 10 minutes | |
| 5 | 20 minutes | |

(b) Calculate the alkaline phosphatase concentration of the unknown sample incubated for 10 minutes, and enter this value in the space below.

_____ I.U./L

(c) Plot a graph, using the graph paper provided, of incubation time ($x$ axis) versus absorbance values ($y$ axis) for tubes 3, 4, and 5.

(d) Is your graph as predicted? Explain.

## C. Assay of Serum Transaminase Activity

1. Enter your absorbance values for the serum samples in the spaces: SGOT _____ ; SGPT _____

2. Enter your absorbance values for the SGOT and SGPT standards in the tables below:

| Units SGOT/ml | Absorbance |
|---|---|
| 22 | |
| 55 | |
| 95 | |

| Units SGPT/ml | Absorbance |
|---|---|
| 25 | |
| 50 | |
| 83 | |

3. Draw two standard curves on the graph paper provided, one for SGOT and one for SGPT, and determine the activity of each enzyme in the unknown serum sample.

    a. SGOT activity = _____ I.U./ml

    b. SGPT activity = _____ I.U./ml

> The normal range for SGOT activity is 8–40 I.U./ml.
> The normal range for SGPT activity is 5–30 I.U./ml.

## Questions for Exercise 2.4

1. What is a "unit" of enzyme activity? Why is enzyme concentration expressed in activity units?

2. What is meant by the pH and temperature "optima" of an enzyme? Why do enzymes exhibit pH and temperature optima?

3. Suppose you were to continue the experiment of measuring the absorbance of product as a function of incubation time for several hours. Would your graph continue to be linear? Explain.

4. The essential amino acids cannot be synthesized by the body and must be included in the diet, while the other amino acids may be absent from the diet. Explain.

Cell Function and Biochemical Measurements

# Genetic Control of Metabolism

Since a different gene codes for the production of each enzyme, a defective gene can result in a specific metabolic disorder. These inborn errors of metabolism can be detected by tests for specific enzyme products.

## Objectives

1. Define the terms *genotype, phenotype, transcription,* and *translation*.
2. Describe how genes regulate metabolic pathways.
3. Describe how inborn errors of metabolism are produced.
4. Explain the etiology (cause) of phenylketonuria (PKU).

## Materials

1. Test tubes, Pasteur pipettes (droppers), urine collection cups
2. Phenistix (Ames), silver nitrate (3 g per 100 ml), 10% ammonium hydroxide, 40% sodium hydroxide, lead acetate (saturated)

The physical appearance and health of an individual (**phenotype**) is determined, to a significant degree, by the individual's genetic endowment (**genotype**). The control of the phenotype by the genotype is achieved by means of the genetic regulation of cellular metabolism.

All of the chemical reactions of cellular metabolism are catalyzed by specific enzymes, and the information for the synthesis of each specific enzyme is coded by a specific gene. That is, one gene makes one enzyme, which is capable of catalyzing one type of reaction (changing $A$ to $B$, for example).

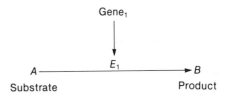

The product of this reaction may become the substrate of a second enzyme, made by a second gene, which converts $B$ into a new product, $C$. A third enzyme, made by a third gene, may then convert $C$ into $D$. Thus, a **metabolic pathway** is formed, where the product of one enzyme becomes the substrate of the next. In a metabolic pathway, the initial substrate (e.g., $A$) is converted into a final product (e.g., $D$) through a number of *intermediates* (e.g., $B$ and $C$).

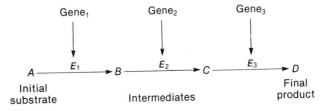

Genes contain the information for the synthesis of all proteins, not only those with enzymatic activity. The genetic code is based on the sequence of DNA components known as nucleotide bases (adenine, guanine, cytosine, thymine). Thus, the sequence of these bases is different in different genes.

The sequence of bases on the DNA that composes one gene is used as a template for the synthesis of one RNA molecule. The RNA molecule consists of a linear sequence of nucleotide bases (uracil, cytosine, guanine, and adenine), which is exactly complementary to the sequence of bases on the region of the DNA (gene) on which it was made. This complementarity is assured by the fact that only a specific base on the RNA can bond to a specific base on the DNA.

DNA  $- A - A - A - A - T - G - C - G - T - T - T - C -$  *Krebs*
                                                          *Cycle* $\leftarrow$
RNA  $- U - U - U - U - A - C - G - C - A - A - A - G -$

A part of the genetic code has thus been transcribed by the synthesis of a specific RNA molecule; this process is called genetic **transcription.** This RNA contains a part of the genetic message and is called *messenger RNA (mRNA).*

The messenger RNA, in association with ribosomes, forms the template for protein synthesis, where the sequence of amino acids in the protein is specified by the sequence of bases in the mRNA. The genetic code is based on the fact that a sequence of three mRNA bases (a *base triplet*) is able to bond to only a specific amino acid through an intermediate compound called *transfer RNA (tRNA).*

PKU

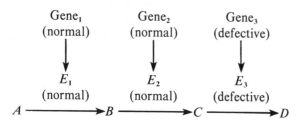

In this way, the sequence of bases in the mRNA determines the sequence of amino acids in the protein; this process is called genetic **translation.** The sequence of amino acids, in turn, determines how the protein will fold (i.e., its three-dimensional structure). The three-dimensional structure of a protein directly determines its function.

## Inborn Errors of Metabolism

When a gene is missing or defective, the enzyme that it makes will also be missing or defective. This will result in a hereditary metabolic disorder in which the intermediates after the step catalyzed by the enzyme are absent and the intermediates before this step accumulate in the blood and body tissues and are excreted in the urine.

Gene$_1$          Gene$_2$          Gene$_3$
(normal)         (normal)         (defective)

$\downarrow$      $\downarrow$      $\downarrow$

$E_1$             $E_2$             $E_3$
(normal)          (normal)          (defective)

$A \longrightarrow B \longrightarrow C \longrightarrow D$

Thus, *D* decreases, and *A, B,* and *C* increase.

There are a number of genetic defects associated with the metabolism of the amino acids phenylalanine and tyrosine. The phenotypic effects of these **inborn errors of metabolism** depend on which enzymes are defective and therefore on which intermediate products either are absent or accumulate in the body tissues.

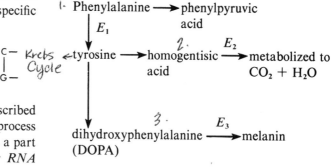

1. Phenylalanine $\longrightarrow$ phenylpyruvic acid
   $E_1$

2. tyrosine $\longrightarrow$ homogentisic acid $\xrightarrow{E_2}$ metabolized to $CO_2 + H_2O$

3. dihydroxyphenylalanine (DOPA) $\xrightarrow{E_3}$ melanin

1. Absence of $E_1$ $\xrightarrow{\text{build up}}$ phenylketonuria (PKU)
2. Absence of $E_2$ $\longrightarrow$ alkaptonuria
3. Absence of $E_3$ $\longrightarrow$ albinism

Probably the best-known phenotypic effect of this group of hereditary disorders is the lack of *melanin* pigment characteristic of the albino. Phenylketonuria (PKU) is the most clinically serious member of this group of disorders, where the accumulation of phenylpyruvic acid can affect the developing central nervous system and produce mental retardation. These odious effects can only be avoided by placing the child with PKU on a low phenylalanine diet.

## Clinical Significance

Since we cannot at present remove defective genes from people and replace them with good genes, the only course available involves early, correct diagnosis and preventive measures. For this reason, newborn babies are routinely tested for PKU so that they can be placed on low phenylalanine diets if they have this disease. Unfortunately, many other inborn errors of metabolism cannot be treated by dietary restrictions; the only way to prevent some of these diseases is by the genetic counseling of potential parents who are carriers of the disease.

When there is a defective enzyme in a metabolic pathway, the molecule that is the substrate of that enzyme accumulates in particular tissues of the body. Such inborn errors of metabolism are not restricted to pathways of amino acid metabolism. In *Tay-Sachs disease,* for example, there is a defect in the enzyme (hexosaminidase A) that breaks down a complex type of lipid known as a ganglioside, resulting in lipid accumulation in the brain and retina. This disease, which is found predominately in Ashkenazi Jews, is invariably fatal. There are also errors in carbohydrate metabolism: in *glycogen storage disease,* for example, the enzyme that breaks down glycogen may be defective, resulting in the excessive accumulation of glycogen and liver disease.

## A. Phenylketonuria

The person with PKU excretes large amounts of phenyl-pyruvic acid because of the inability to convert the amino acid phenylalanine into the amino acid tyrosine.

### Procedure

1. Dip the test end of a Phenistix[8] strip into a sample of urine.
2. Compare the color of the strip with the color chart provided.

## B. Alkaptonuria

The person with alkaptonuria excretes large amounts of homogentisic acid, which reacts with silver to form a black precipitate. This condition does not appear to have any adverse effects on the health of the individual.

### Procedure

1. Add 10 drops of urine to a test tube containing five drops of 3% silver nitrate ($AgNO_3$).
2. Add 5 drops of 10% ammonium hydroxide ($NH_4OH$) to the tube and mix.
3. A positive test is indicated by the presence of a black precipitate.

---

8. From Ames Laboratories.

## C. Cystinuria

The renal tubules can normally reabsorb all of the amino acids filtered in the glomerulus. People with the *recessive trait* known as **cystinuria,** however, have an impaired ability to reabsorb the amino acid cystine and the related amino acids lysine, arginine, and ornithine.

Cystine is the least soluble amino acid and may precipitate in the urinary tract to form stones. This condition accounts for 1%–2% of the cases of renal stones in the United States. (About 10% are uric acid stones, and the remainder are formed from calcium salts, primarily calcium oxalate.)

### Procedure

1. Add 1.0 ml of 40% NaOH to a test tube containing 5.0 ml of urine. Allow the tube to cool.
2. Add 3.0 ml of lead acetate. A brown to black precipitate indicates the presence of cystine in the urine.

1. What do the terms *genotype* and *phenotype* mean? How does the genotype control the phenotype?

2. Define the terms *metabolic pathway* and *inborn errors of metabolism*. Illustrate by describing the etiology of albinism.

3. Explain the etiology of phenylketonuria.

# Diffusion, Osmosis, and Tonicity

Osmosis occurs passively when a membrane that is permeable to water separates two solutions that have different total concentrations of solutes to which the membrane is relatively impermeable. There is no osmosis when a membrane separates two isotonic solutions.

## Objectives

1. Define the terms *osmosis, osmotic pressure,* and *osmolality.*
2. Define the terms *isotonic, hypotonic,* and *hypertonic.*
3. Calculate the osmolality of solutions when the concentration of solute (in g/L) and the molecular weight of a solute are known.
4. Describe osmosis and the effect on red blood cells when these cells are placed in isotonic, hypotonic, and hypertonic solutions.

## Materials

1. Test tubes, thistle tubes, dialysis tubing
2. Beakers, ring stands, burette clamp
3. Lancets, alcohol swabs
4. Microscopes, slides, cover slips, and transfer pipettes
5. Sucrose (30 g per 100 ml) and various sodium chloride solutions (0.20 g, 0.45 g, 0.85 g, 3.5 g, and 10 g per 100 ml each)
6. Benzene, potassium permanganate crystals, vegetable oil, laboratory detergent

If you were to drop a pinch of sugar (the *solute*) into a beaker of water (the *solvent*), the resulting *solution* would, after a time, have a uniform sweetness. The uniform sweetness would result because all the solute and solvent molecules in the solution are in a constant state of random motion, producing a net movement of solute molecules from regions of higher concentration to regions of lower concentration. This net movement of solute molecules is known as **diffusion.**

The rate of diffusion is proportional to the concentration differences that exist in the solution. The diffusion rate will steadily decrease as the solute becomes evenly distributed in the solvent, and net diffusion will cease entirely when the solution becomes uniform.

A molecule may move into or out of a cell by diffusion if (1) a difference in the concentration of that molecule (*concentration gradient*) exists between the intracellular and extracellular compartments and (2) the cell membrane will allow the passage of that molecule.

The movement of a molecule across the cell membrane by diffusion is called **passive transport.** The term *passive* is used because the cell need not expend energy in the process. In contrast, cells often must move molecules across the cell membrane from lower to higher concentrations; that is, cells must "fight" diffusion and maintain a concentration difference across the membrane. To move molecules "uphill" against their concentration gradients, the cells must expend energy. The process is called **active transport.** Sodium, for example, is maintained at a higher concentration outside the cell than inside the cell, whereas potassium is maintained at a higher concentration inside the cell than outside the cell.

The *permeability* of a membrane refers to the ease with which substances can pass through (permeate) it. A membrane that is completely permeable to all molecules is not a barrier to diffusion, whereas a membrane that is completely impermeable to all molecules essentially divides the solutions into two noncommunicating compartments. Since a living cell must selectively interact with its environment, taking in raw materials and excreting waste products, the cell is surrounded by a membrane that is **semi-** (or **selectively**) **permeable.** A semipermeable membrane is completely permeable to some molecules, slightly permeable to others, and completely impermeable to still others.

The cell membrane is composed primarily of two semifluid phospholipid layers, where proteins float partially submerged on both the inner and outer surfaces. The membrane is not continuous but behaves as if it has tiny *pores* that can serve as channels for diffusion, allowing the passage of small molecules while excluding the passage of molecules larger than the pore size. These channels may consist of proteins that span the complete thickness of the membrane.

## A. Solubility of Compounds in Polar and Nonpolar Solvents

Most of the molecules that a cell encounters are water soluble (easily dissolved in water). Such molecules have charged groups and are said to be *polar*. The lipids of the cell membrane are *nonpolar* and serve as a barrier to the passage of polar molecules across the membrane. Small polar molecules may pass through the pores in the lipid barrier, but large polar molecules (e.g., proteins and polysaccharides) are restricted by the pore size.

Many organic solvents (e.g., benzene) are nonpolar; that is, they are soluble in lipids but not in water. Such nonpolar molecules are not limited by the membrane pores and can rapidly diffuse into the cells by going through the lipid layers of the membrane.

### Procedure

1. Pour about 2.0 ml of water and 2.0 ml of benzene into a test tube.
2. Shake the tube, and record your observations in the laboratory report.
3. Using forceps, drop 2–3 crystals of potassium permanganate ($KMnO_4$) into the tube. Shake the tube, and record your observations in the laboratory report.
4. Add about 1.0 ml of yellow vegetable oil to the tube. Shake the tube, and record your observations in the laboratory report.
5. Add a pinch of laboratory detergent to the tube. Shake it, and record your observations in the laboratory report.

**Note:** *One end of the detergent molecule is polar (charged), the other end is nonpolar. The detergent can thus act as a bridge between the two phases.*

Detergent

Nonpolar end          Polar end

**Figure 2.12.** A model of osmosis, where solution A is separated from solution B by a semipermeable membrane. Since solution B is more dilute than solution A, and since the membrane is impermeable to solute molecules (open circles), there is a net movement of water molecules (solid circles) from solution B to solution A. The solid arrows indicate the direction of the net movement of water molecules, whereas the broken arrows indicate the movement of water molecules in a direction that is canceled by the movement of water molecules in the opposite direction.

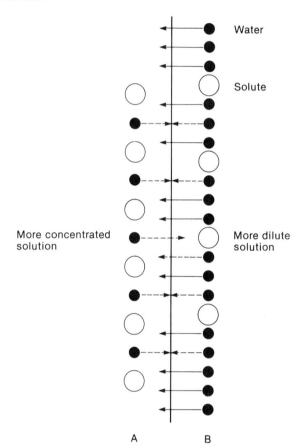

## B. Osmosis across an Artificial Semipermeable Membrane

Imagine a solution divided into two compartments by a membrane. If the membrane is completely permeable to solute and solvent molecules, these molecules can diffuse across it so that the solute/solvent ratio (concentration) is the same on both sides of the membrane. Suppose, however, that the membrane is permeable to the solvent but not to the solute. If the solvent is water, the water will diffuse from the region where the solute/solvent ratio is *lowest* (relatively more water) to the region where the solute/solvent ratio is *highest* (relatively less water) until the solute/solvent ratio (concentration) is the same on both sides of the membrane. This process is called **osmosis** (fig. 2.12).

In osmosis, water diffuses into the more highly concentrated (greater solute/solvent ratio) solution from the less highly concentrated solution. The more highly concentrated solution is said to have a greater **osmotic pressure** than the less concentrated solution. The osmotic pressure is a measure of the ability of a solution to pull in water from another solution that is separated from it by a semipermeable membrane. Since the osmotic pressure of a solution is proportional to its concentration, the osmotic pressure of distilled water is zero. Keep in mind, however, that the "pulling" is a metaphor; since osmosis is simply the diffusion of water through a membrane, water moves into the more concentrated solution as a result of its concentration gradient.

## Procedure

1. Cut a 2½-inch piece of dialysis tubing. Soak this piece in tap water until the layers separate. (You can speed this process by rotating the tubing between two fingers.) Slide one blade of the scissors between the two sides, and cut along the margin, producing a single rectangular sheet of dialysis tubing.

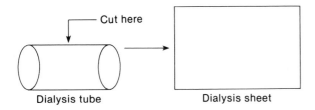

**Note:** *Dialysis tubing is a plastic porous material that can be used to separate molecules on the basis of their size. It is an artificial semipermeable membrane. Molecules that are larger than the pore size remain inside the tubing, whereas smaller molecules (including water) can move through the membrane by diffusion. This technique of biochemical separation is called dialysis.*

2. Hold a thistle tube vertically with the mouth upward. While one person closes the lower opening with one finger, another pours 30% sucrose solution into the mouth of the tube until the solution is about to overflow the tube.

3. Place the rectangular piece of dialysis tubing tightly over the mouth of the thistle tube, so that no air is trapped between the dialysis tubing and the sucrose. Keeping the dialysis tubing taut, secure it to the thistle tube with several wrappings of a rubber band.

4. Invert the thistle tube, and check for leaks. If leaks are observed, remove the dialysis tubing and repeat step 3.

**Figure 2.13.** A thistle tube setup for the osmosis exercise.

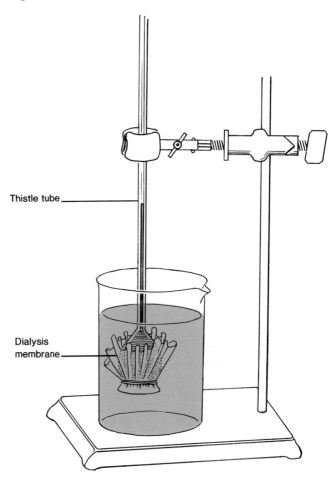

5. With the thistle tube inverted, immerse it into a large beaker of water (fig. 2.13). Secure the thistle tube in this position, using a ring stand and a burette clamp. A folded wad of paper towel will enable you to safely clamp the narrow part of the thistle tube.

6. Mark the meniscus of the 30% sucrose solution with a marking pen, and record the change in the level of this meniscus (in centimeters) every 15 minutes for a 1-hour period in the laboratory report.

## C. Concentration and Tonicity

Osmosis is the diffusion of water across a semipermeable membrane. For osmosis to occur, the membrane must be completely permeable to water but only partially permeable or completely impermeable to the solute. Such solutes are said to be *osmotically active.* Solutes that are as freely permeable as water are not osmotically active. Osmosis is caused by a difference in the concentration of osmotically active solutes, and the osmotic pressure of a solution is proportional to the concentration of osmotically active solute.

A number of different ways exist to describe the concentration of a solution. The simplest is to take the weight of the solute in grams or milligrams per 100 ml of solution. For example, 150 mg in 100 ml may be expressed as 150 mg per 100 ml—or as 150 mg%, or 150 mg/dl.

It is frequently more advantageous to express concentration in terms of *molarity* or *molality*. These measurements take into account the different molecular weights of the solutes; for example, a 1-molar (1 $M$) or a 1-molal (1 $m$) solution of sodium chloride (NaCl) would require you to weigh out a different amount of solute than you would for a 1 $M$ or a 1 $m$ solution of glucose ($C_6H_{12}O_6$). The common unit of weight in a 1 $M$ NaCl solution and a 1 $M$ glucose solution is the **mole.** The significance of this unit of measurement is that *solutions with equal molarities have equal numbers of molecules.* Although they weigh different amounts, a mole of NaCl contains the same number of molecules (Avogadro's number—$6.02 \times 10^{23}$) as a mole of glucose.

One mole is equal to the molecular weight of the solute in grams. The molecular weight is obtained by adding the atomic weights of the elements in the molecule.

*NaCl*

Atomic weights

| | | |
|---|---|---|
| Na | = | 23.0 |
| Cl | = | 35.5 |

Molecular weight = 58.5

*Glucose* ($C_6H_{12}O_6$)

Atomic weights

| | | | |
|---|---|---|---|
| $C_6$ | $12 \times 6$ = | 72 |
| $H_{12}$ | $1 \times 12$ = | 12 |
| $O_6$ | $16 \times 6$ = | 96 |

Molecular weight = 180

A 1-molar (1 $M$) solution contains 1 mole of solute in 1 L of solution. Thus, 1 $M$ NaCl contains 58.5 g of NaCl per liter, whereas 1 $M$ glucose contains 180 g glucose per liter. A 1-molal (1 $m$) solution of NaCl contains 1 mole of NaCl (58.5 g) dissolved in 1,000 g of solvent. If water is the solvent, 1,000 g equals 1,000 ml (at 4° C). A 1 $M$ solution has a final volume of 1,000 ml, whereas a 1 $m$ solution has a final volume that usually exceeds 1,000 ml.

It is obvious that decreasing the solute and the solvent by the same proportion does not change the concentration of the solution. A 1 $M$ glucose solution can be made by dissolving 90 g of glucose in a final volume of 500 ml or by dissolving 180 mg of glucose in 1 ml of solution.

If the concentration of osmotically active solute is the *same* on both sides of a membrane (the osmotic pressures are equal), osmosis will not occur (water movement is equal in both directions). These two solutions are said to be **isotonic** to each other (*iso* means "same"). If the concentration of a third solution is *less* than that of the first two solutions, it is said to be **hypotonic** to the first two solutions (*hypo* means "beneath"). Water will diffuse from the third solution into the first two solutions if these solutions are separated by a semipermeable membrane. If the concentration of a fourth solution is *greater* than that of the first two solutions, it is said to be **hypertonic** (*hyper* means "above") to the first two solutions. Water will diffuse out of the first two solutions and into the fourth if these solutions are separated by a semipermeable membrane. In all cases, water diffuses from the solution of lower osmotic pressure to the solution of greater osmotic pressure.

The osmotic pressure of a solution is proportional to the number of solute molecules in solution. A 1-molal solution of glucose, for example, has 1 mole of glucose molecules in solution. This solution would have the same osmotic pressure as a 1-molal solution of sucrose or a 1-molal solution of urea. These solutions are said to have the same **osmolality** (1.0 osmole/kg water). A solution containing 1 mole of glucose and 1 mole of urea would have an osmolality of 2 (2.0 Osm). The osmolality of a solution can be defined as the sum of all the moles of solute in a solution.

Some molecules *dissociate* when they are dissolved in solution. Common table salt (NaCl), for example, completely dissociates in solution to $Na^+$ and $Cl^-$. Thus, a 1-molal solution of NaCl has an osmolality of 2 (2.0 Osm). This solution would be isotonic to a 2-molal solution of glucose, which does not dissociate in solution.

$$1 \text{ mole NaCl} \longrightarrow 1 \text{ mole Na}^+ + 1 \text{ mole Cl}^-$$

It is frequently convenient to express concentration in terms of milliosmolality (mOsm). A 0.1-molal solution of NaCl, for example, has an osmolal concentration of 200 mOsm, whereas a 0.1-molal solution of glucose has an osmolal concentration of 100 mOsm.

## Tonicity of Saline Solutions Using Red Blood Cells as Osmometers

The red blood cell (RBC) has the same osmolality and, thus, the same osmotic pressure as plasma. When a red blood cell is placed in a hypotonic solution, it will expand or perhaps even burst (*hemolysis*) as a result of the influx of water, extruding hemoglobin into the solution. When it is placed in a hypertonic solution, it will shrink (*crenation*) as a result of the efflux of water (fig. 2.14).

Red blood cells can thus be used as *osmometers* to determine the osmolality of plasma, since the cells will neither expand nor shrink in an isotonic solution.

**Figure 2.14.** A scanning electron micrograph of a crenated red blood cell attached to a fibrin thread. Note the notched or scalloped appearance. From Kessel, R. G., and Kardon, R. H.: *Tissues and Organs: A Text-Atlas of Scanning Electron Microscopy.* © W. H. Freeman and Company, 1979.

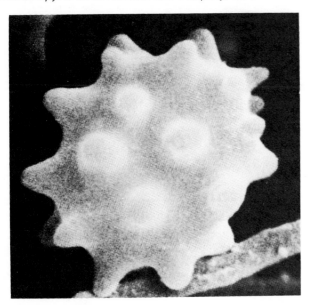

## Procedure

1. Measure 2.0 ml of the solutions indicated in part *C* of the laboratory report into each of five numbered test tubes.
2. Wipe the tip of your finger with alcohol, and using a sterile lancet, prick your finger to draw a drop of blood.
3. Allow the drop of blood to drain down the side of test tube 1. Mix the blood with the saline (salt) solution by inverting the test tube a few times.
4. Repeat the above procedure for test tubes 2–5. Additional drops of blood can be obtained by milking the finger.
5. Using a transfer pipette, place a drop of solution 1 on a slide, and cover it with a cover slip. Observe the cells using the 45× objective.
6. Repeat step 5 for the other solutions, and record your observations in the laboratory report.

## Clinical Significance

Osmolality determines the distribution of fluids between the intracellular compartments and the extracellular compartments of the body. An accumulation of fluid in the tissues (edema), for example, can result when the osmolality of the tissue spaces increases due to an accumulation of proteins. *Blood volume* and, therefore, blood pressure are maintained by an osmotic equilibrium between the plasma and the tissue fluids. Intravenous infusions for the purpose of maintaining blood volume and pressure must be isotonic to prevent the expansion or crenation of the body cells.

# Laboratory Report 2.6

Name _____

Date _____

Section _____

## Data for Exercise 2.6

### A. Solubility of Compounds in Polar and Nonpolar Solvents

1. Describe the appearance of the solutions after completing steps 2 and 3.

2. Describe the appearance of the solutions after completing steps 4 and 5.

### B. Osmosis across an Artificial Semipermeable Membrane

1. Enter your data in the table below.

| Time | Distance Meniscus Has Moved |
|------|------------------------------|
| 15 minutes | |
| 30 minutes | |
| 45 minutes | |
| 60 minutes | |

2. Explain your results.

## C. Concentration and Tonicity

1. Enter your data in the table below.

| Tube and Contents | Molality | Milliosmolality | Appearance of RBC | Diameter of RBC (micrometers) |
|---|---|---|---|---|
| 1  10 g/dl NaCl | | | | |
| 2  3.5 g/dl NaCl* | | | | |
| 3  0.85 g/dl NaCl | 0.145 *m* | 290 mOsm | | |
| 4  0.45 g/dl NaCl | | | | |
| 5  0.20 g/dl NaCl | | | | |

*Approximately the concentration of seawater.
Note: dl = 100 ml.

2. Which solution is isotonic? _____

3. Which solutions are hypotonic? _____

4. Which solutions are hypertonic? _____

# Questions for Exercise 2.6

1. Define the term *osmosis:* _____

_____

2. Define the term *isotonic:* _____

_____

3. Red blood cells _____ in a hypertonic solution.

4. A 0.10 M NaCl solution is _____ (iso/hypo/hypertonic) to a 0.10 M glucose solution.

5. Suppose a salt and a glucose solution are separated by a membrane that is permeable to water but not to the solutes. The NaCl solution has a concentration of 1.95 g per 250 ml (molecular weight = 58.5). The glucose solution has a concentration of 9.0 g per 250 ml (molecular weight = 180).

   Calculate the molality, millimolality, and milliosmolality of both solutions. Describe if and in which direction osmosis occurs, and explain your answer.

6. When the body needs to conserve water, the kidneys excrete a hypertonic urine. What does this mean, and how does this help to conserve water?

7. The receptors for thirst are located in a part of the brain called the *hypothalamus*. They are *osmoreceptors;* that is, they are stimulated by an increase in blood osmolality. Imagine a man who has just landed on a desert island. Trace the course of events leading to his sensation of thirst. Can he satisfy his thirst by drinking seawater? Explain.

8. Before the invention of refrigerators, pioneers preserved meat by salting it. Explain how meat can be preserved by this procedure.

# The Nervous System and Sensory Physiology

Despite changes in external temperature, the availability of foods, presence of toxic and threatening agents, and other influences, the internal environment of the body is remarkably constant. The science of physiology is largely a study of the *regulatory mechanisms* that maintain this internal constancy (or homeostasis). These regulatory mechanisms exist at a variety of interacting levels, including the (1) genetic control of enzyme synthesis; (2) enzymatic control of cellular metabolism; (3) local "intrinsic" feedback loops within organs; (4) regulation of one organ by the metabolic products of another; and (5) orchestration of the preceding regulatory mechanisms to meet the needs of the entire organism by the endocrine system and the nervous system.

To maintain homeostasis in the face of changing external conditions, the organism must be able to recognize specific environmental factors and make appropriate responses. At its simplest level, recognition is achieved through the stimulation of a specific type of *sensory receptor.* A given receptor will usually be affected by only one modality of stimulus; for example, the photoreceptors of the eye are stimulated by light. The receptor transduces the environmental stimulus into electrical nerve impulses, which then go to the specific part of the brain where the sensation is identified. This is known as the **law of specific nerve energies.**

The appropriate response to the environmental stimulus is made by the neural activation of *effector organs,* that is, *muscles* and *glands.* The activation of skeletal muscles by somatic motor nerves may produce a simple reflex action or may involve complex motor behavior. Autonomic motor nerves stimulate smooth muscles, exocrine glands (e.g., sweat glands, gastric glands), and some endocrine glands (e.g., the adrenal medulla). Many other endocrine glands are indirectly regulated by the hypothalamus through its control of the anterior pituitary, thus wedding the endocrine system to the nervous system. Interposed between these *afferent* (sensory) and *efferent* (motor) pathways, of course, are millions of *association neurons,* which integrate these activities and allow the individual to remember and learn from the experiences so that a more appropriate response may be given in the future.

# 3.1 Recording the Action Potential

The potential difference across axon membranes undergoes changes during the production of action potentials. As the axons of a nerve produce action potentials, the surface of the nerve at this region has a difference in potential compared to the surface of an unstimulated region. The polarity of this potential difference and its magnitude in millivolts can be seen in an oscilloscope.

## Objectives

1. Describe the resting membrane potential and the distribution of $Na^+$ and $K^+$ across the axon membrane.
2. Describe the events that occur during the production of an action potential.
3. Demonstrate the recording of action potentials in a frog sciatic nerve, and explain how this recording is produced.

## Materials

1. Frogs
2. Dissecting equipment and trays, glass probes, thread
3. Oscilloscope, nerve chamber
4. Frog Ringer's solution (see exercise 4.2)

A nerve cell (neuron) consists of three regions that are specialized for different functions: (1) the *dendrites* receive input from sensory receptors or from other neurons; (2) the *cell body* contains the nucleus and serves as the metabolic center of the cell; and (3) the *axon* conducts the nerve impulse to other neurons or to effector organs (fig. 3.1). A bundle of axons that leave the brain or spinal cord is known as a peripheral *nerve*.

## Membrane Potentials

If one lead of a voltmeter is placed on the surface of an axon and the other lead is placed in the cytoplasm, a *potential difference* (or voltage) will be measured across the axon membrane. The inside of the cell is 60 to 80 millivolts negative ($-80$ mV) with respect to the outside. (The surface of the axon is positive with respect to the cytoplasm.) This **resting membrane potential** is maintained by the unequal distribution of ions on the two sides of the membrane; $Na^+$ is present in higher concentrations outside the cell than inside, whereas $K^+$ is more concentrated inside the cell. These differences are maintained, in part, by active transport processes (the "sodium-potassium pump").

When a neuron is appropriately stimulated, the barriers to $Na^+$ are lifted and the positively charged $Na^+$ is allowed to diffuse into the cell along its concentration gradient. The flow of positive ions into the cell first abolishes the potential difference across the membrane and then continues until the polarity is actually reversed and the inside of the cell is positive with respect to the outside (about $+15$ mV); this phase is termed *depolarization*. At this point, the barriers to $K^+$ are lifted, and the flow of

Sodium comes through
Sodium gates

**Figure 3.1.** (a) A motor neuron. (b) A sensory neuron. Other types of neurons have different appearances, but all have the same basic components. Arrows indicate the direction of conduction.

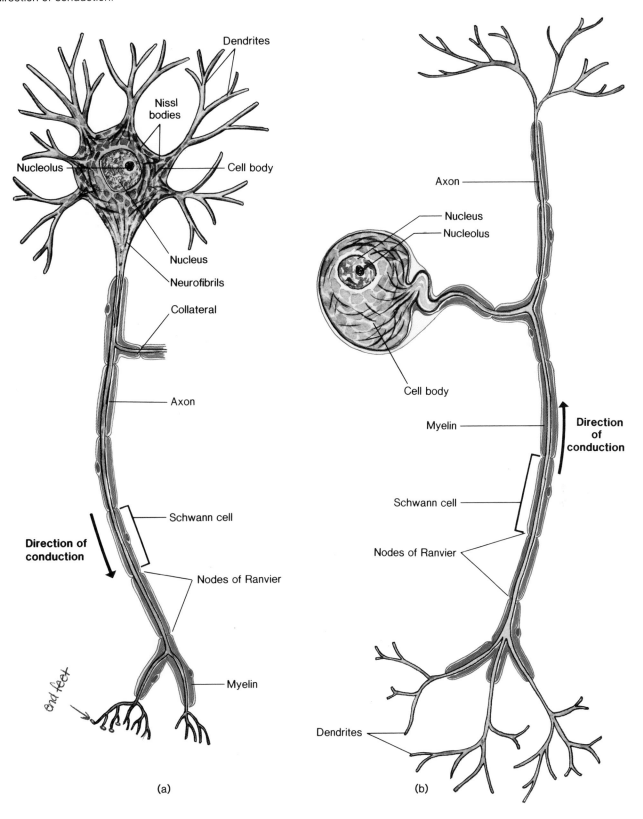

(a)

(b)

this positively charged ion out of the cell along its concentration gradient helps to reestablish the resting potential (*repolarization*). During the time of repolarization, the diffusion of $Na^+$ into the cell is blocked and the neuron is refractory to further stimulation, that is, in a *refractory period*. The momentary reversal and reestablishment of the resting potential is known as the **action potential** (fig. 3.2).

In this exercise, a frog sciatic nerve will be dissected and placed on two pairs of electrodes. One pair of electrodes (the "stimulating electrodes") will deliver a measured pulse of electricity to one point on the nerve, while the other pair (the "recording electrodes") will be connected to a cathode-ray tube of an oscilloscope, which is adjusted to sweep an electron beam horizontally across a screen when the nerve is unstimulated. The delivery of a small pulse of electricity through the stimulating electrodes produces a small vertical deflection at the beginning of the horizontal sweep. This vertical deflection (the *stimulus artifact*) increases in amplitude as the strength of the stimulating voltage is increased (fig. 3.3).

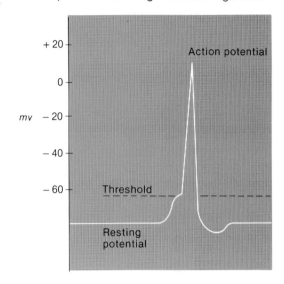

**Figure 3.2.** The action potential of a single nerve fiber. This is an all-or-none change in the membrane potential in response to a depolarizing stimulus above a threshold value. The action potential of a single nerve fiber is observed when a recording electrode is inserted into the cytoplasm of a neuron. Compare this recording with that of figure 3.3.

**Figure 3.3.** As the stimulus voltage is increased (from a through d), the amplitude of the stimulus artifact and nerve action potential (circled areas) are also increased, up to a maximum value (shown in d). This results from the fact that the sciatic nerve contains hundreds of nerve fibers. The number of individual nerve fibers stimulated to produce all-or-none action potentials is increased with increasing stimulus intensity, because some fibers are located closer to the stimulating electrodes than others.

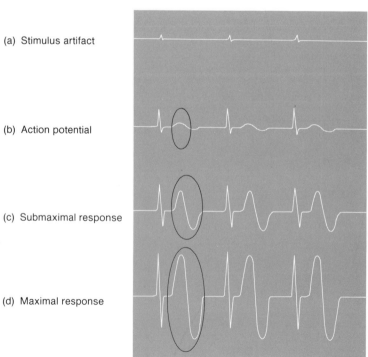

**Figure 3.4.** Nerve impulses are conducted from one region of a nerve fiber to the next by small circuits between the depolarized region and the adjacent region. These circuits depolarize the adjacent region to a threshold value, at which point the permeability of the membrane to Na$^+$ greatly increases. The resulting influx of Na$^+$ further depolarizes that region and produces the upshoot phase of the action potential.

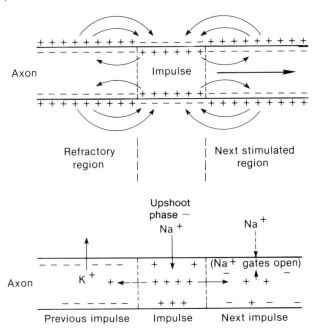

will increase the *amplitude* of each action potential up to a maximum level. This is because the action potential recorded from the nerve is the sum of the action potentials of the stimulated nerve fibers (axons); and as the strength of the stimulus is increased, the number of nerve fibers depolarized increases.

When impulses are recorded from individual nerve fibers (axons), the amplitude of the action potentials does not increase with increasing strength of stimulation. A neuron either does not "fire" (to any subthreshold stimulus) or it "fires" maximally (to any suprathreshold stimulus). This is known as the **all-or-none law** of nerve physiology. The strength of a stimulus, therefore, is coded in the nervous system by the *frequency*, not the amplitude, of action potentials; the stronger the stimulus, the greater the number (not the size) of action potentials carried by a nerve fiber in a given time.

*Brain interprets # of impulses, not amplitude — how many — not how much.*

## Use of the Oscilloscope

Electrical activity in nerves and nerve fibers is frequently observed with the use of an oscilloscope. In this instrument an electron beam, emitted from a cathode, strikes a phosphorescent screen and produces a light dot. Movement of the dot upward or downward is proportional to the voltage of the input from a nerve preparation. The oscilloscope, through vertical deflections of the electron beam, can thus function as a very sensitive voltmeter.

The electron beam is made to sweep from left to right across the screen at a particular rate. The image on the screen is thus a plot of voltage ($y$ axis) against time ($x$ axis). If the sweep of the electron beam is triggered by a stimulus to the nerve preparation, the electrical response of the nerve will always appear at the same time after the sweep has begun and thus at the same location on the screen. Since the phosphor in the screen continues to emit light long after it has been struck with electrons, an action potential produced in response to a second stimulus will be superimposed on the one produced in response to the previous stimulus. An observer will thus see an apparently stable image of an action potential, even though each action potential only lasts for about 3 msec.

Vertical deflections of the electron beam are produced when there is a potential difference, or voltage, developed between two *recording electrodes*, which touch the nerve some distance away from a pair of *stimulating electrodes* (fig. 3.5). Action potentials produced in the region of the nerve in contact with the recording electrodes result from the conduction of nerve impulses away from the region in contact with the stimulating electrodes. The first action potential, produced near the stimulating electrodes, results from a depolarizing current whose voltage, duration, and frequency (number of "shocks" per second) can be varied by adjustments of the stimulator module in the oscilloscope.

When the stimulating voltage reaches a sufficient level (the *threshold*), the region of the nerve next to the stimulating electrodes becomes depolarized (the outside of the nerve becomes negative with respect to the inside). By the creation of "minicircuits," this region depolarizes the adjacent region of the nerve, while it (the region nearest the stimulating electrodes) is being repolarized (fig. 3.4). In this manner, a wave of "surface negativity" is conducted from the stimulating electrodes toward the recording electrodes. When this wave reaches the first recording electrode, it becomes electrically negative with respect to the second electrode, since both are on the *surface* of the nerve and the depolarization wave has not yet reached the region of the second electrode. The potential difference between the two recording electrodes produces a vertical deflection of the electron beam a few milliseconds (msec) after the stimulus artifact. This is the action potential of the nerve.

The electrical activity of the nerve can be increased by increasing either the frequency or the strength of stimulation. Increasing the frequency of stimulation will increase the number of impulses conducted by the nerve in a given time up to a maximum amount. This maximum (impulses about 2 msec apart) is due to the refractory period of the nerve and ensures that the action potentials will remain discrete units at high frequencies of stimulation. Similarly, increasing the strength of each stimulus

**Figure 3.5.** A nerve is laid across a pair of stimulating electrodes and a pair of recording electrodes. A stimulator delivers a square wave pulse of a given voltage and duration to the nerve via the stimulating electrodes. This can be seen at the recording electrodes as the stimulus artifact (not shown). The action potential observed after the stimulus artifact represents the bioelectrical response of the nerve to the stimulus.

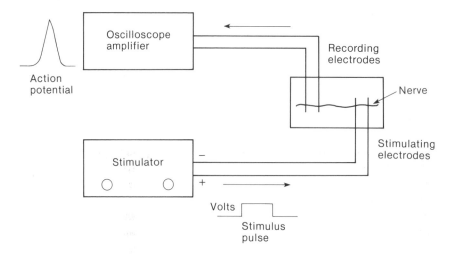

## Procedure

1. Double pith a frog (see section 4 for this procedure), skin its legs and the lower portion of its back, and place it in a prone position in a dissecting tray.
2. Make a 1-inch incision on both sides of its spine from the anal region toward the head. Lift the portion of spine free from surrounding muscle, and excise it to expose the right and left sciatic nerves, which run lateral to the spine.
3. Lift one of the sciatic nerves with a glass probe, tie it with a few inches of thread, and cut the nerve beyond the tie.

**Note:** *Be careful not to touch the nerve with fingers or metal tools and not to let the nerve touch the surface of the frog's skin or cut muscle. Keep the nerve moist with Ringer's solution.*

4. Separate the muscles of the thigh to expose the distal portion of the sciatic nerve, and lift it with a glass probe.

**Note:** *The sciatic nerve is easily identified because it runs in the same connective tissue sheath as the sciatic artery. Tie the nerve with a few inches of thread, and cut the nerve beyond the tie.*

5. Lift the two ends of the nerve with the two lengths of thread (fig. 3.6) and carefully free it from attached muscle and fascia.
6. Lay the nerve across the stimulating and recording electrodes of the nerve chamber, keeping the nerve moist with Ringer's solution.
7. Connect the stimulating electrodes to the stimulator and the recording electrodes to the preamplifier of the oscilloscope.
8. Adjust the horizontal sweep, and set the stimulus frequency, duration, and amplitude at their lowest values.
9. Slowly increase the stimulus amplitude until the threshold voltage is obtained (the lowest stimulus that produces an action potential). Threshold stimulus: _____ V

**Note:** *The first deflection on the screen is the stimulus artifact, and a deflection to the right of this is the action potential.*

10. Slowly increase the strength of the stimulating voltage until the action potential is at its maximum amplitude.
    Stimulus producing maximum response: _____ V
11. With the stimulating voltage set at a slightly suprathreshold level, gradually increase the frequency of stimulation, and note the effect on the size of the action potential.

**Figure 3.6.** The sciatic nerve of a frog has been exposed with the aid of glass probes. The two ends have been tied with thread just proximal to the points where they will be cut.

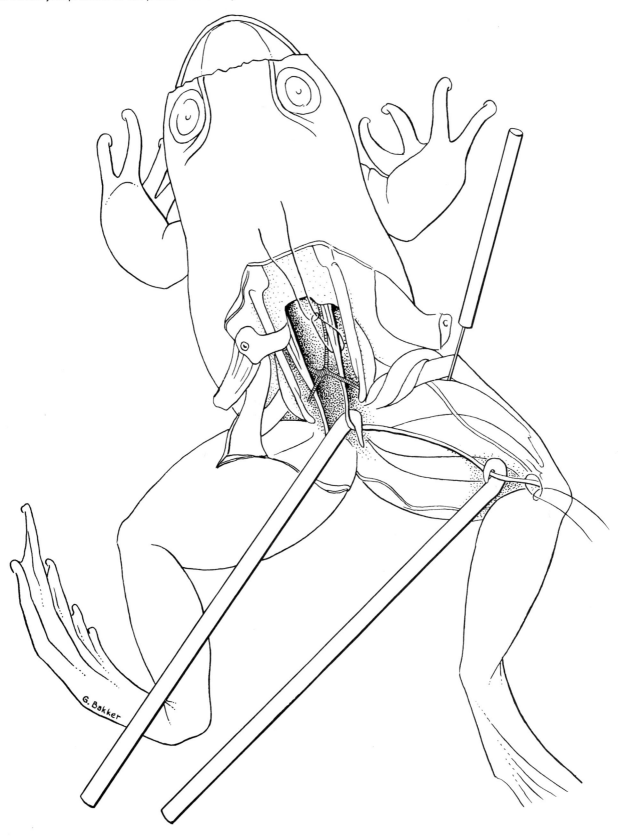

G. Bakker

1. The part of a neuron that receives input from sensory receptors or from other neurons is the _____ .

2. The voltage across the membrane of a particular axon is $-65$ mV; this is its _____

_____ .

3. During an action potential the membrane polarity momentarily reverses.

   (a) This is called _____ .

   (b) This is caused by the diffusion of _____ into the axon.

4. The height of the action potential recording is a measure of its _____ ; the number

   of action potentials per unit time is a measure of its _____ .

5. Since both recording electrodes in this exercise were placed on the surface of the nerve (both were extracellular), a resting membrane potential was not recorded. In order to record a resting membrane potential, one electrode must be extracellular and one must be intracellular. Explain why this is true.

6. How is the strength of a stimulus coded in the nervous system?

7. The amplitude of the action potential recorded from the frog sciatic nerve increased when the stimulating voltage increased, yet neurons follow an all-or-none law. Explain.

Action Potentail ⟶ Release of Transmitters :

Depolorization               Hyperpolarization
        ↓           or                ↓
      ESPS                           IPSP


Exitation occurs = EPSP  >  IPSP —
Inhibition occurs = IPSP  >  EPSP —

# Electroencephalogram (EEG)

Chemical neurotransmitters released by presynaptic nerve fibers produce excitatory or inhibitory postsynaptic potentials. These synaptic potentials account for most of the electrical activity of the brain and contribute to the electroencephalogram recorded by surface electrodes over the brain.

## Objectives

1. Describe the structure of a chemical synapse.
2. Describe EPSPs and IPSPs, and explain their significance.
3. Demonstrate the recording of an electroencephalogram, and explain how it is produced.

## Materials

1. Oscilloscope and EEG selector box (Phipps and Bird), or physiograph and high-gain coupler (Narco)
2. EEG electrodes and surface electrode
3. Long ECG elastic band and ECG electrolyte gel

The basic unit of neural integration is the **synapse,** or functional connection between the axon of one neuron and the dendrites or cell body (occasionally even the axon) of another neuron. A train of action potentials that travels down the axon of the first neuron stimulates the release of packets (vesicles) of chemical transmitter substances. These chemical transmitters (such as acetylcholine, or ACh) diffuse across the small space separating the two neurons (the *synaptic cleft*) and reach the membrane of the second neuron (the *postsynaptic membrane*).

These chemical transmitters may stimulate a depolarization of the postsynaptic membrane. Unlike an action potential, this *excitatory postsynaptic potential,* or *EPSP,* is a graded response—the larger the number of transmitter vesicles released, the larger the depolarization.

When the EPSP reaches a critical level of depolarization (the threshold), an action potential is generated, which can then be conducted down the axon of the second neuron to the next synapse. Chemical transmitters released by other neurons that synapse with the second cell may produce an opposite response—a hyperpolarization of the postsynaptic membrane (the inside of the cell becomes even more negative with respect to the outside). This is called an *inhibitory postsynaptic potential* (or *IPSP*). The production of action potentials by the second cell, as well as their frequency, will be determined by the algebraic sum of these EPSPs and IPSPs produced by the convergence (fig. 3.7) of neurons on the second cell.

These electrical activities—action potentials, EPSPs and IPSPs—are not equal in two different regions of the brain at the same time. An extracellular potential difference (which fluctuates between 50 and 100 millionths of a volt) can therefore be measured by placing two electrode leads on the scalp over two different regions of the brain. The recording of these "brain waves" is known as an **electroencephalogram (EEG).**

In actual practice, nineteen electrodes are placed at various standard positions on the scalp, with each pair of electrodes connected to a different recording pen. The record obtained shows periodic waxing and waning of synchronous neuronal activity, producing complex wave forms that are characteristic of the regions of the brain sampled and the state of the subject.

The first of the brain waves to be discovered, the **alpha rhythm** (8–12 cycles per second, cps), can be seen with a single pair of electrodes. These waves are produced by the visual association areas of the occipital lobe and predominate when the subject is relaxed with eyes closed. These waves can be suppressed by opening the eyes or by doing mental arithmetic (fig. 3.8) and are normally absent in a significant number of people.

The **beta rhythm** (above 13 cps) is common in tense subjects and is enhanced by barbiturates. Other rhythms include the **theta rhythm** (4–7 cps), which is dominant in some children, and the **delta rhythm** (0.5–3 cps), which is

**Figure 3.7.** The convergence of large numbers of presynaptic nerve fibers on the cell body of a spinal motor neuron.

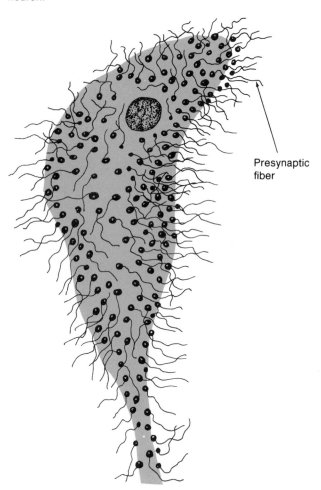

Presynaptic fiber

**Figure 3.8.** Electroencephalograph (EEG) rhythms.

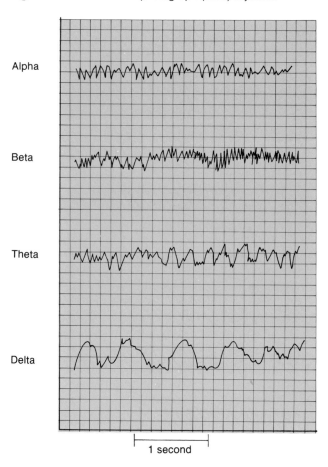

Alpha

Beta

Theta

Delta

1 second

seen in subjects who are in deep sleep. During an attack of petit mal epilepsy, the EEG pattern may show regular spikes and waves at 3 cps. Abnormal patterns not observed in the "resting" EEG can often be revealed by stimulation of the subject through hyperventilation or flashing a strobe light at different frequencies.

## Clinical Significance

Use of the electroencephalograph may help diagnose a number of brain lesions, including epilepsy, intracranial infections, and encephalitis. Hypoglycemia may also be revealed by starvation of the subject for twenty-four hours before taking an EEG and then by repeating the EEG after the administration of glucose. It should be emphasized that the EEG alone is not sufficient for diagnosis, and the absence of abnormal rhythms does not exclude the presence of a pathological state.

It has been discovered that meditation, as performed by Zen monks and yogis, results in the production of slow alpha waves (7–8 cps) of increased amplitude and regularity (even with the eyes partially open) and that this change is associated with a decrease in metabolism and sympathetic nerve activity. The clinical applications of this discovery are as yet unexplored.

### Procedure

1. If an **oscilloscope** will be used
   a) connect the EEG selector box to the preamplifier of the oscilloscope, and adjust the horizontal sweep and sensitivity (fig. 3.9);
   b) plug the lead for the forehead into the EEG selector box outlet labeled *L. Frontal* and the lead for the earlobe into the outlet for the *ground*.

2. If a **physiograph** will be used
   a) insert a *high-gain coupler* into the physiograph;
   b) set the *gain* on ×*100*, the *sensitivity* on *2* or *5*, and the *time constant* on *0.03* or *0.3*;
   c) connect two *EEG electrodes* and one *surface electrode* to the high-gain coupler.

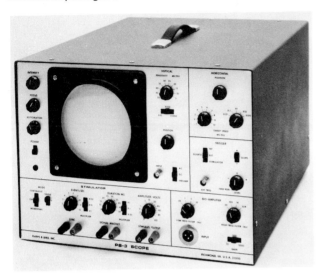

**Figure 3.9.** An oscilloscope for recording an electroencephalogram.

4. Dab a little electrolyte gel onto the ground electrode (the surface electrode for the physiograph), and with your fingers, press this electrode against the skin behind the ear.

5. With the subject in a relaxed position (no muscular movements), with eyes closed, observe the EEG pattern, checking particularly for the presence of alpha waves. Since many people do not produce alpha waves in this situation, test a number of subjects.

**Note:** *Interference from room electricity at 60 cps sometimes occurs. This will appear as regular, fast, low-amplitude waves usually superimposed on the slower, more irregular brain waves of larger amplitude.*

6. Observe the effect of opening the eyes, mental arithmetic, and hyperventilation on the production of alpha waves.

3. Obtain a long elastic ECG strap, and tie it around the forehead (with the knot on the back of the head) to form a snug headband.
   a) If an oscilloscope will be used for recording, dab a little electrolyte gel onto the single electrode from the left frontal outlet, and place it under the headband in the middle of the forehead.
   b) If a physiograph will be used for recording, dab electrolyte gel onto both EEG electrodes, and place them under the headband on the right and left sides of the forehead.

1. A depolarization of the postsynaptic membrane is called a(n)

   _____ .

2. A hyperpolarization of the postsynaptic membrane is called a(n)

   _____ .

3. Action potentials are all-or-none; postsynaptic potentials, in contrast, are _____ .

   Match the following:

   ____  4. alpha rhythm          (a) common in tense subjects
   ____  5. beta rhythm           (b) observed in some relaxed subjects
   ____  6. theta rhythm          (c) observed in deep sleep
   ____  7. delta rhythm          (d) seen in some children

8. Describe how an EPSP is produced, where it is produced, and its significance. Compare the properties of an EPSP with those of an action potential.

9. Compare the EEG with the nerve impulse (see exercise 3.1) with respect to their methods of measurement and the origin of their electrical activities.

# Reflex Arc

In a reflex, specific sensory stimuli evoke characteristic motor responses very rapidly due to the low number of synapses between the sensory input and the motor output. Since a specific simple reflex arc occurs at a specific spinal cord segment and involves limited numbers of nerves, tests of simple reflex arcs are very useful in the diagnosis of neurological disorders.

## Objectives

1. Describe the neurological pathways involved in a simple reflex arc.
2. Describe the structure and function of muscle spindles.
3. Demonstrate muscle stretch reflexes, and explain the clinical significance of these tests.
4. Demonstrate a test for the Babinski reflex, and explain the clinical significance of this test.

## Materials

1. Rubber mallets
2. Blunt probes

The speed of a motor response to an environmental stimulus depends, in part, on the number of synapses to be crossed between the afferent flow of impulses and the activation of efferent nerves. A **reflex** is a relatively simple motor response that is made without the necessary involvement of large numbers of association neurons.

The simplest reflex requires only one synapse between the sensory and motor neurons (e.g., the knee jerk, or patellar reflex). Impulses traveling on the sensory axons enter the CNS in the *dorsal root* of the peripheral nerve, make a single synapse with a motor neuron within the central gray matter, and then leave the CNS in the *ventral root* of the spinal nerve (fig. 3.10). In more complicated reflexes, the sensory impulses may travel longitudinally and transversely within the gray matter, stimulating other motor neurons. This may lead to the contraction of other flexor muscles on the same side (*ipsilateral*) and the contraction of extensor muscles on the opposite side (*contralateral*), while inhibiting the contraction of antagonistic muscles (ipsilateral extensors and contralateral flexors).

## A. Tests for Spinal Nerve Stretch Reflexes

In this exercise, a number of reflex arcs will be tested that are initiated by stretch receptors within muscles. These receptors, called **muscle spindles,** are embedded within the connective tissue of the muscle and consist of specialized thin muscle fibers (*intrafusal fibers*), which are connected to a sensory (afferent) nerve. The intrafusal fibers are arranged in parallel with the normal muscle cells (*extrafusal fibers*), so that stretch of the muscle places tension on the intrafusal fibers and stimulates the sensory neuron (fig. 3.10). In a typical clinical examination, these receptors are stimulated by the momentary stretch created by striking the tendon with a rubber mallet. The sensory neuron arising from the intrafusal fiber synapses with a motor neuron that innervates the extrafusal fibers. Contraction of the muscle (extrafusal fibers) releases tension of the intrafusal fibers and decreases stimulation of the stretch receptors.

*withdrawal reflex - more complex than stretch involve at least 3 neurons.*

*inhibition - one muscle must relax while another contracts - both can't contract at once.*

**Figure 3.10.** The knee jerk reflex, an example of a monosynaptic stretch reflex.

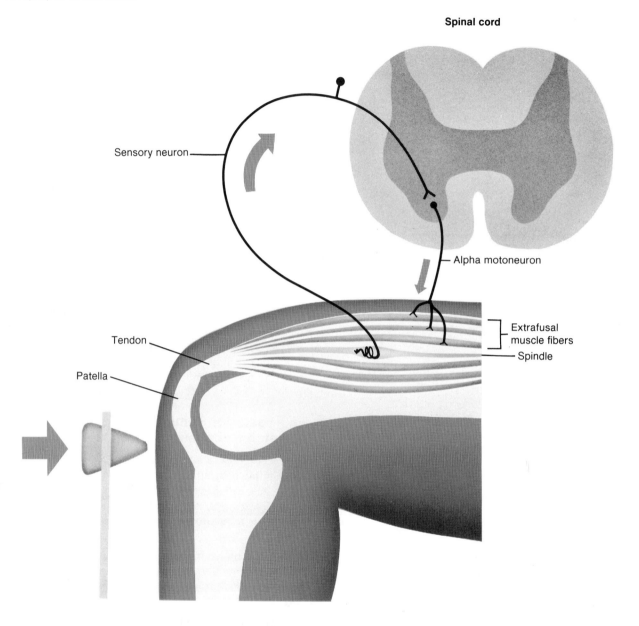

## Procedure for Knee Jerk (fig. 3.11)
*Tests Femoral Nerve*

1. The subject is allowed to sit comfortably with his or her legs free.
2. Strike the patellar tendon, just below the patella (kneecap), and observe the resulting contraction of the quadriceps muscles and extension of the leg.

## Procedure for Ankle Jerk (fig. 3.11)
*Tests Medial Popliteal Nerve*

1. The subject kneels on a chair, with his or her back to the examiner and feet (shoes and socks off) projecting over the edge.
2. Strike the Achilles tendon at the level of the ankle, and observe the resulting plantar extension of the foot.

**Figure 3.11.**  Some reflexes of clinical importance.

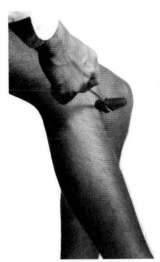

1. Knee (patellar) reflex

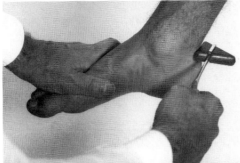

2. Ankle (Achilles) reflex

3. Biceps reflex

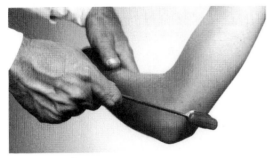

4. Triceps reflex

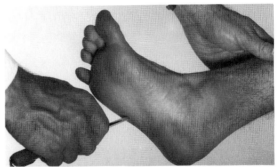

5. Babinski reflex

## Procedure for Biceps Jerk (fig. 3.11)
*Tests Musculocutaneous Nerve*

1. With the subject's arm relaxed on the desk, gently press the biceps tendon in the antecubital fossa with the thumb or forefinger, and strike this finger with the mallet.
2. If this procedure is performed correctly, the biceps muscle will twitch (the contraction is not usually strong enough to cause arm movements).

## Procedure for Triceps Jerk (fig. 3.11)
*Tests for Radial Nerve*

1. The subject is supine with the elbow bent so that the arm lies loosely across the abdomen.
2. Strike the triceps tendon about 2 inches above the elbow. If there is no response, repeat this procedure, striking to either side of the original point.
3. If this procedure is correctly performed, the triceps muscle will twitch but will not usually contract strongly enough to produce arm movements.

## B. A Cutaneous Reflex: The Babinski (Plantar) Reflex

The Babinski, or plantar, reflex, elicited by cutaneous receptors in the sole of the foot, is one of the most important neurological tests. The proper stimulation of these receptors in the normal individual results in the flexion (i.e., downward movement) of the great toe while the other toes flex and come together. Damage to the pyramidal motor tracts produces a Babinski response to this stimulation, in which the great toe extends (i.e., moves upward).

### Clinical Significance

Tests for simple muscle reflexes are basic to any physical examination when motor nerve or spinal damage is suspected. If there is spinal cord damage, these easily performed tests can help locate the level of the spinal cord that is damaged: motor nerves that exit the spinal cord above the damaged level may not be affected, whereas nerves that originate at or below the damaged level may not be able to produce their normal reflexes. In this regard, the Babinski test is particularly useful, because damage to the pyramidal motor tract at any level may result in a positive Babinski reflex.

### Procedure

1. The subject is supine, knees slightly bent, with the thigh rotated so that the lateral (outer) side of the foot rests on the couch.
2. Applying firm (but not painful) pressure, draw the tip of a blunt probe along the lateral border of the sole, starting at the heel and ending at the base of the big toe (fig. 3.11). Observe the response of the toes to this procedure.

(facilitation.)
facilitain - make easier (knee jurk + clench fists)
Synapse - junction between 2 nuerons

# Laboratory Report 3.3

Match the following tests with the nerve involved:

___ 1. biceps jerk

___ 2. triceps jerk

_c_ 3. knee jerk

___ 4. ankle jerk

(a) femoral nerve

(b) musculocutaneous nerve

(c) medial popliteal nerve

(d) radial nerve

5. Describe the sequence of events that occurs between striking the patellar tendon and extension of the leg (knee jerk reflex).

6. Failure to elicit a given stretch reflex may indicate damage to a specific motor nerve or region of the spinal cord, whereas the presence of a Babinski reflex (positive Babinski test) may be produced by damage to the spinal cord at any level. Explain why this statement is true.

7. The intrafusal and extrafusal muscle fibers are innervated by different motor nerves. The intrafusal fibers are innervated by *gamma* efferent nerves, and the extrafusal fibers are innervated by *alpha* efferent nerves. Describe the sequence of events by which stimulation of the intrafusal fibers by gamma efferents could produce contraction of extrafusal fibers. (This mechanism is responsible for the maintenance of muscle tone.)

Summation?

Fatigue → accumation of waste products

# Cutaneous Receptors

Specialized sensory organs and free nerve endings in the skin provide four modalities of cutaneous sensation. The modality and location of each sensation is determined by the specific sensory pathway in the brain; the acuteness of sensation depends on the density of the cutaneous receptors.

## Objectives

1. Describe the punctate distribution of cutaneous receptors.
2. Describe the structures of cutaneous receptors and the modality of sensations they mediate.
3. Determine the two-point touch threshold in different areas of the skin, and explain the physiological significance of the differences obtained.
4. Define and demonstrate sensory adaptation, and explain its significance.

## Materials

1. Thin bristles, cold and warm metal rods
2. Calipers, cold and warm water baths

Four independent modalities of cutaneous sensation have traditionally been recognized—warmth, cold, touch, and pain. (Pressure is excluded because it is mediated by receptors deep in the dermis, and the sensations of itch and tickle are usually excluded because of their mysterious origin.) Mapping of these sensations on the surface of the skin has revealed that the receptors are not generalized throughout the skin but are clustered at different points (*punctate distribution*).

Since the punctate distribution is different for each of the four sensory modalities, earlier physiologists believed that each sensation was mediated by a different sensory receptor, and this view was supported by the histological identification of different cutaneous receptors (table 3.1 and fig. 3.12). Excision of areas of the skin from different sensory maps, however, failed to reveal a different distribution of receptors, and more recent experiments have suggested that the four sensations may arise from an analysis of complex patterns of sensory (afferent) impulses in the brain.

## A. Mapping the Temperature and Touch Receptors of the Skin

### Procedure

1. With a ball-point pen, draw a square 2 cm² on the ventral surface of the subject's forearm.
2. With the subject's eyes closed, gently touch an ice-cold metal rod to different points in the square. Mark the points of cold sensation with a dark dot.
3. Heat the metal rod to about 45° C in a water bath, wipe the rod, and repeat the mapping procedure, drawing open circles at the points where heat sensation is felt.
4. Gently touch a thin bristle to different areas of the square, and indicate the points of touch sensation with small *x's*.
5. Reproduce this map in your laboratory report.

**Table 3.1**   Some of the modalities of sensation and the sensory receptors they stimulate.

| Classification | Sensory Modality | Receptor |
|---|---|---|
| Special senses | Light | Eye |
| | Smell | Nasal mucosa |
| | Taste | Taste buds |
| | Sound | Inner ear |
| | Equilibrium | Vestibular apparatus |
| Proprioceptors | Muscle stretch | Muscle spindles |
| | Muscle contraction | Tendon organs |
| | Limb position | Joint receptors |
| Cutaneous senses* | Cold | Krause's end bulbs |
| | Heat | Ruffini's end organs |
| | Touch | Meissner's corpuscles |
| | Pain | Free nerve endings |
| | Tickle | Free nerve endings |
| | Itch | Free nerve endings |
| | Pressure | Pacinian corpuscles |
| Visceral senses | Blood pressure | Aortic arch / Carotid sinus |
| | Blood $P_{O_2}$, $P_{CO_2}$, pH | Aortic bodies / Carotid bodies |
| | Plasma osmotic pressure | Hypothalamus |
| | Plasma temperature | Hypothalamus |
| | Pain | Free nerve endings |

*These sensory modalities are probably not served by specific receptors but rather by the pattern of afferent nerves stimulated.

## B. The Two-Point Threshold in Touch Perception

The density of touch receptors in some parts of the body is greater than in other parts; therefore, the areas of the **sensory cortex** (postcentral gyrus of the central fissure) that correspond to different regions of the body are of different sizes. Those areas of the body that have the largest density of touch receptors also receive the greatest motor innervation; the areas of the **motor cortex** (precentral gyrus) that serve these regions are correspondingly larger than other areas. A map of the sensory and motor areas of the brain therefore reveals that large areas are devoted to the touch perception and motor activity of the face (particularly the tongue and lips) and hands, whereas relatively small areas are devoted to the trunk, hips, and legs.

The density of touch receptors is measured by the two-point threshold test. The two points of a pair of adjustable calipers are simultaneously placed on the subject's skin with equal pressure, and the subject is asked if two separate contacts are felt. If so, the points of the divider are brought closer together, and the test is repeated until only one point of contact is felt. The *minimum distance* at which two points of contact can be discriminated is the two-point threshold.

### Clinical Significance

Sensory information from the cutaneous receptors project to the postcentral gyrus of the cerebral cortex. Direct electrical stimulation of this area therefore produces the same sensations as those felt when the cutaneous receptors are stimulated. Much of this information has been gained by the electrical stimulation of the brain of awake patients undergoing brain surgery; the surgeon must often map the areas of the brain in order to locate the site of the lesion and avoid damage to healthy tissue. Since the cutaneous receptors are more densely arranged in the face, tongue, and hands than on the back and thighs, larger areas of the brain are involved in analyzing information from the former areas than from the latter. Consequently, the areas of the brain map representing the face, tongue, and hands are larger than those representing the back and thighs. The map is also upside down, with the feet represented near the superior surface and the head represented more inferiorly and laterally in the cortex.

**Figure 3.12.** A diagrammatic section of skin showing cutaneous receptors.

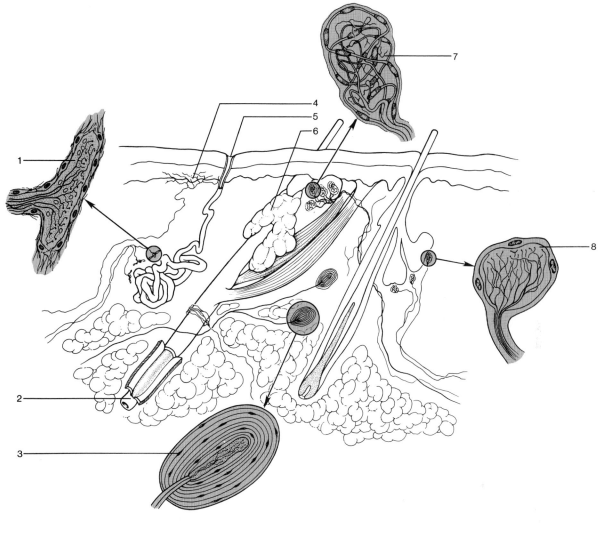

1. Organ of Ruffini
2. Hair follicle
3. Pacinian corpuscle
4. Free nerve endings
5. Opening of sweat gland
6. Sebaceous gland
7. Meissner's corpuscle
8. Bulbs of Krause

## Procedure

1. Starting with the calipers wide apart and the subject's eyes closed, determine the two-point threshold on the back of the hand. (Randomly alternate the two-point touch with one-point contacts, so that the subject will not try to second guess the examiner.)
2. Repeat this procedure with the palm of the hand, fingertip, and back of the neck.
3. Write the results in the table provided in your laboratory report.

## C. Adaptation of Temperature Receptors

Many of our sense receptors respond strongly to acute changes in our environment and then cease responding when these stimuli become constant. This phenomenon is known as **sensory adaptation.** Our sense of smell, for example, quickly adapts to the odors of the laboratory, and our touch receptors soon cease to inform us of our clothing, until these stimuli change.

When one hand is placed in warm water and another in cold water, the strength of stimulation gradually diminishes until both types of temperature receptors have adapted to their new environment. If the two hands are then placed in water at an intermediate temperature, the hand that was in the cold water will feel warm, and the hand that was in the warm water will feel cold. The "baseline," or "zero," of the receptors has obviously changed— the sensations of temperature are therefore not absolute but relative to the baseline previously established by sensory adaptation.

## Procedure

1. Place one hand in warm water (about 40° C) and the other in cold water, and leave them in the water for about 3 minutes.
2. Now place both hands in lukewarm water (about 22° C), and record your sensations in your laboratory report.

# Laboratory Report 3.4

## Data from Exercise 3.4

### A. Mapping the Temperature and Touch Receptors of the Skin

Reproduce the map of the temperature and touch receptors in the square on your forearm in the box below:

### B. The Two-Point Threshold in Touch Perception

Write your results in the data table below:

| Location | Two-Point Threshold (mm) |
|---|---|
| Back of hand | |
| Palm of hand | |
| Fingertip | |
| Back of neck | |

### C. Adaptation of Temperature Receptors

Record your observations and conclusions in the space below:

1. What is meant by the punctate distribution of cutaneous receptors? Describe the distribution of touch receptors in the skin as an example.

2. What does the term *sensory adaptation* mean? Which senses adapt quickly? Which senses adapt slowly, if at all?

3. Most textbooks of anatomy and physiology show a picture of an upside-down, odd-looking person in the brain. What does this picture represent, and how was it obtained?

# Referred Pain

Damage to an area of the body may elicit a perception of pain in a different area. Such referred pains are very important in clinical diagnosis.

## Objectives

1. Define the meaning of the term *referred pain,* and explain how it is produced.
2. Demonstrate the referred pain produced by striking the ulnar nerve with a mallet, and describe the clinical significance of other referred pains in the body.

## Materials

Rubber mallets (those used to produce knee jerk reflexes)

Receptor organs are sensory transducers, changing environmental stimuli into afferent nerve impulses. Since the action potentials in one nerve are the same as another, the perception of the sensation is determined entirely by the area of the brain stimulated, which is different for each sensory nerve. Although a given sensory nerve is normally stimulated by a specific receptor, trauma to the nerve proximal to the receptor may also evoke action potentials, and this will be interpreted by the brain as the normal sensation (e.g., seeing flashes of light—"stars"—when punched in the eye).

Amputees frequently report feelings of pain in their missing limbs (this is known as the *phantom limb phenomenon*). The source of nerve stimulation is trauma to the cut nerve fibers, but the pain is perceived as coming from the amputated region of the body that normally produces action potentials along these nerves. This is a referred pain because the source of nerve stimulation is different from the perceived location of the stimulus.

## Clinical Significance

Referred pains are important clinically, particularly for deep visceral pain, which is characteristically dull and poorly localized. In ischemic heart disease, for example, the pain is referred to the left pectoral region and shoulder areas (fig. 3.13)—this is called **angina pectoris**. In many patients with stomach ulcers, the pain is referred to the region between the scapulae of the back. In general, the deep pain is referred to a surface location served by nerves from the same segmental level of the spinal cord.

## Procedure

1. Gently tap the ulnar nerve where it crosses the median epicondyle of the elbow.
2. Describe the locations where sensation is felt.

**Figure 3.13.** Sites of referred pain are perceived cutaneously but actually originate from specific visceral organs.

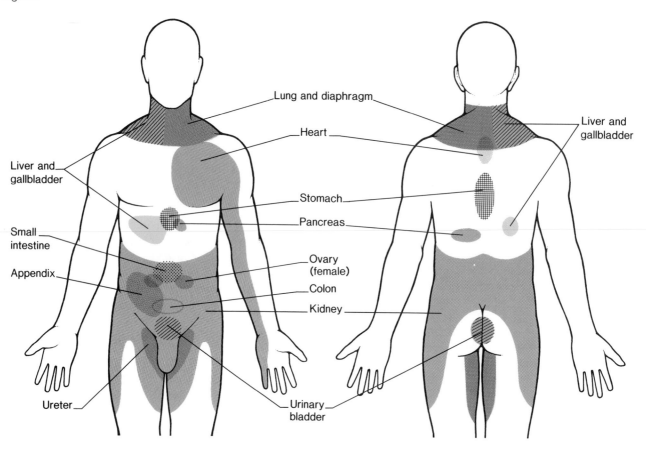

1. Describe the locations where pain was felt, and explain why pain was perceived in these locations when this exercise was performed.

2. Describe the importance of referred pain in the diagnosis of deep visceral pain, and give examples.

3. "Our perceptions of the external world are created by our brains." Discuss this concept, using the phantom limb phenomenon to support your argument.

# Eyes and Vision

The elastic properties of the lens allow its refractive power to be varied, so that the image of an object at almost any distance can be focused on the retina. Photoreceptors—rods and cones—are located in the retina. The refractive abilities of the eye and the functions of its inner structures are routinely tested in eye examinations.

## Objectives

1. Describe the structure of the eye and the functions of its component parts.
2. Test for visual acuity and accommodation, and describe common refractive problems.
3. Identify the extrinsic eye muscles, and describe their functions.
4. Describe the optic disc and fovea centralis, and explain their significance.
5. Demonstrate the presence of a blind spot, and explain how it is produced.

## Materials

1. Snellen eye chart and astigmatism chart
2. Wire screen and meter stick
3. Ophthalmoscope
4. Lamp
5. Red, blue, and yellow squares on larger sheets of black paper or cardboard

The student should be familiar with the gross structure of the eye (fig. 3.14). The eye has three walls, or tunics, that form an outer fibrous layer (the *sclera* and *cornea*), a middle vascular layer (the *choroid*), and an inner layer (the *retina*). The *lens,* suspended by *suspensory ligaments* attached to the *ciliary muscle,* divides the eye into an anterior and posterior chamber filled with *aqueous humor.* The semigelatinous *vitreous humor* (*body*) fills the rest of the eye and lends structural support. Light is admitted into the eye through the aperture (*pupil*) of a colored muscular diaphragm, the *iris.*

## A. Refraction: Test for Visual Acuity and Astigmatism

Light rays are bent (*refracted*) when they pass from air to a medium of greater density, where their rate of transmission is slower. The light rays that diverge from a point in the visual field are thus refracted by the cornea, lens, and vitreous humor of the eye so that they converge on a point (i.e., are focused) on the retina and form an inverted image (fig. 3.15).

Whereas the refractive power of the cornea and vitreous humor is constant, the strength (i.e., the ability to bend light) of the lens can be varied by making it more or less *convex.* The greater the degree of convexity, the greater the strength of the lens (i.e., the greater the ability to bring parallel rays of light to a focus). A lens that brings light to a focus 0.25 m from its center is stronger (more convex) than a lens that brings light to a focus 1 m from its center. The strength of a lens is expressed in **diopters.**

$$\text{Strength (diopters)} = \frac{1}{\text{focal length (meters)}}$$

The lens that brings light to a focus 0.25 m from its center has a *focal length* of 0.25 m and a strength of 4 diopters, whereas the lens that brings parallel waves of light to a focus 2 m from its center has a focal length of 2 m and a strength of 0.5 diopters. The refractive power of the normal eye when an object is 20 feet or more away is 67 diopters.

When the light rays that diverge from two adjacent points in the visual field are each brought to a perfect focus on the retina, two points will clearly be perceived. If, however, the light rays converge on a point (i.e., are focused)

**Figure 3.14.** A cross section of the eye.

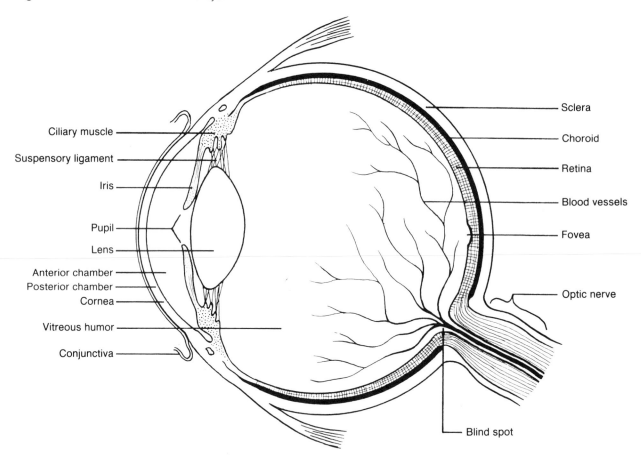

Ciliary muscle

Suspensory ligament

Iris

Pupil

Lens

Anterior chamber
Posterior chamber
Cornea

Vitreous humor

Conjunctiva

Sclera

Choroid

Retina

Blood vessels

Fovea

Optic nerve

Blind spot

**Figure 3.15.** The refraction of light by the cornea and lens of the eye producing an inverted image on the retina.

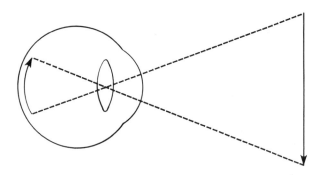

in front of or behind the retina, the two points in the visual field will be perceived as one fuzzy or blurred point. To correct this defect in **visual acuity,** the individual must either adjust the distance between the eye and the object or wear corrective lenses, which change the degree of refraction.

When a distant object (20 feet or more) is brought to a focus in front of the retina, the individual is said to have **myopia** (nearsightedness). Myopia is usually due to an

elongated eyeball (excessive distance from lens to retina) and is corrected by a *concave lens.* In the opposite condition, **hyperopia** (hypermetropia, or farsightedness), the image is brought to a focus behind the retina; this condition is usually due to an eyeball that is too short. In this case, an increase in refractive power is needed, and a convex lens is used. Normal visual acuity is called *emmetropia.*

Visual acuity is frequently tested by means of the Snellen eye chart. A person with normal visual acuity can read the line marked 20/20 from a distance of 20 feet. An individual with 20/40 visual acuity must stand 20 feet away from a line that a normal person can read at 40 feet. An individual with 20/15 visual acuity can read a line at a distance of 20 feet that the average, normal young adult could not read at a distance greater than 15 feet. The person with 20/40 vision has myopia, but the person with 20/15 vision does not necessarily have hyperopia. The farsighted person has a decreased ability to see near objects but cannot see distant objects any better than a person with normal vision.

An **astigmatism** is a visual defect produced by an abnormal curvature of the cornea or lens or an irregularity in their surface. Because of this abnormality, the refraction of light rays in the horizontal plane is different from that in the vertical plane. At a given distance, therefore, lines in the visual field oriented in one plane will be clear while lines oriented in the other plane will be blurred. Astigmatism is corrected by means of a *cylindrical lens.*

The strength of corrective lenses prescribed is given in diopters, preceded by either a plus sign (convex lens for hyperopia) or a minus sign (concave for myopia), for example +4 or −5 diopters. The correction for astigmatism indicates both the strength of the cylindrical lens (e.g., +2) and the axis of the defect (90° for vertical plane, 180° for horizontal plane). A correction for both myopia and astigmatism may be indicated, for example, as −3+2 axis 180°.

---

### Procedure

1. Stand 20 feet (6 m) from the Snellen eye chart, and covering one eye, attempt to read the line with the smallest letters you can see (with glasses off if applicable). Walk up to the chart, and determine the visual acuity of that eye.
2. Repeat this procedure using the other eye (glasses off if applicable).
3. Repeat this procedure for each eye with glasses on (if applicable).
4. Stand about 20 feet away from an astigmatism chart, and cover one eye (glasses off). This chart consists of a number of dark lines radiating from a central point, like spokes on a wheel. If astigmatism is present, some of the spokes will appear sharp and dark, whereas others will appear blurred and lighter because they come to a focus either in front of or behind the retina. Still covering the same eye, slowly walk up to the chart while observing the spokes.
5. Repeat this procedure using the other eye.
6. Repeat the test for astigmatism for both eyes with glasses on (if applicable).
7. If astigmatism has been corrected with glasses, this can be verified by holding the glasses in front of the face while standing 10 feet from the chart and rotating the glasses 90°. The shape of the wheel will change when the glasses are rotated.

## B. Accommodation

If the refractive power (strength) of a lens is constant, the distance between the lens and the point of focus (focal length) will increase as an object moves closer to the lens. If the image of an object that is 20 feet away is in focus on the retina (or on the photosensitive film of a camera), for example, the image of an object 10 feet away will be focused behind the retina (or the camera film) and will appear blurred. A camera can focus on an object 10 feet away by moving the lens outward until the focal length of the image equals the distance between the lens and the film (or retina). The object 10 feet away will now be in focus, but the object 20 feet away will be blurred because its image will come to a focus in front of the film (or retina).

Unlike a camera, the distance between the retina and the lens of a human eye cannot be changed to bring objects into focus. Since the human lens is elastic, however, its degree of convexity (and therefore its refractive power) can be altered by changing the tension placed on it by the suspensory ligament; this, in turn, is regulated by the degree of contraction of the ciliary muscle. When the ciliary muscle is relaxed, the suspensory ligament pulls on the lens, thereby decreasing its convexity and power; distant objects (greater than 20 feet) are thus brought to a focus on the retina. Near objects are brought to a focus on the retina by contraction of the ciliary muscle. The contraction places slack in the suspensory ligament, allowing the lens to spring to a more convex shape. The ability of the eye to focus objects that are different distances from the lens is called **accommodation.**

The convexity of the normal lens can be adjusted to give it a range of power from 67 diopters (distant vision—least convex) to 79 diopters (near vision—most convex). The elasticity of the lens and therefore the degree of convexity it can assume for near vision decreases with age (**presbyopia,** or *old eyes*). Lens elasticity can be tested by measuring the *near point* of vision—the closest an object can be brought to the eyes while still maintaining visual acuity. The near point of vision changes dramatically with age, averaging about 8 cm at age 10 and 100 cm at age 70. Presbyopia is corrected with *bifocals,* which contain two lenses of different refractive strengths. → focus like Hyper.

---

### Clinical Significance

In addition to tests of refraction, measurements of intraocular pressure are frequently performed with a device known as a *tonometer.* About 6 ml of aqueous humor is formed per day by the *ciliary body.* This fluid is drained by the *venous sinus (canal of Schlemm).* If the drainage of aqueous humor is blocked, the intraocular pressure may rise (a condition known as **glaucoma**), resulting in damage to the optic nerve and blindness. Glaucoma may also damage the cornea, resulting in replacement of the normally transparent tissue with opaque scar tissue. When this happens the cornea can be surgically removed and replaced with either a contact lens or a grafted cornea. Because the cornea is avascular, corneal grafts can be performed with less fear that the transplanted tissue will be immunologically rejected.

**Figure 3.16.** Ocular muscles of the left eyeball: (a) a lateral view; (b) a superior view.

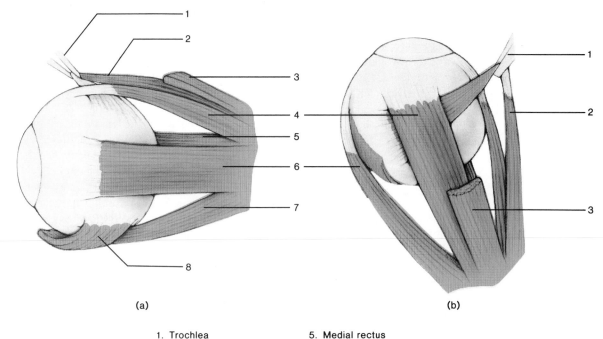

(a)                                                   (b)

1. Trochlea                    5. Medial rectus
2. Superior oblique            6. Lateral rectus
3. Levator palpebrae           7. Inferior rectus
   superioris (cut)            8. Inferior oblique
4. Superior rectus

**Procedure**

1. Place a square of wire screen about 10 inches in front of the eyes, and observe a distant object through the screen.
2. After closing your eyes momentarily, open them and notice whether the screen or the distant object is in focus.
3. Repeat this procedure, this time focusing the eyes on the screen before opening them.
4. To measure the near point of vision, place a meter stick just under one eye, and holding a pin at arm's length, gradually bring the pin toward the eye.
5. Record the distance at which the pin first appears blurred or doubled.
6. Repeat this procedure, determining the near point of vision of the other eye.

## C. The Extrinsic Muscles of the Eye and Nystagmus

The six extrinsic muscles of the eye, their innervations, and their actions are presented in figure 3.16 and table 3.2. These muscles allow the eyes to follow a moving object while maintaining the image on the same location of the retina of each eye (the *fovea centralis,* which provides maximum visual acuity). These muscles also allow the visual field of each eye to maintain the correct amount of overlap. (The medial regions of each visual field overlap, while the more lateral regions are different for each eye; this *retinal disparity* helps in three-dimensional vision.) When an object is brought closer, the correct amount of overlap and retinal disparity is maintained by the medial movement (**convergence**) of the eyes.

The ocular muscles normally maintain the eyes in a midline position by the balance between antagonistic muscles. If the tone of one muscle is weak as a result of muscle or nerve damage, the eyes will drift slowly in one direction followed by a rapid movement back to the correct position. This phenomenon is known as **nystagmus.**

**Table 3.2**    The ocular muscles.

| Muscle | Cranial Nerve Innervation | Movement of Eyeball |
|---|---|---|
| Lateral rectus | Abducens | Lateral |
| Medial rectus | Oculomotor | Medial |
| Superior rectus | Oculomotor | Superior and medial |
| Inferior rectus | Oculomotor | Inferior and medial |
| Inferior oblique | Oculomotor | Superior and lateral |
| Superior oblique | Trochlear | Inferior and lateral |

In a typical examination of the ocular muscles, the subject is asked to follow an object (such as a pencil) with his or her eyes as it is moved up and down, right and left. Continued oscillations of the eye (slow phase in one direction, fast phase in the opposite direction) indicate the presence of nystagmus. Inability to move the eye outward indicates damage either to the abducens nerve (VI) or the lateral rectus muscle (table 3.2). Inability to move the eye downward when it is moved inward indicates damage to the trochlear nerve (IV) or the superior oblique muscle. All other defects in eye movement may be due either to damage of the oculomotor nerve (III) or to damage of the specific muscles involved.

### Procedure

1. Observe retinal disparity by holding a pencil in front of the face with one eye closed and then quickly changing eyes and noting the apparent position of the pencil.
2. Observe convergence by asking the subject to focus on the tip of a pencil as it is slowly brought from a distance of 2 feet in front of the face to the bridge of the nose. Notice the change in the diameter of the pupil during this procedure.
3. Hold a pencil about 2 feet away from the bridge of the subject's nose, and then move it to the left, to the right, and up and down, leaving the pencil at least 10 seconds in each position. Observe the movement of the eyes, and note the presence or absence of nystagmus.

### D. The Pupillary Reflex

The correct amount of light is admitted into the eye through an adjustable aperture (the *pupil*) surrounded by the *iris*. The pupillary reflex, mediated by the autonomic nervous system, decreases the size of the pupil in bright light and increases the size of the pupil in dim light.

### Procedure

1. The examiner and the subject remain in a darkened room for at least 1 minute, allowing their eyes to adjust to the dim light.
2. The examiner shines a narrow beam of light (e.g., from an ophthalmoscope or a pen flashlight) from the right side into the right eye. Observe the pupillary reflex in the right eye and in the left eye (this is the consensual reaction).
3. Repeat this procedure (first dark-adapting the eyes again) from the left side with the left eye.

### E. Examination of the Eye with an Ophthalmoscope

An ophthalmoscope is a device used to observe the posterior inner part of the eye (the *fundus*). A mirror situated at the top of the instrument deflects light at a right angle into the eye, enabling an observer to see the interior of the eye through a small slit in the mirror. Different depths of focus are attained by changing the lens, which is positioned in the slit; the lenses are carried on a wheel in regular order according to their focal lengths. The strength of each lens is given in diopters preceded by a plus (+) for a convex lens or a minus (−) for a concave lens, with 0 indicating no lens.

In this exercise, the arteries and veins of the fundus and two regions of the retina—the **optic disc** (the region where the optic nerve exits the eye, otherwise known as the *blind spot*) and the **macula lutea**—will be observed. The macula lutea is a yellowish region containing a central pit, the **fovea centralis,** where the highest concentration of the photoreceptors responsible for visual acuity (the cones) is located. This is the region on which an image is focused when the eyes look directly at an object.

**Figure 3.17.** The optic fundus.

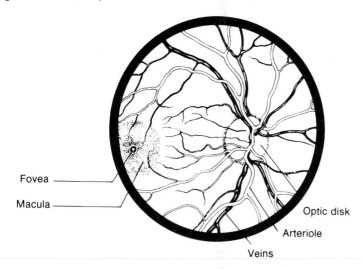
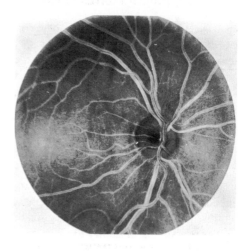

Fovea

Macula

Optic disk

Arteriole

Veins

## Clinical Significance

Clinical examination of the fundus (ophthalmoscopy) can aid the diagnosis of a number of ocular and systemic diseases. The features noted in these examinations include the condition of the blood vessels; the color and shape of the disc; the presence of particles, exudates, or hemorrhage; the presence of edema and inflammation of the optic nerve (*papilledema*); and myopia or hyperopia.

## Procedure

1. The subject is seated in a darkened room and is asked to look at a distant object (blinking is allowed).
2. The examiner and subject position themselves face to face. The examiner holds the ophthalmoscope with his or her right hand and uses the right eye when observing the subject's right eye. (The situation is reversed when viewing the left eye.)
3. With the examiner's forefinger on the lens adjustment wheel and eye as close as possible to the small hole in the ophthalmoscope (glasses off if applicable), the instrument is brought as close as possible to the subject's eye. (The examiner's hand can be steadied by resting it on the subject's cheek.)
4. The eye will be examined from the front to the back. Looking from the side of the eye (not in front), the iris and lens can be examined using a +20 to +15 lens (this will be different if the examiner wears glasses).

5. Rotate the wheel counterclockwise to examine the fundus. If both the examiner's and the subject's eyes are normal, the fundus can be clearly seen without the need of a lens (set on 0; the refractive strength of the subject's eye is sufficient to focus the light on the fundus).
   a) If a positive (convex) lens is necessary to focus on the fundus and the examiner's eyes are normal, the subject has hyperopia (hypermetropia).
   b) If a negative (concave) lens is necessary to focus on the fundus and the examiner's eyes are normal, the subject has myopia.
6. Observe the arteries and veins of the fundus, and follow them to their point of convergence. This will enable you to see the optic disc (fig. 3.17).
7. Finally, at the end of the examination, observe the macula lutea by asking the subject to look directly into the light of the ophthalmoscope.

## F. The Blind Spot

The retina contains two types of photoreceptors, **rods** and **cones.** These synapse with other cells (*bipolar neurons*), which in turn synapse with *ganglion cells,* whose axons carry the sensory information along the optic nerve to the brain. In the fovea only one cone will synapse with one bipolar cell, whereas several rods may converge on a given bipolar cell. Thus, the rods are more sensitive to low levels of illumination, whereas the cones provide greater visual acuity (fig. 3.18). The rods, therefore, are responsible for night (scotopic) vision, when sensitivity is most important, whereas the cones are responsible for day (photopic)

**Figure 3.18.** The organization of cells in the retina. Note that the light must pass through layers of nerve fibers, ganglion cells, and bipolar cells before reaching the photoreceptors (rods and cones). The cones synapse in a 1:1 ratio with bipolar cells, allowing greater visual acuity, whereas a number of rods can synapse with a single bipolar cell, allowing greater visual sensitivity.

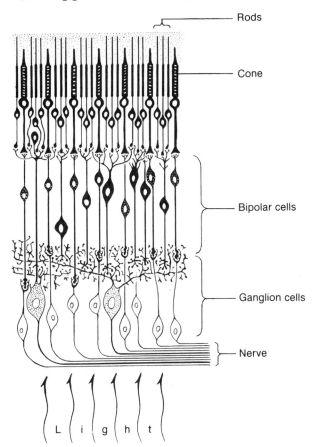

Rods

Cone

Bipolar cells

Ganglion cells

Nerve

L i g h t

vision, when visual acuity is most important. The cones also provide color vision—colors are seen during the day whereas night vision is in black and white.

The axons for all of the ganglion cells gather together as the optic nerve and leave the eye at one point in the retina, the *optic disc* (blind spot). There are no rods or cones in this spot, and an object whose image is focused here will not be seen.

## Procedure

1. Hold the drawing of the circle and the cross (fig. 3.19) about 20 inches from your face with the left eye covered or closed. Focus on the circle; this is most easily done if the circle is positioned in line with the right eye.

**Figure 3.19.** A diagram for demonstrating the blind spot.

2. Keeping your right eye focused on the circle, slowly bring the drawing closer to your face until the cross disappears. Continue to move the drawing slowly toward your face until the cross reappears.
3. Repeat this procedure with the right eye closed or covered and the left eye focused on the cross. Observe the disappearance of the circle as the drawing is brought closer to the face.

## G. The Afterimage

The light that strikes the receptors of the eye stimulates a photochemical reaction in which the pigment **rhodopsin** (within the rods) dissociates to form the pigment *retinene* and the protein *opsin*. This chemical dissociation produces electrical changes in the photoreceptors, which trigger a train of action potentials in the axons of the optic nerve. These events cannot be repeated in a given receptor until the rhodopsin is regenerated, and this requires a series of chemical reactions in which one isomer of retinene is converted to another through the intermediate compound *vitamin $A_1$*. In other words, after the visual pigment has been "bleached" by the image of an object (i.e., after the rhodopsin has dissociated under the influence of light), a certain period of time is required before that receptor can again be stimulated.

When an eye that has adapted to a bright light, such as a light bulb, is closed or quickly turned toward a wall, the bright image of the light bulb will still be seen. This is called a *positive afterimage* and is caused by the continued "firing" of the photoreceptors. After a short period, the dark image of the light bulb (the *negative afterimage*) will appear against a lighter background due to the "bleaching" of the visual pigment of the affected receptors.

According to the **Young-Helmholtz theory** of color vision, there are three systems of cones that respond respectively to red, green, and blue (or violet) light, and all other colors are seen by the brain's interpretation of mixtures of impulses from these three systems. Color discrimination will of course be impaired if one system of cones is defective (color blindness), or if one system of cones has been "bleached" by the continued viewing of an object. In the latter case, the positive afterimage of the object will appear in the complementary color.

## Clinical Significance

It is important to remember that the eye is a receptor, transducing light into electrical nerve impulses. We actually see with our brain. Impulses from the retina pass, via the *lateral geniculate bodies,* to the *visual cortex* of the occipital lobe, where the patterns of impulses are integrated to produce an image. The importance of the visual cortex in vision is illustrated by **strabismus,** a condition in which weak extrinsic eye muscles prevent the eyes from converging on an object and fusing the images. To avoid confusion, the cortical cells eventually stop responding to information from one eye, making that eye functionally blind. Visual information is integrated with input from the other senses in the cortex of the *inferior temporal lobe.* If this area is damaged (the **Klüver-Bucy syndrome**), visual recognition is impaired so that although the image is seen, it lacks meaning and emotional content.

## Procedure

1. Stare at a light bulb, then suddenly shift your gaze to a blank wall. Observe the appearance of the negative afterimage.
2. For 1 minute, stare at a small red square that has been pasted on a larger sheet of black paper.
3. Suddenly shift your gaze to a sheet of white paper and note the color of the positive afterimage.
4. Repeat this procedure using blue squares and yellow squares.

Match the following:

_____ 1. myopia
_____ 2. hyperopia
_____ 3. presbyopia
_____ 4. astigmatism
_____ 5. glaucoma

(a) abnormal curvature of cornea or lens
(b) eye too long
(c) abnormally high intraocular pressure
(d) eye too short
(e) loss of lens elasticity

6. Define the following terms:

(a) visual acuity _____

_____

(b) accommodation _____

_____

(c) convergence of eyes _____

_____

(d) nystagmus _____

_____

7. What is the function of the iris? What muscles are responsible for pupil constriction and dilation?

8. List, in proper sequence, the structures through which light passes as it enters the eye and travels to the photoreceptors. Which of these structures refracts light?

9. A person with myopia does not have to accommodate for near vision as much as a person with normal vision does. Explain why this is true.

10. Explain why the rods provide greater visual sensitivity than the cones and why the cones provide greater visual acuity than the rods.

11. "You see with your brain, not with your eyes." Explain this statement, using the Young-Helmholtz theory of color vision and the optic disc as examples.

12. Carrots contain large amounts of the compound *carotene,* a precursor of vitamin A. How can eating carrots improve eyesight?

# Ears and Hearing

Sound is conducted by the middle ear to the inner ear, where events within the cochlea result in the production of nerve impulses. Clinical tests of middle (conductive) and inner (sensory) ear function aid in the diagnosis of hearing disorders.

## Objectives

1. Describe the function of the middle ear, and explain how the ossicles function.
2. Describe the structure of the inner ear, and explain how the cochlea functions.
3. Demonstrate the Rinne test and Weber's test, and explain their significance.
4. Explain how the source of a sound is localized.

## Materials

1. Tuning forks
2. Rubber mallets

The student should be familiar with the gross structure of the ear (fig. 3.20). Sound waves are conducted through the **outer ear** (the *pinna* and the *external auditory meatus*) to the *tympanic membrane* (eardrum), causing it to vibrate. The movement of the tympanic membrane causes the three ossicles of the **middle ear**—the *malleus* (hammer), *incus* (anvil), and *stapes* (stirrup)—to vibrate, thus pushing the footplate of the stapes against a flexible membrane, the *oval window.* Vibration of the oval window produces compression waves in the fluid-filled *cochlea* of the **inner ear.**

The compression waves of cochlear fluid (*endolymph*) flow over a thin, flexible membrane within the cochlea called the *basilar membrane,* causing it to vibrate. Within the **organ of Corti,** the basilar membrane is coated with sensory *hair cells,* which are displaced upward by this vibration into a stiff, overhanging structure, called the *tectorial membrane* (fig. 3.21). The distortion of the hair cells produced by this action stimulates a train of action potentials that travels along the cochlear branch of the vestibulocochlear (VIII) nerve to the brain, where it is interpreted as the sound of a specific pitch that is determined by the location of the stimulated hair cells on the basilar membrane, and of a specific loudness, which is coded by the frequency of action potentials.

## A. Conduction of Sound Waves through Bone: Rinne and Weber's Tests

Although hearing is normally produced by the vibration of the oval window in response to sound waves conducted through the movements of the middle ear ossicles, the endolymph can also be made to vibrate in response to sound waves conducted through the skull bones, which bypass the middle ear. This fact is used clinically to differentiate between deafness due to middle ear damage (**conduction deafness**—e.g., due to damage to the ossicles in *otitis media* or immobilization of the stapes in *otosclerosis*) and deafness caused by damage to the cochlea or vestibulocochlear nerve (**sensory deafness**—e.g., due to infections, streptomycin toxicity, or prolonged exposure to loud sounds).

**Figure 3.20.** The outer, middle, and inner ear.

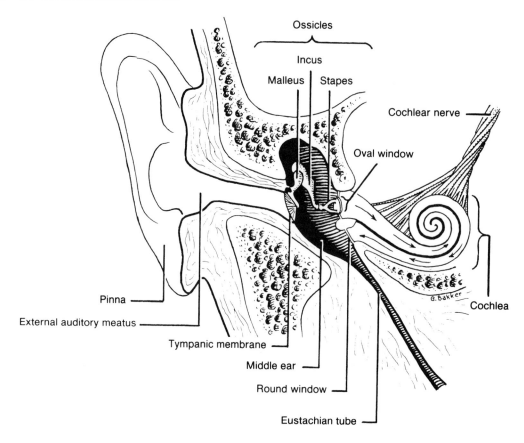

**Figure 3.21.** The organ of Corti.

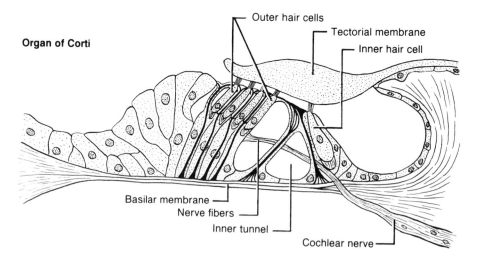

## Clinical Significance

Conduction deafness may be caused by infections of the middle ear (otitis media), infections of the tympanic membrane (tympanitis), or an excessive accumulation of ear wax (also called *cerumen*). People with conduction deafness often wear hearing aids over the mastoid process of the temporal bone, which amplify sounds and transmit them by bone conduction to the cochlea. Hearing aids do not help in cases of complete sensory (nerve) deafness.

### Procedure

1. Produce vibrations in a tuning fork by striking it with a rubber mallet.
2. Perform the Rinne test by placing the *handle* of a vibrating tuning fork against the mastoid process of the temporal bone (the bony prominence behind the ear), with the tuning fork pointed down and behind the ear. When the sound almost dies away, move the tuning fork (by the handle) near the external auditory meatus. If there is no damage to the middle ear, the sound will reappear.
3. Simulate conductive deafness by repeating the Rinne test with a plug of cotton in the ear.
4. Perform Weber's test by placing the handle of a vibrating tuning fork on the midsagittal line of the head.
5. Repeat Weber's test with one ear plugged with your finger. Notice that the sound will appear louder in the plugged ear because external room noise is excluded.

**Note:** *In conduction deafness, therefore, the sound will seem loudest in the affected ear (room noise is excluded), whereas in sensory deafness the sound will be loudest in the normal ear.*

## B. Binaural Localization of Sound

Just as binocular vision provides valuable clues for viewing scenes in three dimensions, binaural hearing helps localize sounds (people have stereoscopic vision and stereophonic hearing). The ability to localize the source of a sound depends partly on the difference in loudness of the sound that reaches the two ears and partly on the difference in the time of arrival of the sound at the two ears. The difference in loudness is most important for high-pitched sounds, where the sound waves are blocked by the head, whereas the difference in the time of arrival is most important for low-pitched sounds, whose wavelengths are large enough to bend around the head.

### Procedure

1. The subject closes his or her eyes and is asked to locate the source of a sound (e.g., a vibrating tuning fork).
2. The vibrating tuning fork is placed at various positions (front, back, sides) about a foot from the subject's head, and the subject is asked to describe the location of the tuning fork.
3. The above procedures are repeated with one ear plugged.

# Laboratory Report 3.7

Name _____

Date _____

Section _____

1. Name the three middle ear ossicles in the correct sequence, from outer to inner:

   _____

2. The scientific name for the eardrum is the _____ .

3. Movements of _____ fluid within the cochlea cause

   the _____ membrane to vibrate.

4. How does the ear transduce sound waves in air into electrical nerve impulses?

5. How are the pitch and loudness of a sound coded in the nervous system?

6. Explain the results that might be obtained by performing the Rinne test and Weber's test on a patient with otosclerosis. How might these results compare with those obtained from a patient with sensory deafness? Explain.

# Vestibular Apparatus

The vestibular apparatus provides a sense of balance and equilibrium. As a result of inertia acting on the structures within the vestibular apparatus, changes in the position of the head result in the production of afferent nerve impulses that are conducted to the brain on the eighth cranial nerve. This information results in eye movements and other motor activities that help to orient the body in space.

## Objectives

1. Describe the structure of the semicircular canals, and explain how movements of the head result in the production of nerve impulses.
2. Describe vestibular nystagmus, and explain how it is produced.

## Materials

Swivel chair

The vestibular apparatus is located in the inner ear above the cochlea and consists of three *semicircular canals* (horizontal, superior vertical, and posterior vertical—oriented in three planes), the *utricle,* and the *saccule* (fig. 3.22). These structures, like the cochlea, are filled with endolymph and contain sensory cells activated by bending. The sensory hair cells of the semicircular canals have cilia embedded in a gelatinous sail (the *cupula*) extending into the endolymph (fig. 3.23). Movement of the endolymph fluid, induced by acceleration or deceleration, bends the hair cells, sending a train of impulses to the brain along the vestibulocochlear (VIII) nerve. The sensory cells of the utricle (and possibly the saccule) serve to orient the head with respect to the gravitational pull of the earth.

Afferent impulses from the vestibular apparatus help make us aware of our position in space and affect a variety of efferent somatic motor nerves (e.g., those regulating the extrinsic eye muscles) and, under intense vestibular activity, autonomic motor nerves (producing vomiting, perspiration, hypotension, etc.). In this exercise, the effect of vestibular activity on the extrinsic eye muscles will be tested by producing **vestibular nystagmus.**

The semicircular canals can be stimulated by rotating a subject in a chair (to stimulate the horizontal canal the head must be flexed 30° forward). When the subject is first rotated to the right, the cupula will be bent to the left because of the inertial lag of the endolymph. This will cause nystagmus in which the eyes drift slowly to the left followed by a quick movement to the right (midline position). Nystagmus will continue until the inertia of the endolymph has been overcome and the cupula returns to its initial position. When the rotation of the subject is abruptly stopped, the inertia of the endolymph will bend the cupula to the right, producing nystagmus with a slow phase to the right and a rapid phase to the left. This is often accompanied by **vertigo** (an illusion of movement) and a tendency to fall to the right.

## Clinical Significance

Activation of the vestibular apparatus can result in vertigo. Vertigo may be accompanied by dizziness, but the two are not the same thing; a person may be dizzy without experiencing vertigo. In the present exercise, activation of the vestibular apparatus by rotation of the subject produces eye movements (nystagmus). The eyes in turn can activate the vestibular apparatus and produce vertigo, as occurs in motion sickness (seasickness, car-sickness, etc.). Vertigo can also accompany diseases unrelated to the special senses (e.g., cardiovascular disease). Many of the unpleasant symptoms associated with vertigo, such as nausea and vomiting, are the result of activation of the autonomic motor system. Drugs taken for motion sickness (e.g., Dramamine) act by suppressing these autonomic responses.

**Figure 3.22.** The vestibular apparatus and the cochlea.

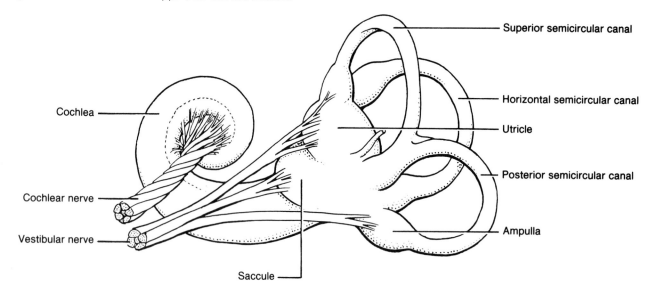

Cochlea

Cochlear nerve

Vestibular nerve

Saccule

Superior semicircular canal

Horizontal semicircular canal

Utricle

Posterior semicircular canal

Ampulla

**Figure 3.23.** The cupula within the semicircular canals.

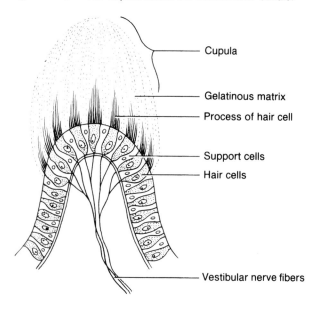

Cupula

Gelatinous matrix

Process of hair cell

Support cells

Hair cells

Vestibular nerve fibers

## Procedure

1. The subject sits in a swivel chair with the head flexed 30° (chin almost touching chest) and is quickly rotated for 20 seconds (10 revolutions). After the initial nystagmus is noted, the subject closes his or her eyes.

**Note:** *The exercise should be stopped immediately if the subject feels sick.*

2. The chair is abruptly stopped, the subject opens the eyes, and the direction of nystagmus is noted.
3. Repeat this procedure (using different subjects) alternating with the head resting on the right shoulder and the left shoulder (this stimulates the vertical canals), and note the direction of the post-rotational nystagmus.

1. Explain how the semicircular canals transduce body movement into electrical nerve impulses.

2. Does nystagmus occur after a person in a rotating chair has achieved constant velocity? Explain.

3. Explain the causes of vertigo and nausea in a seasick person.

# Taste Buds

Taste buds that have the greatest sensitivity to one of the four taste modalities—sweet, sour, bitter, and salty—have a characteristic distribution on the tongue. Each of these taste modalities is therefore perceived most acutely in a particular tongue region.

## Objectives

1. Describe the structure of a taste bud and the location of taste buds on the tongue.
2. List the four primary taste modalities, and describe their distribution on the tongue.

## Materials

1. Cotton-tipped applicator sticks
2. Solutions of 5% sucrose, 1% acetic acid, 5% NaCl, and 0.5% quinine sulfate

The taste buds consist of epithelial cells arranged in the form of barrel-shaped receptors (fig. 3.24), associated with sensory (afferent) nerves. In adults, these receptors are located primarily on the dorsal surface of the tongue, with a lesser number on the soft palate and epiglottis; in children, the sense of taste is more diffuse with additional receptors on the inside of the cheeks.

It is generally believed that all the nuances of taste are due to different mixtures of only four basic taste stimuli—*sweet, sour, bitter,* and *salty*—in addition to information derived from olfactory and touch receptors. Although a given taste bud can be stimulated by all four modalities, different taste buds will respond more readily (i.e., have a lower threshold) to one or two stimuli than to the others. Thus, a sweet stimulus is most easily perceived at the tip of the tongue, bitter at the back, sour at the edge, and salty at the tip and edge of the tongue.

*proteins also give sweet sensation*
*Bitter - quinine*
*Salt - Cl*
*Sour → H ion or acid*

**Figure 3.24.** A taste bud.

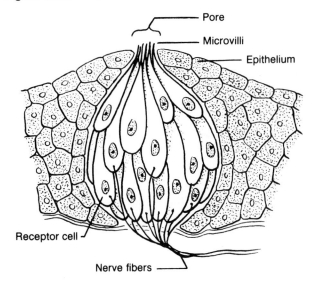

- Pore
- Microvilli
- Epithelium
- Receptor cell
- Nerve fibers

The sour taste of solutions is due to their acid ($H^+$) content, and the salty taste is produced by the presence of $Cl^-$ (but this is modified by the cation—NaCl tastes saltier than KCl, for example). The chemical basis for bitter and sweet taste is largely unknown, since these can be produced by a variety of seemingly unrelated compounds. (Fructose tastes the sweetest, followed by sucrose, and then by glucose. The artificial, nonsugar sweeteners, however, taste sweeter than any of these.)

The afferent pathway from the taste buds to the brain involves two cranial nerves (fig. 3.25). Taste buds on the posterior one-third of the tongue have a sensory pathway through the glossopharyngeal nerve, whereas the anterior two-thirds of the tongue is served by the facial nerve. The vagus nerve also has limited innervation in the epiglottis area, and the trigeminal nerve sends sensory fibers to the sides and tip of the tongue. Impulses in the nerves originating in the taste buds are conducted through the medulla oblongata and thalamus to the cerebral cortex of the parietal lobe where they are interpreted.

133

**Figure 3.25.** Tongue innervation.

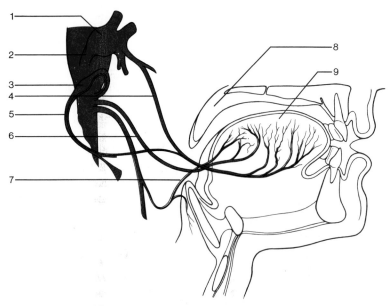

1. Gasserian ganglion
2. Trigeminal nerve
3. Geniculate ganglion
4. Lingual nerve
5. Facial nerve
6. Glossopharyngeal nerve
7. Laryngeal branch of vagus nerve
8. Soft palate
9. Tongue

## Clinical Significance

The sensations of taste and olfaction are often grouped together in a single category—the chemical senses. These function together to provide the proper nuances of taste, which are extremely well developed in some people (e.g., wine tasters). Since the sense of smell is so important in tasting, a stuffy nose from a cold or allergy greatly affects the taste of foods.

**Procedure**

1. Dry the tongue with a paper towel, and using an applicator stick, apply a dab of 5% sucrose solution to the tip, sides, and back of the tongue.
2. Repeat this procedure using 1% acetic acid, 5% NaCl, and 0.5% quinine sulfate, being sure to rinse the mouth and dry the tongue between solutions.
3. Using the sketch provided in the laboratory report, record the location where each solution was tasted. Use the symbols *sw* for sweet, *sl* for salty, *sr* for sour, and *b* for bitter.

## Data from Exercise 3.9

Map the areas of the tongue as described in the last procedure in the diagram below.

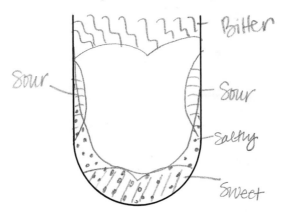

## Questions for Exercise 3.9

1. Describe the areas of the tongue where the following tastes are best perceived:

    (a) sweet _____

    (b) salty _____

    (c) bitter _____

    (d) sour _____

2. Which taste modalities would be most affected by the destruction of the glossopharyngeal nerve? Which would be most affected by the destruction of the facial nerve? Explain why this is true.

# Skeletal Muscles

The basic mechanism of contraction for striated muscles (skeletal and cardiac muscle) can be divided into three parts: (1) electrical excitation of the muscle cell; (2) excitation-contraction coupling; and (3) sliding of the muscle filaments and contraction.

At rest, there is a potential difference across the muscle cell membrane equal to approximately $-80$ mV (millivolts). The negative sign indicates that the inside of the membrane is negatively charged in comparison to the outside of the cell. When the cell is appropriately stimulated—by a direct electric shock or by the motor nerve that innervates the muscle—the permeability of the membrane to cations changes. The diffusion of $Na^+$ into the cell *depolarizes* the membrane and momentarily reverses its polarity. This is immediately followed by the outward diffusion of $K^+$, which *repolarizes* and reestablishes the resting membrane potential. This rapid depolarization and repolarization of the membrane at the stimulated point is called an **action potential.**

As action potentials are conducted along the cell membrane they stimulate a rise in the cytoplasmic concentration of $Ca^{++}$, which in skeletal muscles comes from a system of intracellular tubules called the sarcoplasmic reticulum. In the absence of this calcium, two proteins that are part of the thin filaments, known as *troponin* and *tropomyosin,* inhibit contraction. When $Ca^{++}$ is released into the cell as a result of electrical stimulation, the calcium ions attach to troponin and release the inhibitory effect of these proteins. Calcium ions are thus said to couple electrical excitation to muscle contraction.

Within the muscle cell (fiber) there are numerous subunits (*fibrils*) that are oriented along the long axis of the fiber. Each fibril, in turn, is composed of numerous repeating subunits called **sarcomeres.** The sarcomere is the functional unit of contraction. When contraction is stimulated by $Ca^{++}$, the thick and thin *filaments* within the sarcomeres slide over each other; this sliding of the filaments allows the sarcomeres to get shorter while the filaments remain the same length (fig. 4.1). As the sarcomeres become shorter, the fibrils and thus the entire fiber shorten, causing muscle contraction.

**Figure 4.1.** A sliding filament model of muscle contraction (see text for discussion).

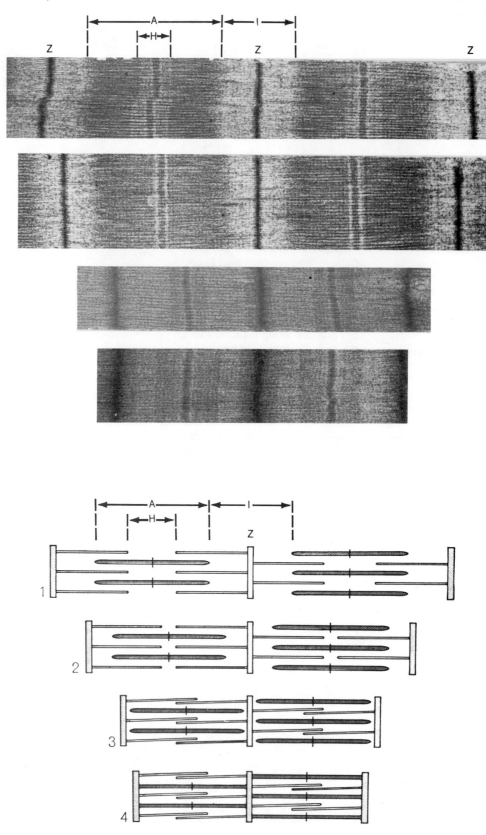

# Neural Control of Muscle Contraction

The physiology of muscle contraction can be studied by using isolated muscles from a pithed frog. Isolated frog muscles can be stimulated directly by an electric shock and indirectly through the activation of the appropriate motor nerve.

## Objectives

1. Prepare a pithed frog for the study of muscle physiology.
2. Describe how muscle contraction can be stimulated by a direct electric shock.
3. Explain how motor nerves stimulate the contraction of skeletal muscles.

## Materials

1. Frogs
2. Surgical scissors, forceps, sharp probes, dissecting trays, glass probes
3. Recording equipment (either kymograph or electrical recorder, such as physiograph), electrical stimulators
4. Straight pins bent into the shape of a *Z,* thread
5. Bone clamp (if kymograph is used) or myograph transducer (if physiograph is used)
6. Frog Ringer's solution: dissolve 6 g NaCl, 0.075 g KCl, 0.10 g $CaCl_2$, and 0.10 g $NaHCO_3$ in a liter of water

### Recording Procedures: Kymograph and Physiograph

The **kymograph,** or moving-drum recorder, is the classical device for measuring the mechanical aspects of muscle contraction in the physiology laboratory. In this technique, glossy white paper on a revolving drum is smoked over a kerosene burner so that the paper becomes uniformly blackened. The muscle (skeletal muscle or heart) is connected with a thread to a movable stylus, so that contractions of the muscle produce deflections of the stylus, which in turn cause soot to rub off the smoked paper, exposing a white line against a black background.

The **physiograph** is a more modern device for recording the mechanical aspects of muscular contraction. It is much more sensitive than the straightforward mechanical coupling mechanism of kymograph recorders because the mechanical movements of the muscle are first *transduced* (changed) into electrical current, which can then be greatly amplified prior to recording. The fact that mechanical energy is transduced into electrical energy also makes the physiograph more versatile than the kymograph recorder, because mechanical events with different energies (from muscle contraction to sound waves) can be recorded, as can primarily electrical events such as the electrocardiograph (ECG), electromyograph (EMG), nerve impulses, and the electroencephalograph (EEG). A number of physiological parameters can simultaneously be recorded on different *channels* of the physiograph, so that the temporal relationship between these events can be studied.

The physiograph consists of four basic parts: (1) the **transducer** changes the original energy of the physiological event into electrical energy; (2) the **coupler,** which is interchangeable, makes the input energy from the transducer compatible with the built-in amplifier; (3) once the input signal has been properly modified by the coupler, the **amplifier** increases the strength of the electrical current so that a galvanometer can be activated; (4) the **galvanometer** measures the current generated by the movement of a pen. The movement of the pen is proportional to the strength of the electrical current generated by the physiological event being measured. Since recording paper moves continuously at a known speed under the pen, both the *frequency* (number per unit time) and the *strength* (amplitude of the pen deflection from a baseline) of the physiological event can be continuously recorded (fig. 4.2).

**Figure 4.2.** The Physiograph Mark III recorder.

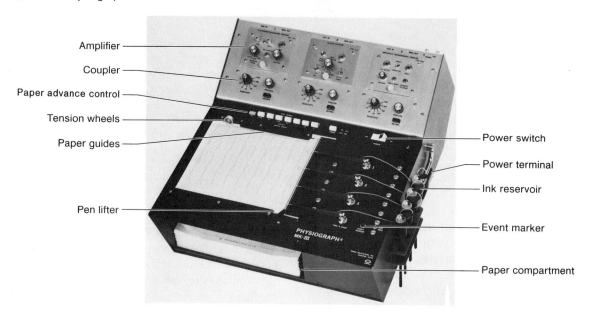

- Amplifier
- Coupler
- Paper advance control
- Tension wheels
- Paper guides
- Pen lifter
- Power switch
- Power terminal
- Ink reservoir
- Event marker
- Paper compartment

## For Kymograph Recording

1. Attach the kymograph paper to the kymograph drum with tape, so that the shiny side of the paper is facing out. Hold the drum over a kerosene burner until the paper is uniformly blackened. (This will go faster if the drum is slowly rotated close to, but not in, the flame.)
2. Place the drum on the motor-driven mechanism. Adjust the height of the drum so that the writing stylus will touch the bottom fourth of the paper, and adjust the speed so that the drum turns slowly.

## For Physiograph Recording

1. Insert the *transducer coupler* into the physiograph, and plug the myograph transducer into the coupler (fig. 4.3).[9]
2. Raise the inkwells and lower the pens onto the paper by lowering the pen lifter (fig. 4.2). Squeeze the rubber bulbs on the inkwells to force ink into the pens.
3. Turn the physiograph on with the rocking switch. Depress the *paper-speed* button that is marked 0.5 cm per second (cm/sec), the *down* position is on. Turn on the paper drive by depressing the *paper advance* button and releasing it, allowing it to rise (the *up* position is on).

9. For Physiograph Mark III, Narco Bio-Systems.

**Figure 4.3.** The Narco Mark III Physiograph with an inserted transducer coupler. The transducer coupler is connected by means of a cable to a myograph transducer.

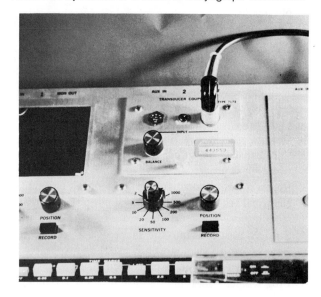

**Figure 4.4.** The procedure for pithing a frog. (a) a probe is first inserted through the foramen magnum into the skull; (b) then it is inserted through the spinal cord. (Procedure was simulated with a preserved frog.)

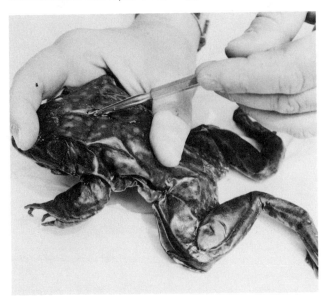

(a)

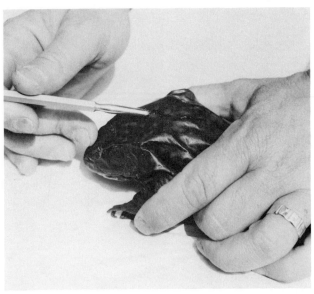

(b)

4. Move the *time* switch to *on.* The bottom pen, labeled *time* and *event,* will make upward deflections every second. Notice that at a paper speed of 0.5 cm/sec, these deflections will be separated by a distance equal to the width of one small box on the recording paper. If the paper speed is increased to 1.0 cm/sec, the deflections of the time-and-event pen will be two small boxes apart.

5. Turn the outer knob of the *sensitivity* control to its lowest number (this will be its greatest sensitivity (fig. 4.3). With the *record* button off (in the *up* position), adjust the position of the recording pen for the appropriate channel with the *position* knob, so that the pen writes exactly on the heavy horizontal line corresponding to the channel being recorded.

6. Depress the *record* button (the *down* position is on). This will cause the pen to move away from the heavy horizontal line. Bring the pen back to the line by rotating the *balance* knob. The pen should now remain on the heavy line whether or not the *record* button is depressed and regardless of the setting of the *sensitivity* knob.

## A. Frog Muscle Preparation

To study the physiology of frog muscle and nerve, the frog must be killed but its tissues kept alive. This can be accomplished by destroying the frog's central nervous system—a procedure called **pithing.** The frog is thus clinically dead (clinical death is defined as the irreversible loss of higher brain function), but its muscles and peripheral nerves are functional as long as their cells remain alive. Under the proper conditions, this can be prolonged for several hours.

There are two techniques for pithing a frog. In the first technique, grasp the frog securely in one hand and flex its head so that the base of the skull can be felt with the fingers of the other hand. Then perform these steps:

1. Insert a sturdy metal probe into the skull through the foramen magnum (the opening in the skull where the spinal cord joins the brain stem). This is shown in figure 4.4a.

2. Move the probe around in the skull. This destroys the brain and prevents the frog from feeling any pain (it is now clinically dead).

3. Partially withdraw the probe, turn it so that it points toward the hind end of the frog (keeping the head flexed), and insert the probe downward into the spinal cord (fig. 4.4b). This destroys spinal reflexes. The frog's legs will straighten out as the probe is inserted. When the spinal nerves are destroyed, the frog will become limp.

Alternatively, the following procedure may be employed. Force one blade of a pair of sharp scissors into the frog's mouth as shown in figure 4.5a. Quickly decapitate the frog by cutting behind its eyes. It should be understood that the frog is dead as soon as its brain is severed from its spinal cord. Insert a probe down into the exposed spinal cord to destroy its spinal reflexes (fig. 4.5b).

**Figure 4.5.** Alternative pithing procedure. (a) the frog is first decapitated; (b) then a probe is inserted into the spinal cord. (Procedure was simulated with a preserved frog.)

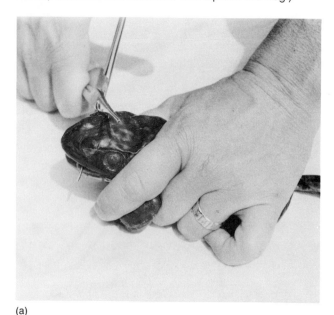

(a)

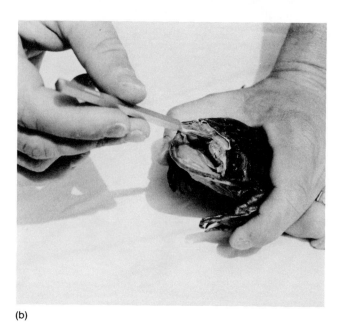

(b)

After the frog has been pithed, skin one of its legs to expose the underlying muscle. Then run one blade of a pair of scissors under the Achilles tendon and cut it, leaving part of the tendon still attached to the gastrocnemius muscle.

---

### Procedure for Kymograph or Physiograph Recordings

1. For **kymograph** recording, prepare the muscle as follows:
   a) Cut the bone at its attachment to the muscle, taking care to leave a short length of femur still attached to the muscle. Place the femur in a bone clamp, and attach the Achilles tendon to the recording stylus by inserting a bent pin through the tendon and hooking the pin through a loop on the stylus.
   b) Raise the bone clamp so that the muscle is under tension, and position the stylus so that it lightly drags across the smoked paper when the kymograph is on. Insert two stimulating electrodes into the muscle (fig. 4.6).
2. For **physiograph** recording, prepare the muscle as follows:
   a) Unlike the procedure for kymograph recording, do *not* cut the attachment of the muscle to the femur. Instead, secure the frog to a dissecting tray by inserting sharp probes through its arms and legs.

b) Push a bent pin through its Achilles tendon, and tie one end of a cotton thread to the hook of a myograph transducer. Position the myograph so that it is directly above the muscle, and adjust the height of the myograph so that the muscle is under tension. Insert two stimulating electrodes into the muscle (fig. 4.7).

3. Establish the **threshold stimulus** (the minimum stimulus that will evoke a particular response). To do this, set the stimulus intensity on 1.0 V, and deliver a single shock. Increase the strength of the stimulus in 0.5 V increments until the muscle responds with a contraction (*twitch*) that is recorded on the kymograph or physiograph. Record this voltage.

Threshold: _____

**Note:** *Rinse the muscle periodically with Ringer's solution (a salt solution balanced to the extracellular fluid of the frog). Do not allow the muscle to dry out.*

## B. Stimulation of Motor Nerve

In the body, or *in vivo,* skeletal muscles are stimulated to contract by **somatic motor nerves.** Action potentials in the motor nerve fibers elicit the release of a chemical neurotransmitter called *acetylcholine (ACh)* from the axon endings. This transmitter combines with a receptor protein in the muscle cell membrane and stimulates the production of action potentials in the muscle fiber. Electrical

**Figure 4.6.** The frog gastrocnemius muscle setup. The muscle is fixed in a muscle clamp so that when an electrical charge is delivered by a stimulator, the contraction causes a pen to write on a moving chart (kymograph).

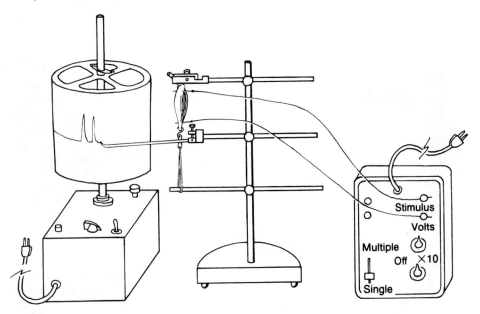

stimulation of the muscle fibers, in turn, cause $Ca^{++}$ to be released from the sarcoplasmic reticulum. The release of $Ca^{++}$ stimulates muscle contraction through the mechanisms previously described.

The electrical activity of somatic motor neurons is normally stimulated in the spinal cord by synapses with other neurons. These other neurons may be association neurons located in the brain or spinal cord, or they may be sensory neurons. Alternatively, action potentials in motor, or *efferent,* nerve fibers may be stimulated by damage to the fibers peripherally. This damage produces an injury current, which stimulates action potentials and muscle contractions when a nerve is pinched, for example.

## Clinical Significance

Some types of muscle degeneration are secondary to nerve damage or to dysfunctions at the neuromuscular junctions. Muscle degeneration follows damage to the motor nerve pathway because proper neuromuscular activity and resulting muscle tone seem to be required for the health of the muscle. In the disease *myasthenia gravis* (*myasthenia* means that a muscle fatigues too easily), antibodies are produced against the muscle membrane receptors for acetylcholine, which is the neurotransmitter of somatic motor neurons. This autoimmune disease thus prevents the muscle from being properly stimulated by somatic motor neurons.

### Procedure

1. Starting at the pelvis, skin the leg that is going to be used for kymograph or physiograph recordings.
2. With the frog on its belly, part the muscles of the thigh around the femur to reveal the sciatic nerve.
3. Using glass probes, free the nerve from its attached connective tissue, and raise it tightly held between two glass probes (fig. 4.7b)
4. Place both stimulating electrodes against the nerve. Starting with the stimulator set at 0 V, gradually increase the stimulus voltage in small increments until the minimum stimulus is attained that will produce a muscle twitch. Record this threshold in the space provided, and compare it with the threshold previously obtained by placing the electrodes directly on the muscle.
   Threshold: _____ V
5. Turn off the stimulator. Using a length of cotton thread, tie a knot in the nerve, and observe the response of the gastrocnemius muscle.

**Figure 4.7.** After the frog's leg is skinned (a), the Achilles tendon is cut (b) and a bent pin is inserted into it (c). A length of thread attaches this pin to the hook of the myograph transducer (not shown). In (b) the sciatic nerve is shown between two glass probes, in preparation for exercise 4B.

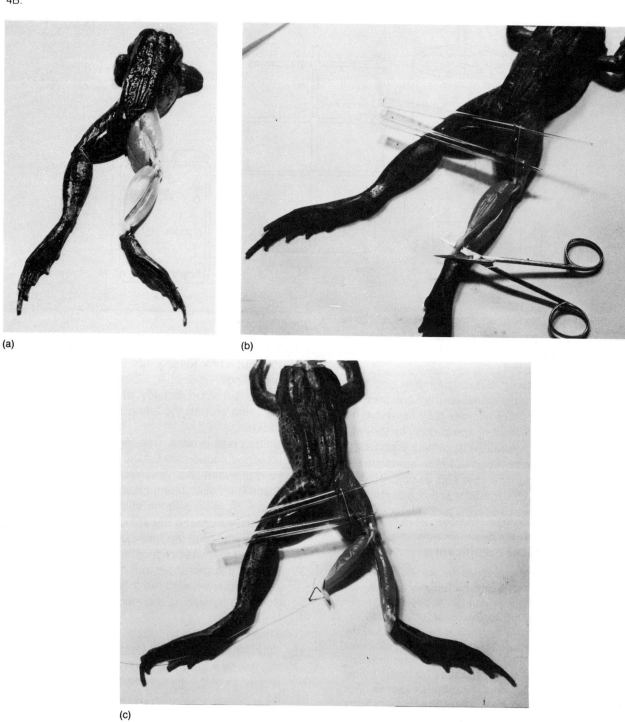

(a)

(b)

(c)

# Laboratory Report 4.1

Name _____

Date _____

Section _____

1. Another name for a muscle cell is a muscle _____ .

2. The electrical events in the muscle cell that stimulate contraction are known as _____ .

3. The basic subunits of contraction in the muscle cell are known as _____ .

4. What couples electrical excitation to muscle contraction? _____

   _____

5. Define the term *threshold:* _____

   _____ .

6. Explain why the threshold stimulus for producing a muscle twitch is lower when the sciatic nerve is stimulated than when the gastrocnemius muscle is stimulated directly.

# Summation, Tetanus, and Fatigue

Twitch, summation, and tetanus can be produced by direct electrical stimulation of frog muscles *in vitro* and by human muscles *in vivo*. These procedures demonstrate how normal muscular movements are produced.

## Objectives

1. Define the terms *twitch, summation, tetanus,* and *fatigue.*
2. Demonstrate twitch, summation, and tetanus in frog and human muscles, and demonstrate fatigue in the frog muscle preparation.
3. Explain how a smooth, sustained contraction is normally produced.

## Materials

1. Frogs
2. Equipment and setup used in exercise 4.1
3. Electrocardiograph plates and electrolyte gel

Individual skeletal muscle fibers cannot sustain a contraction; they can only twitch. Muscle fibers likewise cannot produce a graded contraction—they can only contract maximally to any stimulus above threshold (they contract all-or-none). Smooth, graded skeletal muscle contractions are produced by the **summation** of fiber twitches. This occurs when fibers twitch asynchronously, so that some are in the process of contraction before the muscle has had time to relax completely from the twitch of the previously stimulated fibers. Maintenance of a sustained muscle contraction is called **tetanus.**

Tetanus can be demonstrated in the laboratory by setting the stimulator to deliver shocks automatically to the muscle at an ever-increasing frequency until the twitches fuse into a smooth contraction. This is similar to what occurs in the body when different motor neurons in the spinal cord are activated at slightly different times.

If the stimulator is left on so that the muscle remains in tetanus, a gradual decrease in contraction strength will be observed. This is due to muscle **fatigue.** True muscle fatigue rarely occurs in the body because the sensations of muscle pain and depletion of the neurotransmitter at the neuromuscular junction usually cause exercise to cease before the muscle's energy stores have been depleted.

## A. Summation, Tetanus, and Fatigue in Frog Gastrocnemius Muscle

Summation, tetanus, and fatigue can be demonstrated with the frog gastrocnemius muscle preparation used in exercise 4.1.

### Procedure

1. Set the stimulus voltage above threshold, and press down rapidly two or three times on the switch that delivers a single pulse to the muscle. If this is done rapidly enough, successive twitches can be made to "ride piggyback" on preceding twitches (fig. 4.8)
2. Set the stimulus switch to deliver shocks automatically to the muscle at a frequency of about one per second. Gradually increase the frequency of stimulation until the twitches fuse into a smooth, sustained contraction.
3. Maintain stimulation until the strength of contraction gradually diminishes because of muscle fatigue.
4. Enter your recordings in the laboratory report.

**Figure 4.8.** A recording of the summation of two muscle twitches on a physiograph recorder. Note that contraction to the second stimulus is greater than contraction to the first stimulus (the intensity of the first and second stimulus is the same).

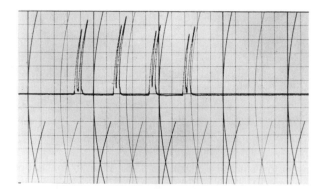

## B. Twitch, Summation, and Tetanus in Human Muscle

The properties of frog muscle observed *in vitro* duplicate the behavior of human muscle *in vivo* in many ways. A single pulse of electrical stimulation produces a single short contraction (twitch), and many pulses of stimulation delivered in rapid succession produce a summation of twitches resulting in a smooth, graded muscular contraction and eventually in tetanus.

### Clinical Significance

Sustained muscular spasm (*tetany*) may be produced by hypocalcemia and alkalosis. (The most common cause of tetany is alkalosis produced by hyperventilation.) Cramps may be caused by a variety of conditions including salt depletion. General muscle weakness may be caused by alterations in plasma potassium levels (due, for example, to excessive diarrhea or vomiting).

*Muscular dystrophy* is a name given to a variety of diseases where there is a progressive weakness of skeletal muscles (although the heart may also be involved) that does not seem to be caused by inflammation or neural disease. In severe forms of these diseases, there is a great loss of myofilaments and sarcomeres, which are replaced with fibrous connective tissue and fat.

### Procedure

1. Rub a small amount of electrolyte gel on the skin near the wrist, and attach an ECG electrode plate to this area with an elastic band. Rub electrolyte gel on a second ECG electrode plate, and place it on the anterior, medial area of the arm just below (distal to) the elbow. Do not attach this electrode to the arm, as this will be the exploring electrode (fig. 4.9).

**Figure 4.9.** The placement of electrodes for eliciting finger twitches in response to electrical stimulation.

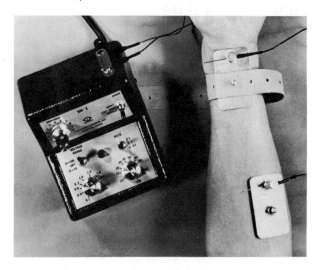

2. Attach the electrode plates to a stimulator. Make sure that the stimulator is *off* at this time.
3. Set the stimulus intensity at 15 V and deliver a single pulse of stimulation. If no twitch is observed or felt in the fingers, move the exploring electrode around the medial area of the forearm until an effect is seen or felt. (See fig. 4.9 for the approximate position of the electrode.)

**Note:** *The stimulus intensity may have to be increased for some people, but **do not exceed 30 V!** Most of the time an effect can be obtained at a lower voltage by moving the exploring electrode to a slightly different position. A tingling sensation means that the stimulus intensity is adequate although the position may have to be changed.*

4. Once a muscle twitch has been observed, set the stimulator so that it automatically delivers one pulse of stimulation per second. Adjust the exploratory plate so that only one finger twitches.
5. Keeping the stimulus intensity constant, increase the **frequency** of stimulation gradually until a maximum contraction is reached. Gradually decrease the stimulus frequency until the individual twitches are reproduced.

# Laboratory Report 4.2

Name _____

Date _____

Section _____

## Data from Exercise 4.2

### A. Summation, Tetanus, and Fatigue in Frog Gastrocnemius Muscle

1. Tape your recording to (or draw a facsimile in) the space below:

2. Label twitch, summation, tetanus, and fatigue in your recording.

### B. Twitch, Summation, and Tetanus in Human Muscle

1. Describe the results of your procedure in the space below.

2. What can you conclude about the production of normal muscular movements?

## Questions for Exercise 4.2

1. Describe how the summation of muscle twitches is produced. Using this information, explain how variations in the strength of muscle contraction are produced.

2. Explain how a sustained muscle contraction was produced *in vitro* in this exercise and how sustained contractions are produced *in vivo* (in the body).

# Electromyogram (EMG)

The electrical activity produced by muscles can be recorded using surface electrodes. This recording can be used to demonstrate the action of antagonistic muscles and to provide biofeedback training of muscles.

## Objectives

1. Demonstrate the antagonism between the action of the biceps and triceps using the electromyogram (EMG).
2. Describe the EMG of the biceps and triceps during flexion and extension of the arm.
3. Explain the importance of antagonist inhibition in skeletal movements.
4. Explain how the EMG can be used in biofeedback techniques.

## Materials

1. Physiograph or other electrical recorder and high-gain coupler
2. EMG plates, disposable adhesive paper washers for EMG plates
3. Electrolyte (ECG) gel or paste, alcohol swabs

Muscle contraction occurs in response to the electrical stimulation of the muscle fibers. In the previous exercises, the mechanical response of the muscles—recorded because of the tension exerted on the myograph transducer—was observed. Although the muscles were stimulated by electric shocks, the electrical activity of the muscle cells was not recorded. It should be recalled, however, that electric shocks delivered to the muscle induce action potentials in the muscle fibers and that it is these action potentials (acting via release of $Ca^{++}$ from the sarcoplasmic reticulum) that stimulate contraction.

## A. Electromyogram during Arm Flexion and Extension

When somatic motor nerves stimulate skeletal muscles to contract, the action potentials produced by the muscles induce potential differences in the overlying skin that can be recorded by a pair of surface electrodes on the skin. The recording thus obtained is called an **electromyogram** (**EMG**). When the pair of electrodes are placed on the anterior surface of the upper arm, they record potentials of the *biceps brachii;* when they are located over the posterior surface of the upper arm, they record the activity of the *triceps brachii*. These two groups of muscles are antagonistic—contraction of the biceps flexes the arm, whereas contraction of the triceps extends the arm. Therefore, during flexion, the activity of the triceps is inhibited, whereas during extension the activity of the biceps is inhibited.

### Clinical Significance

The activity of antagonistic muscle groups is controlled in the central nervous system, so that when one group of muscles (the *agonist*) is stimulated, the antagonistic group is inhibited. The inhibition of antagonistic muscle groups occurs largely through the action of descending motor tracts that originate in the brain. When a person has spinal cord damage that blocks these descending inhibitory influences, the antagonistic muscles may contract when they are stretched by the movement of a limb. Flexion, for example, stretches the extensor muscles, and extension causes the flexor muscles to be stretched. Without inhibitory influences, stretch reflexes in a person with spinal cord damage may cause antagonistic muscles to alternately stretch and contract, producing a *flapping tremor* or *clonus*.

**Figure 4.10.** Electrode plates and adhesive washers needed for performing an electromyograph procedure.

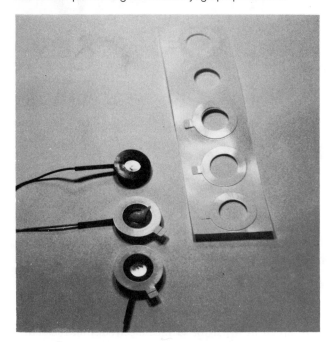

**Figure 4.11.** Placement of the EMG electrodes for recording from (a) the biceps (b) and triceps.

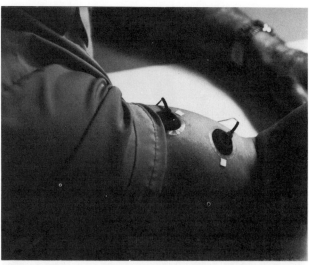

(a)

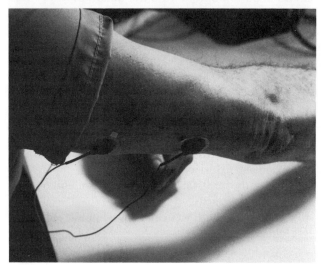

(b)

## Procedure

1. Using cotton or a paper towel soaked in alcohol, cleanse the skin over the biceps and triceps.
2. Apply the self-sticking paper washers to the raised plastic area around the electrode plates (fig. 4.10). Squeeze electrolyte gel onto the metal electrode plates. Use a paper towel to smooth the gel so that it completely fills the well between the metal plates and the surrounding plastic.
3. Remove the paper coverings over the adhesive area of the washers, and apply the electrodes to the skin over the biceps. Apply one electrode to the skin over the proximal portion of the biceps and one over the distal portion in a parallel line (fig. 4.11). Apply the ground electrode over the triceps muscle.
4. Plug the electrodes into the **high-gain coupler** module of the physiograph. Set this module to a *gain* of X100, a *time constant* of 0.03, and a *sensitivity* between 20 and 100.
5. Set the chart speed at 0.5 cm/sec. With the arm relaxed and hanging down, establish a baseline in the recording. Then flex the arm (bringing the hand upward), and observe the recording. Extend the arm back to its previous position, and flex it again so that the difference between flexion and extension can be seen in the recording.

6. Flex the arm again, this time lifting a chair or other weight. Observe the effect of this activity on the recording. Now "make a muscle," and observe the recording.
7. Change the position of the electrodes so that the two recording electrodes are over the triceps muscle (one proximal and one distal) and the ground electrode is over the biceps. Flex and extend the arm as before, and observe the recording.
8. Place the hand on a table with the elbow bent, and then extend the arm, as if doing a push-up. Observe the effect of this action on the EMG.

## B. Biofeedback and the Electromyograph

A person's behavior can be changed as a result of the pleasant or unpleasant consequences of his or her actions. That is, positive and negative feedback modify behavior; this represents a type of learning that experimental psychologists call *operant conditioning*. The pairing of a particular behavior—such as cigarette smoking—with unpleasant sensations has been used successfully to shape human behavior through negative feedback.

**Biofeedback** techniques similarly effect learning, usually through the positive feedback afforded by electronic monitors of specific physiological states. The electromyogram, for example, provides a visual display of muscle stimulation that can be used as a psychological reward for effort spent attempting to contract specific muscle groups. In this exercise, biofeedback will be demonstrated by the use of the EMG to learn how to increase the strength of contraction of the triceps muscle.

## Clinical Significance

Biofeedback techniques serve a variety of clinical functions. The EMG is sometimes used to train people with neuromuscular disorders to use affected limbs. Physiological monitoring of the heart rate and blood pressure have served to train patients with high blood pressure to lower their pulse, and EEG recordings have been used to teach people techniques for relaxation (when alpha rhythms are produced). Future health applications of biofeedback may become widespread as physiological monitoring equipment becomes available to the general population.

## Procedure

1. Prepare the EMG electrodes as described in the previous procedure. Place the two recording electrodes over the triceps muscle and the ground electrode over the biceps muscle. Be sure to cleanse the skin with alcohol before applying the electrodes.
2. Set the *high-gain coupler* to a gain of X100, a time constant of 0.03, and a sensitivity of 20 or 50. Set the chart speed of the recorder to 0.5 cm/sec.
3. Extend the arm, and observe the highest amplitude of the recording. Attempt a forced extension, and observe the amplitude of the recording. Attempt to increase the amplitude of the EMG by various procedures. (*Hint:* Try to extend the arm with the back of the hand against a table.)

1. During arm flexion the biceps is the _____ (agonist/antagonist) and the triceps is the _____ .

2. With the recording electrode over the biceps muscle, the amplitude of the EMG is greater when a chair is lifted than when the arm is flexed without lifting a weight. What causes this increase in amplitude?

3. Describe the activity of the biceps and triceps muscles during arm flexion and extension, and explain how the central nervous system controls this activity.

4. Define the term *biofeedback*, and describe some of the health benefits of this technique.

# The Cardiovascular System

Glucose, amino acids, fatty acids, and other monomers are carried by the **blood** from the digestive tract, liver, and adipose tissue to all the cells of the body. The waste products of cellular metabolism are carried by the blood to the kidneys and lungs for elimination. Regulatory molecules—hormones—are secreted by endocrine glands and carried by the blood to target organs. Blood is thus the major channel of communication between the different specialized organs of the body.

The interchange of molecules between blood and tissue cells occurs across the walls of **capillaries,** which are composed of only a single layer of epithelial cells (known as an endothelium). Blood is delivered to the capillaries in **arterioles,** microscopic vessels with walls of endothelium, smooth muscle, and connective tissue. Blood is drained from the capillaries in microscopic vessels known as **venules.** The arterioles receive their blood from larger, more muscular vessels called **arteries.** The venules drain their blood into larger vessels known as **veins,** which are less muscular and more distensible than arteries.

Since the tissue cells must be within 0.10 mm of a capillary for molecules to diffuse at an adequate rate, the vascular system within an organ is highly branched, creating a *vascular tree.* The many narrow, muscular arterioles of this tree offer great resistance to blood flow *(peripheral resistance)* through the organs. For organs to receive adequate blood (to be adequately *perfused*), therefore, the blood must be under sufficient pressure to overcome the resistance to blood flow.

The pressure required to overcome peripheral resistance and maintain adequate tissue perfusion is generated by a muscular pump, the **heart.** The heart has four chambers. The *right atrium* receives blood from the two largest veins in the body— the superior and inferior venae cavae—which carry blood low in oxygen from the body cells. The *left atrium* receives oxygen-rich blood from the pulmonary vein. When the two atria contract, they empty blood into two ventricles. The *right ventricle* pumps blood into the pulmonary arteries, which carry it to the lungs, where it becomes enriched in oxygen and depleted in carbon dioxide. The *left ventricle* pumps blood into a large artery called the aorta, which by means of its many branches perfuses all the organs in the body. Since the blood pumped out of the heart by the two ventricles (the **cardiac output**) is carried by arteries to the body's organs, and since blood from the organs is returned by veins to the heart (valves in the veins ensure a one-way flow of blood), the cardiovascular system forms a closed circle (the circulatory system).

The heart's ability to maintain adequate perfusion of the body's organs (maintain circulation) depends on proper electrical stimulation and muscular contraction; proper functioning of its *valves,* which direct the blood flow within the heart; and integrity of the blood vessels. These functions can be assessed by various techniques, which will be explored in the following exercises.

# 5.1 Effects of Drugs on the Frog Heart

The heart of a pithed frog may continue to beat automatically after the frog's central nervous system has been destroyed. The function of the heart and the effect of various drugs can thus be studied.

## Objectives

1. Describe the pattern of contraction in the frog heart.
2. Describe the effect of various drugs on the heart, and explain their mechanisms of action.

## Materials

1. Frogs, dissecting instruments, and trays
2. Copper wire and thread
3. Recording apparatus: physiograph, transducer coupler, and myograph transducer (Narco); or kymograph, kymograph paper, and kerosene burner
4. Ringer's solution (see exercise 4.1—all drugs to be made in Ringer's solution as a solvent); calcium chloride (2.0 g/100 ml); digitalis (2.0 g/100 ml); pilocarpine (2.5 g/100 ml); atropine (5.0 g/100 ml); potassium chloride (2.0 g/100 ml); epinephrine (adrenalin chloride solution, supplied in vials); caffeine (saturated); and nicotine (0.2 g/100 ml)

A *drug* is a substance that affects some aspects of physiology when given to the body. Drugs may be identical to substances found in the body, such as minerals, vitamins, and hormones, or they may be molecules that are uniquely produced by particular plants or fungi. Many drugs that are marketed by pharmaceutical companies are natural products whose chemical structure has been slightly modified to alter the biological activity of the native compounds.

The biological effects of endogenous compounds (those normally found in the body) vary with their concentration. A normal blood potassium concentration, for example, is necessary for health, but too high a concentration can be fatal. Similarly, the actions exhibited by many hormones at abnormally high concentrations may not occur when the hormones are at their normal concentrations. It is therefore important to distinguish between the *physiological effects* (normal effects) of these substances and their *pharmacological effects* (those that occur when the substances are administered as drugs). A study of the pharmacology of various substances can, however, reveal much about the normal physiology of the body.

In this exercise, the effects of various pharmacological agents will be tested on the heart of a pithed frog. Although the heart, like skeletal muscle, is striated, it differs from skeletal muscles in several respects. The heartbeat is *automatic;* unlike skeletal muscles, the heart does not have to be stimulated by nerves or electrodes to contract. This is because action potentials begin spontaneously in the *pacemaker region* (called the SA node) in the right atrium and spread through the ventricles in an automatic, rhythmic cycle. As can be seen in the exposed frog heart, this causes the atria to contract before the ventricles. (Unlike mammals, however, frogs only have one ventricle.)

When the frog heart is connected by a thread to the recording equipment, contractions of the atria and ventricle produce two successive peaks in the recordings. The strength of contraction is related to the amplitude of these peaks, and the rate of beat can be determined by the distance between the ventricular peaks (if the chart speed is known). The rate of impulse conduction between the atria and ventricle is related to the distance between the atrial and ventricular peaks in the recording of each cycle. The effects of various drugs on the strength of contraction, rate of contraction, and rate of impulse conduction from the atria to the ventricle can therefore be determined.

**Figure 5.1.** A procedure for exposing the frog heart. (a) first the skin is cut; (b) then the body cavity is exposed by cutting through the muscles to the sternum. The sternum will next be split to expose the heart.

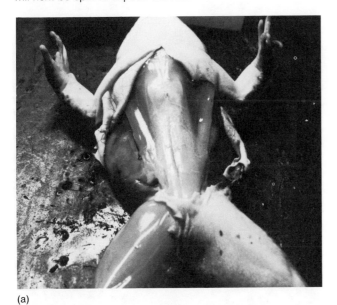

(a)

(b)

**Figure 5.2.** A frog heart setup. The contractions of the heart pull a lever that writes on a moving chart (kymograph).

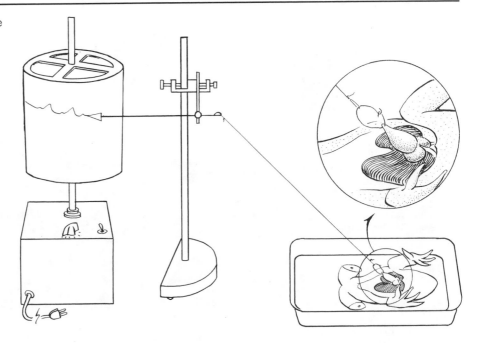

## Preparation for Recording

1. Double pith a frog, and expose its heart (fig. 5.1). Skewer the apex of the heart muscle with a short length of thin copper wire, being careful not to let the wire enter the chamber of the ventricle. (The frog heart has only one ventricle and two atria.)

2. Bend the copper wire into a loop, and tie one end of cotton thread to this loop (see enlarged insert in fig. 5.2).

3. Procedure for **kymograph** recording:

   a) Tie the other end of the thread to a heart lever. The thread and heart should be pulled fairly tightly so that contractions of the heart produce movements of the lever.

Effects of Drugs on the Frog Heart    159

**Figure 5.3.** A procedure for setting up to record the frog's heart contractions. (a) a small length of thin copper wire is passed through the tip of the ventricle. (b) this wire is then twisted together to form a loop, (c) which is tied by a cotton thread to the hook in the myograph transducer.

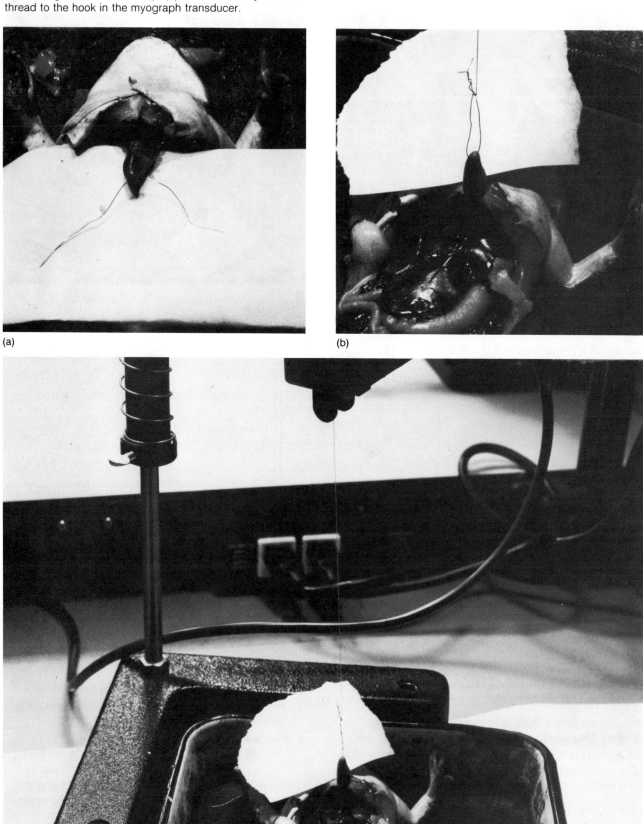

(a)

(b)

(c)

**Figure 5.4.** A recording of frog heart contractions on a physiograph recorder. The arrow points to a recording of a smaller atrial contraction, which is followed by a recording of a larger ventricular contraction.

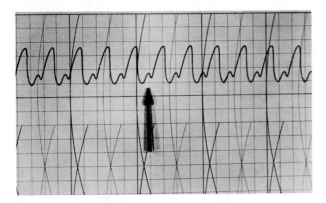

b) Attach kymograph paper (shiny side out) to the kymograph drum, and rotate the drum slowly over a kerosene burner until the paper is uniformly blackened. Arrange the heart lever so that it lightly drags across the smoked paper. (Too much pressure of the writing stylus against the kymograph will prevent movement of the heart lever.) See figure 5.2 for the proper setup.

4. Procedure for **physiograph** recording:
   a) Tie the other end of the thread to the hook below the myograph transducer. (Make sure the myograph is plugged into the transducer coupler on the physiograph.) The heart should be positioned directly below the myograph. Adjust the height of the myograph on its stand so that the heart is pulled out of the chest cavity (fig. 5.3).
   b) Make sure the physiograph is properly balanced, and set the paper speed at 0.5 cm per second. Push the *record* button *in,* and set the *paper advance* button *out* when you are ready to record.

5. Observe the pattern of the heartbeat prior to the addition of drugs (see example in fig. 5.4). Be sure you can distinguish atrial and ventricular beats and that you can measure the rate (in beats per minute) and strength (in millimeters deflection above baseline) of the heartbeat.

## A. Effect of Calcium Ions on the Heart

In addition to the role of calcium in coupling excitation to contraction, the extracellular $Ca^{++}/Mg^{++}$ ratio also affects the permeability of the cell membrane. An increase in the extracellular concentration of calcium (above the normal concentration of 4.5–5.5 mEq/L) affects both the electrical properties and the contractility of muscle.

The heart is thus affected in a number of ways by an increase in extracellular calcium: (1) increased force of contraction, (2) decreased cardiac rate, and (3) the appearance of ectopic pacemakers in the ventricles, producing abnormal rhythms (extrasystoles and idioventricular rhythm).

### Procedure

1. Obtain a record of the normal heartbeat. Then, using a dropper, bathe the heart in a 2.0% solution of calcium chloride ($CaCl_2$). On the recording paper, indicate the time at which calcium was added. Observe the effects of the added calcium solution over a period of a few minutes.
2. Tape the recording or draw a facsimile of the normal heartbeat and of the heartbeat after the calcium solution was added in the table in your laboratory report.
3. Rinse the heart thoroughly with Ringer's solution until the heartbeat returns to normal.

## B. Effect of Digitalis on the Heart

The effects of digitalis are believed to be due to its inhibition of the $Na^+/K^+$ (ATPase) pump. This inhibition results in an influx of $Na^+$ and an efflux of $K^+$ and is accompanied by an enhanced uptake of calcium ions. The effects of digitalis and of increased extracellular calcium on the heart are thus very similar.

### Procedure

1. Obtain a record of the normal heartbeat, and then bathe the heart in a 2.0% solution of digitalis.
2. Tape the recording or draw a facsimile of the heartbeat after adding digitalis in the table in your laboratory report.

## C. Effect of Pilocarpine on the Heart

Pilocarpine is a *parasympathomimetic* drug; that is, it mimics the effect of parasympathetic nerve stimulation. Pilocarpine acts to facilitate the release of the neurotransmitter acetylcholine from the vagus nerve, resulting in a decrease in the cardiac rate.

### Procedure

1. Thoroughly rinse the heart with Ringer's solution until the beat returns to the normal rate.
2. Bathe the heart in a 2.5% solution of pilocarpine, and tape the recording or draw a facsimile in the table in your laboratory report.

## D. Effect of Atropine on the Heart

Atropine is an alkaloid drug derived from the nightshade plant (the species name, *belladonna,* is often used as the drug name). Atropine blocks the effects of acetylcholine and inhibits the effects of parasympathetic activity on the heart, smooth muscles, and glands. If the cardiac rate is decreased as a result of vagal stimulation, therefore, the administration of atropine will increase this rate.

### Procedure

1. Bathe the heart in a 5.0% solution of atropine while it is still under the influence of pilocarpine.
2. Tape the recording or draw a facsimile of the effects of atropine in the table in your laboratory report.

## E. Effect of Potassium Ions on the Heart

Since the resting membrane potential is dependent, in part, on the maintenance of a higher concentration of $K^+$ on the inside of the cell than on the outside, an increase in the concentration of extracellular $K^+$ results in a *decrease in the resting membrane potential*. This, in turn, produces a decrease in the force of contraction and the conduction rate of the action potentials. In extreme *hyperkalemia* (high blood potassium), the conduction rate may be so depressed that ectopic pacemakers appear in the ventricles and fibrillation may develop.

### Procedure

1. Rinse the heart in Ringer's solution until the beat returns to normal, and then bathe the heart in a 2.0% solution of potassium chloride (KCl).
2. Tape the recording or draw a facsimile of the effects of $K^+$ on the heartbeat in the table in your laboratory report.

## Clinical Significance

Digitalis is a drug frequently used clinically in cases of congestive heart failure, atrial flutter, and atrial fibrillation. Digitalis is helpful in these cases because (1) it increases the force of contraction; (2) it decreases the cardiac rate, directly by inhibiting the SA node and indirectly by stimulating the vagus nerve, which in turn inhibits the SA node; and (3) it decreases the rate of conduction of the bundle of His, thus increasing the P-R interval (see exercise 5.2).

The ability of atropine to block the effects of parasympathetic nervous stimulation is useful in a variety of clinical situations. It is used, for example, in ophthalmology to dilate the eyes (parasympathetic nerves cause constriction of the pupils) and in surgery to dry the mouth, pharynx, and trachea. (Glandular secretions that wet these mucous membranes are stimulated by parasympathetic nerves.)

Since the resting membrane potential of all cells is determined in large part by the concentration gradient of potassium across the membrane, elevations in extracellular potassium concentration cause a decrease in the resting potential. In hyperkalemia (high plasma potassium), therefore, the strength of myocardial contraction is reduced and the cells become more electrically excitable, because their resting potential is closer to the threshold required for generating an action potential. Ectopic pacemakers may appear, resulting in fibrillation.

## F. Effect of Epinephrine on the Heart

Epinephrine is a hormone secreted by the **adrenal medulla** which, together with norepinephrine released as a neurotransmitter by sympathetic nerves, acts to increase both the strength of contraction of the heart and the cardiac rate. Exogenous epinephrine is a *sympathomimetic* drug, since it mimics the effect of sympathetic nerve stimulation.

### Procedure

1. Rinse the heart with Ringer's solution until the heartbeat returns to normal, and then bathe the heart in epinephrine (adrenaline).
2. Tape the recording or draw a facsimile of the effect of epinephrine on the heartbeat in the table in your laboratory report.

## G. Effect of Caffeine on the Heart

Caffeine is a mild central nervous system stimulant that also acts directly on the myocardium to increase both the strength of contraction and the cardiac rate. Its usefulness as a central nervous system stimulant is limited by the fact that, in high doses, it can promote the formation of *ectopic pacemakers* (*foci*), resulting in major arrhythmias.

**Procedure**

1. Bathe the heart with Ringer's solution until the beat returns to normal, and then bathe the heart with a saturated solution of caffeine.
2. Tape the recording or draw a facsimile in the table in your laboratory report.

## H. Effect of Nicotine on the Heart

Nicotine promotes transmission at the sympathetic ganglia, resulting in an enhancement of sympathetic nerve activity and of the secretion of epinephrine from the adrenal medulla.

**Procedure**

1. Rinse the heart in Ringer's solution until the beat returns to normal, and then bathe the heart in a 0.2% solution of nicotine.
2. Tape the recording or draw a facsimile in the table provided in your laboratory report.
3. Analyze your data, and record your results for parts A through H in the "Results" table of your laboratory report.

## Data from Exercise 5.1

| Condition | Effect (Tape the Recording or Draw a Facsimile) |
|---|---|
| Normal | |
| $Ca^{++}$ | |
| Digitalis | |
| Pilocarpine | |
| Atropine | |
| $K^+$ | |
| Epinephrine | |
| Caffeine | |
| Nicotine | |

# Results from Exercise 5.1

| Condition | Rate (Beats/min.) | Strength (mm above Baseline) | Distance (mm) between Atrial and Ventricular Peaks | Conclusions about Drug Effects |
|---|---|---|---|---|
| Normal | | | | |
| Ca++ | | | | |
| Digitalis | | | | |
| Pilocarpine | | | | |
| Atropine | | | | |
| K+ | | | | |
| Epinephrine | | | | |
| Caffeine | | | | |
| Nicotine | | | | |

# Questions for Exercise 5.1

Match the following:

_____ 1. Endogenous substance that makes the beat stronger and faster

_____ 2. Substance that makes the beat slower and stronger

_____ 3. Substance that facilitates the release of ACh from parasympathetic nerve endings

_____ 4. Substance that promotes the activity of the sympathetic nervous system

(a) digitalis
(b) nicotine
(c) caffeine
(d) epinephrine
(e) pilocarpine

5. What are the effects of hyperkalemia on the heart? How are these effects produced?

6. What is a sympathomimetic drug? What are its effects on the heart?

7. What effect did $Ca^{++}$ have on the amplitude of the recording of the heartbeat? Explain why $Ca^{++}$ had this effect.

8. Explain the effect of digitalis on the heart and the clinical uses of this drug.

# Electrocardiogram

The regular pattern of electrical impulse production and conduction in the heart results in contraction of the myocardium and the cardiac cycle of systole and diastole. These events can be followed by an electrocardiogram, which can also reveal abnormal patterns associated with abnormal cardiac rhythms.

## Objectives

1. Describe the normal pattern of impulse production and conduction in the heart and the conducting tissues of the heart.
2. Describe the normal ECG, and explain how it is produced.
3. Obtain an electrocardiogram using the limb leads, identify the waves, determine the P-R interval, and measure the cardiac rate.
4. Describe common abnormalities that can easily be seen in an electrocardiogram.

## Materials

1. Electrocardiograph
2. Electrode plates, rubber straps, electrolyte gel or
. paste

Since the heart (fig. 5.5) is a functional syncytium, electrical stimulation at any point in the heart musculature (myocardium) results in the almost simultaneous contraction of the individual muscle cells (myocardial fibers). This allows the heart to function as an effective pump, its chambers contracting (**systole**) and relaxing (**diastole**) as integrated units.

Unlike skeletal muscles, the myocardium is able to stimulate itself electrically in the absence of neural input. This is called *automaticity*. The sympathetic and parasympathetic nerves that innervate the heart only modulate the rate of depolarization-contraction and repolarization-relaxation (i.e., the rate of systole and diastole) that is intrinsic to the heart. The intrinsic regulation of contraction and relaxation, unique to heart muscle, is termed *rhythmicity*.

Although each individual myocardial cell is potentially capable of initiating its own cycle of depolarization-contraction and repolarization-relaxation, a single group of cells usually regulates the cycle of the entire myocardium. This *pacemaker* region establishes its dominance because its cycle is more rapid than other areas, depolarizing the other myocardial cells before they can depolarize themselves. A region of the right atrium, the **sinoatrial node (SA node)**, serves as the normal **pacemaker** of the heart. The wave of depolarization initiated by the SA node spreads across the right and left atria as a result of the close association of the myocardial cells. The depolarization wave cannot, however, easily spread from the myocardial cells of the atria to the myocardial cells of the ventricles. For this to occur, the depolarization wave must be carried from the atria to the ventricles along the specialized conducting tissue of the heart.

After a brief delay, the depolarization wave that spreads over the atria stimulates a node called the **atrioventricular node (AV node)**, which is located at the base of the interatrial septum. The depolarization wave in the AV node is quickly transmitted over a bundle of specialized conducting tissue, the **atrioventricular (or AV) bundle,** otherwise known as the **bundle of His.** The bundle of His splits to form right and left "bundle branches," carrying the depolarization wave to the apex of the ventricles. The impulse is then carried to the innermost cells of the ventricles on a network of branching **Purkinje fibers** (fig. 5.5).

**Figure 5.5.** A diagram of the heart showing conduction tissue.

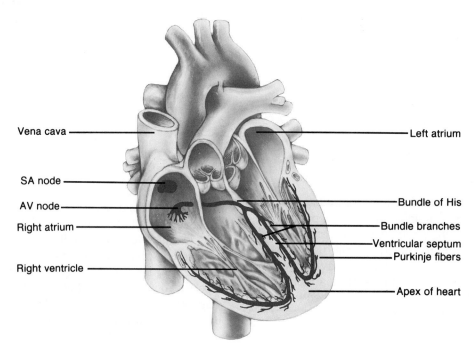

Vena cava

SA node

AV node

Right atrium

Right ventricle

Left atrium

Bundle of His

Bundle branches

Ventricular septum

Purkinje fibers

Apex of heart

As a result of electrical stimulation, the atria contract as a single unit (atrial systole), followed quickly by depolarization and contraction of the ventricles (ventricular systole). Contraction of the atria forces blood into the ventricles, and contraction of the ventricles forces blood into the pulmonary arteries and aorta, pumping blood through the pulmonary and systemic circulations. During the period of repolarization and relaxation (diastole), the atria once more fill with blood, and the cycle is ready to be initiated again by the spontaneous depolarization of the SA node.

Since the body fluids contain a high concentration of electrolytes, the electrical activity generated by the heart travels throughout the body and can easily be monitored by placing a pair of electrodes on different areas of the skin (fig. 5.6). A graphic representation of these electrical activities is called an **electrocardiogram** (**ECG,** or **EKG**), and the instrument producing this record is called an *electrocardiograph*. A normal ECG is shown in figure 5.7.

The *P wave* represents depolarization of the atria; the *QRS complex* occurs during the depolarization and contraction of the ventricles; and the *T wave* represents repolarization of the ventricles at the beginning of diastole. An incompletely understood *U wave* sometimes follows the T wave.

In the following exercises the *standard limb leads* I, II, and III will be used. These leads record the difference in potential (that is, the voltage) between two electrodes placed on the arms and legs (fig. 5.6). In clinical electrocardiography, however, *unipolar leads* are also used. These are the *AVR* (right arm), *AVL* (left arm), *AVF* (left leg), and the chest leads labeled $V_1$ to $V_6$.

At a chart speed of 25 mm per second, the thin vertical lines are 0.04 second apart, and the distance between every fifth, heavier line represents an interval of 0.20 second. In this way, the length of time between depolarization of the atria (P wave) and depolarization of the ventricles (QRS complex) can easily be measured. This interval is known as the **P-R interval** (although it is actually measured from the beginning of the P wave to the Q wave, fig. 5.7) and is equal to less than 0.20 second in the normal ECG.

## Abnormal ECG Patterns

Interpretations of the electrocardiogram can provide information about the heart rate, rhythm, presence or absence of hypertrophy, ischemia (inadequate blood supply), necrosis (area of dead cells), and other factors that produce abnormalities of electrical conduction. According to the standards set by the National Conference on Cardiopulmonary Resuscitation and Emergency Cardiac Care, the arrhythmias that all health professionals should be able to recognize include (1) bradycardia (ventricular rate less than 60 per minute); (2) the difference between supraventricular and ventricular rhythms; (3) premature ventricular contractions; (4) ventricular tachycardia; (5) atrioventricular block; (6) atrial fibrillation and flutter; and (7) ventricular fibrillation.

**Figure 5.6.** The placement of electrodes for the standard limb leads. The electrodes measure the potential difference (voltage) between the right and left arms (lead 1), between the right arm and the left leg (lead 2), and between the left arm and left leg (lead 3).

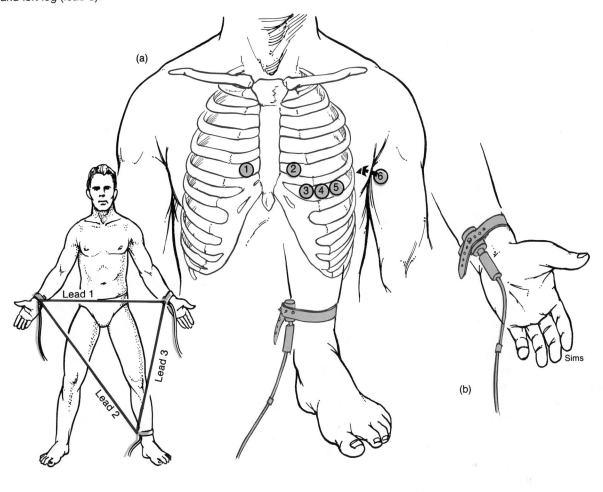

**Figure 5.7.** The normal electrocardiogram (simulated).

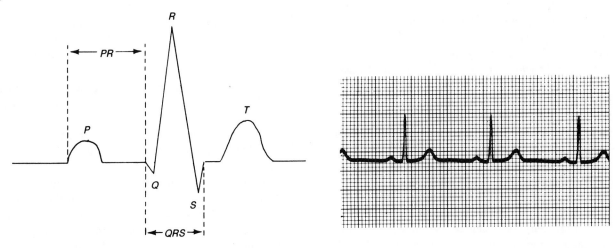

**Figure 5.8.** (a) an atrial flutter; (b) an atrial fibrillation (simulated).

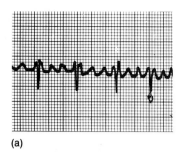

(a)

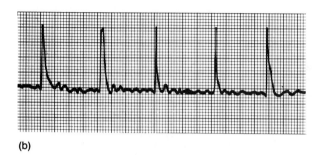

(b)

**Figure 5.9.** (a) first-degree heart block, where the P-R interval is greater than 0.20 second (one large square); (b) a second-degree heart block, where beats (i.e., QRS complexes) are missed (a 3:1 heart block is shown); (c) a third-degree, or complete, heart block, where a slower than normal heart rate is set by an ectopic focus in the ventricles, producing broad QRS complexes that are independent of the sinus rhythm (P waves) (simulated).

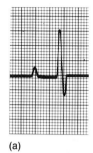

(a)

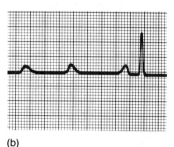

(b)

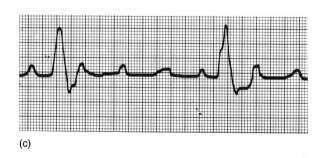

(c)

When *ectopic beats* (beats that are out of place) occur in the atria as a result of the development of an *ectopic pacemaker* (a pacemaker that develops in addition to the normal one in the SA node) or as a result of a derangement in the normal conduction pathway, a condition of **atrial flutter** or **atrial fibrillation** may be present. Atrial flutter is characterized by very rapid atrial waves (about 300 per minute), producing a saw-toothed baseline. The atrial waves occur with such high frequency that the AV node can only beat to every second, third, or fourth wave that reaches it (fig. 5.8a). A person with atrial flutter may have a normal pulse rate, since the pulse is produced by ventricular contraction.

In atrial fibrillation, the depolarization waves occur so rapidly (350–400 per minute) that the atria no longer function effectively, and the P waves of the ECG are replaced by a wavy baseline (fig. 5.8b). Atrial fibrillation is characteristic of atrial enlargement, as might be produced by *mitral stenosis* (narrowing of the mitral valve), but it may occur in all forms of heart disease and occasionally in apparently healthy individuals. Digitalis is often used in atrial flutter and fibrillation to decrease the excitability of the AV node, thus maintaining the ventricular rate within the normal range.

A delay in the conduction of the impulse from the atria to the ventricles is known as **atrioventricular (AV) block.** When the ECG pattern is otherwise normal, but the P-R interval is greater than 0.20 second, a *first-degree* AV block is present (fig. 5.9a). First-degree AV block may be a result of inflammatory states, rheumatic fever, or digitalis treatment.

When the excitability of the AV node is further impaired so that two or more atrial depolarizations are required before the impulse can be transmitted to the ventricles, a *second-degree* AV block is present. This is seen on the ECG as a dropped beat (i.e., a P wave without an associated QRS complex). In *Wenckebach's phenomenon,* the cycle after the dropped beat is normal, whereas the P-R interval of successive cycles lengthens until a beat (i.e., a QRS complex) is again dropped (fig. 5.9b).

*Third-degree,* or complete, AV block occurs when none of the impulses from the atria reach the ventricles. When this happens, the myocardial cells of the ventricles are freed from their subservience to the SA node, and one or more ectopic pacemakers appear in the ventricles. The rhythm produced by these ectopic foci in the ventricles

**Figure 5.10.** (a) premature ventricular contraction; (b) ventricular tachycardia; (c) ventricular fibrillation (simulated).

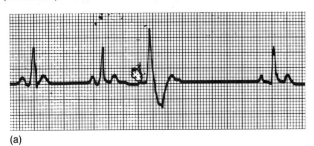

(a)

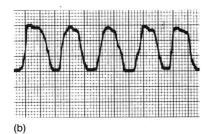

(b)

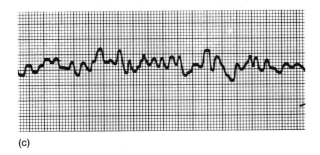

(c)

(*idioventricular rhythm*) is usually very slow (20–45 beats per minute) in comparison with the normal pace set by the SA node (fig. 5.9c).

**Premature ventricular contractions (PVCs)** are produced by ectopic foci in the ventricles when the sinus rhythm is normal. This results in *extrasystoles* (i.e., extra beats or QRS complexes without preceding P waves) in addition to the normal cycle, often subjectively described by patients as "palpitations." The ectopic QRS complexes are broad and deformed and may be coupled to the preceding normal beats. (This coupling is termed *bigeminy*—fig. 5.10a). This condition is often seen in digitalis toxicity.

When an ectopic focus in the ventricles discharges at a rapid rate, a condition of **ventricular tachycardia** (usually 100–150 beats per minute) develops (fig. 5.10b). The ECG shows a widened and distorted QRS complex, and the P waves are usually difficult, and often impossible, to observe (although the atria are discharging at a slower, regular rate). This serious condition should be distinguished from the less serious **supraventricular tachycardia,** in which an ectopic focus above the ventricles

results in rapid running of the heart (150–250 beats per minute) that begins and ends abruptly. This condition is appropriately named **paroxysmal tachycardia.**

The most serious of all arrhythmias is **ventricular fibrillation** (fig. 5.10c), in which the development of multiple ectopic foci, or circus movements of depolarization waves around the heart, results in an impotent tremor rather than a coordinated contraction of the myocardium. Under these conditions, the pumping activity of the ventricles ceases, and death shortly results unless emergency measures (including electrical defibrillation) are successful.

## Procedure

1. With the subject lying comfortably on a cot, rub a small amount of electrolyte gel on the medial surface of the arms and legs, about 2 inches above the wrists and ankles, into an area about the size of a silver dollar. Attach electrode plates to these four spots, using the rubber straps provided.
2. Attach the four ECG leads to the appropriate plates.
3. Adjust the instrument panel as follows:
   a) Turn on the power switch.
   b) Set the speed selector switch to 25 mm per second.
   c) Set the sensitivity to *1.*
   d) Set the lead selector switch to the first dot to the left of the *STD* position.
   e) Turn the control knob to the *run* position.
4. Turn the position knob until the stylus is centered on the ECG paper.
5. Turn the lead selector switch to the *1* position; the ECG obtained will be due to the voltage difference between the right and left arms. As the paper is running, depress the *mark* button, so that a single dash will be made at the top of the chart to indicate that this is the record from lead I. Allow enough time so that each member of the subject's group can cut off a sample of the record, then turn the lead selector switch to the dot above the *1* position. The dots are the *rest* positions, which prevent the chart from running between the recordings from different leads.
6. Turn the lead selector switch to the *2* position; the ECG obtained will be due to the voltage difference between the right arm and left leg. As the chart is running, depress the *mark* button twice so that the two dashes produced at the top of the chart will indicate that this is the record from lead II. Turn the lead selector switch to the dot above the *2* position.

7. Repeat this procedure with lead III; this samples the voltage between the left arm and the left leg.

8. After recordings from leads I, II, and III have been obtained, turn the lead selector switch to the *STD* position. This will run the record out of the machine, allowing members of the group to cut samples of each lead.

9. Remove the electrode plates from the subject's skin, and thoroughly wash the electrolyte gel from both the plate and the skin.

10. Tape samples of the recordings in your laboratory report, and label all the waves.

11. Determine the P-R interval of lead II. This can be done by counting the number of small boxes between the beginning of the P and the Q and multiplying this number by 0.04 second.

_____ second

> The normal P-R interval is 0.12–0.20 second.

12. Determine the cardiac rate by the following methods:

    a) Count the number of QRS complexes in a 3-second interval (the distance between two vertical lines at the top of the ECG paper), and multiply by 20.

    Beats per minute = _____

    b) Count the number of QRS complexes in a 6-second interval, and multiply by 10.

    Beats per minute = _____

    c) At a chart speed of 25 mm per second, the time interval between one light vertical line and the next is 0.04 second. The time interval between heavy vertical lines is 0.20 second. The cardiac rate in beats per minute can thus be calculated if one knows the time interval between two R waves in two successive QRS complexes.

    For example, suppose that the time interval from one R wave to the next is exactly 0.60 second. Therefore,

    $$\frac{1 \text{ beat}}{0.60 \text{ sec}} = \frac{x \text{ beats}}{60 \text{ sec}}$$

    $$x = \frac{1 \text{ beat} \times 60 \text{ sec}}{0.60 \text{ sec}}$$

    $$= 100 \text{ beats per minute}$$

    Beats per minute = _____

    d) The values obtained by method c can be approximated by counting the number of heavy vertical lines between one R wave and the next according to the memorized sequence: 300, 150, 100, 75, 60, 50.

**Example**

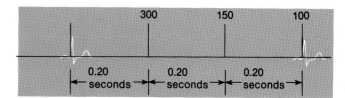

The cardiac rate in the above example is 100 beats per minute.

Beats per minute = _____

> The normal cardiac rate is 60–100 beats per minute.

## Data from Exercise 5.2

Tape your recording in the spaces below

*Lead I*

*Lead II*

*Lead III*

## Questions for Exercise 5.2

1. The cells with the fastest spontaneous cycle of depolarization-contraction are located in the _____ .

2. Indicate the electrical events that produce each of the following waves:

    (a) P wave: _____

    (b) QRS wave: _____

    (c) T wave: _____

3. An occasional extra beat, which can be seen as an ectopic QRS complex, is called a _____ .

4. An abnormally long P-R interval indicates a condition called _____ .

5. A condition where the ventricles are unable to contract as a pump and a circus rhythm of electrical activity may be present is known as _____ .

6. Explain why the SA node functions as the normal pacemaker.

7. Compare ventricular tachycardia with paroxysmal supraventricular tachycardia in terms of its etiology, ECG pattern, and seriousness.

8. On initial examination, a patient is found to have a P-R interval of 0.24 sec. This patient is examined again a year later and found to have a resting pulse of 40 beats per minute with very little increase after exercise. Explain what happened.

# Effects of Exercise on the Electrocardiogram

During exercise there is a decrease in the activity of parasympathetic and an increase in the activity of sympathetic innervation to the SA node, conductive tissue, and myocardium. More rapid discharge of the SA node, more rapid conduction of impulses, and a faster rate of contraction all result in an increased cardiac rate with exercise.

## Objectives

1. Describe the effects of the sympathetic and parasympathetic innervation to the heart.
2. Obtain an ECG before and immediately after exercise, and explain the differences observed.

## Materials

1. Electrocardiograph
2. ECG plates, straps, and gel

The heart is innervated by both sympathetic and parasympathetic fibers. At the beginning of exercise, the activity of the parasympathetic fibers that innervate the SA node decreases. Since these fibers have an inhibitory effect on the pacemaker, a decrease in their activity results in an increase in cardiac rate. As exercise becomes more intense, the activity of sympathetic fibers that innervate the SA node increases. This has an excitatory effect on the SA node and causes even greater increases in cardiac rate.

Sympathetic fibers also innervate the conducting tissues of the heart and the ventricular muscle. Through these innervations, sympathetic stimulation may increase the velocity of both impulse conduction and ventricular contraction. These effects are most evident at high cardiac rates and contribute only slightly to the increased cardiac

**Figure 5.11.** The relationship between changes in intraventricular pressure and the electrocardiogram (ECG) during the cardiac cycle of systole and diastole. Notice that the QRS wave occurs at the beginning of systole, whereas the T wave occurs at the beginning of diastole.

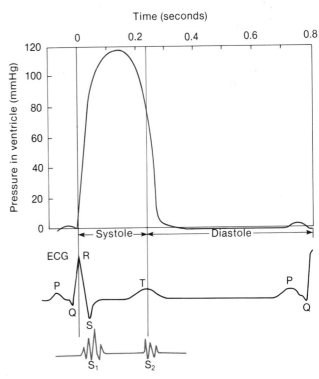

rate during exercise. Thus, the increased cardiac rates are mainly due to a shortening of the ventricular diastole (from the end of one QRS complex to the beginning of the next) and only secondarily due to a shortening of ventricular systole (measured by the duration of the QRS complex). These intervals are shown in figure 5.11.

**Figure 5.12.** During myocardial ischemia, the S-T segment of the electrocardiogram may be depressed, as illustrated in this figure.

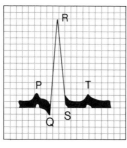

Normal                                    Ischemia

## Clinical Significance

A portion of the cardiac muscle may receive insufficient blood flow because of a clot in a coronary artery (*coronary thrombosis*) or because of narrowing of the vessel due to *atherosclerosis*. A condition of insufficent blood flow—or **ischemia**—may, however, be relative. The rate of blood flow may be adequate to meet the aerobic requirements of the heart at rest, but it may not be adequate when the metabolic energy demands of the heart are increased during exercise. In these cases exercise tests are required to diagnose the ischemia, which may be revealed by a change in the S-T segment of the ECG (fig. 5.12).

### Procedure

1. After the resting ECG has been recorded (from exercise 5.2), unplug the electrode leads from the electrocardiograph.
2. With the subject holding the lead wires, he or she should exercise by walking up and down stairs or hopping.

**Note:** *The intensity of exercise should be such that 80% of the maximum cardiac rate is not exceeded. This should not be performed by students who are not in good health.*

3. Immediately after exercise, the subject lies down and the electrode leads are plugged into the electrocardiograph. Record lead II. Wait 2 minutes and record lead II again.
4. Calculate the cardiac rate, period of ventricular diastole, and the duration of the QRS complex for the resting ECG and for the two postexercise ECG recordings. Enter these data in the table in your laboratory report.

## Data from Exercise 5.3

Enter your data in the table below:

| | Cardiac Rate (Beats/Min) | Ventricular Diastole (Seconds) | Duration of QRS Complex (Seconds) |
|---|---|---|---|
| Resting ECG | | | |
| Immediate postexercise ECG | | | |
| 2-minute postexercise ECG | | | |

## Questions for Exercise 5.3

1. The ECG wave that occurs at the beginning of ventricular systole is the _____ wave.

2. The ECG wave that occurs at the end of systole and beginning of diastole is the _____ wave.

3. The ECG wave that occurs at the end of ventricular diastole is the _____ wave.

4. Describe the regulatory mechanisms that produce an increase in cardiac rate during exercise. Explain how these changes affect the electrocardiogram.

5. Explain why a person may have a normal electrocardiogram at rest but may show evidence of myocardial ischemia after moderate exercise.

# Mean Electrical Axis of the Ventricles

The voltage changes in the ECG measured by two different leads can be compared and used to determine the mean electrical axis, which corresponds to the average direction of depolarization as the impulses spread into the ventricles. Significant deviations from the normal axis may be produced by specific heart disorders.

## Objectives

1. Describe the electrical changes in the heart that produce the ECG waves.
2. Determine the mean electrical axis of the ventricles in a test subject, and explain the clinical significance of this measurement.

## Materials

1. Electrocardiograph
2. ECG plates, straps, and gel

Depolarization waves spread through the heart in a characteristic pattern. Depolarization begins at the SA node and spreads from the pacemaker to the entire mass of both atria. This produces the P wave in an electrocardiogram. After the AV node is excited, the interventricular septum becomes depolarized as the impulses spread through the bundle of His. Since at this point the septum is depolarized while the lateral walls of the ventricles maintain their original polarity, there is a potential difference (or voltage) between these two locations in the ventricles. This produces the R wave. When the entire mass of the ventricles is depolarized, there is no longer a potential difference within the ventricles, and the voltage returns to zero (completing the QRS complex).

The direction of the depolarization waves depends on the orientation of the heart and on the particular instant of the cardiac cycle being considered. It is clinically useful, however, to determine the average, or mean, direction (axis) of depolarization during the cardiac cycle. This can be done by observing the voltages of the QRS complex from two different perspectives using two different leads. Lead I provides a horizontal axis of observation (from left arm to right arm); lead III has an axis of about 120° (from left arm to left leg). Using the recordings from leads I and III, the normal mean electrical axis of the ventricles is about 59°. This is shown in figure 5.13.

## Clinical Significance

**Hypertrophy** of one ventricle shifts the mean axis of depolarization toward the hypertrophied ventricle because it takes longer to depolarize. A left axis deviation thus occurs when the left ventricle is hypertrophied (as a result of hypertension or narrowing of the aortic semilunar valve). A right axis deviation occurs when the right ventricle hypertrophies. The latter condition may be secondary to narrowing of the pulmonary semilunar valve or to such congenital conditions as a septal defect or the tetralogy of Fallot.

The depolarization wave normally spreads through both the right and left ventricles at the same time. If there is a conduction block in one of the branches of the bundle of His, however, depolarization will be much slower in the blocked ventricle. If there is a left **bundle branch block,** for example, depolarization will occur more slowly in the left ventricle than in the right ventricle, and the mean electrical axis will deviate to the left. Conversely, if there is a right bundle branch block, there will be a right axis deviation. Deviations of the electrical axis also occur to varying degrees as a result of myocardial infarction.

**Figure 5.13.** (a) the convention by which the axis of depolarization is measured; the bottom half of the circle (with the heart at the center) is considered the positive pole (LA = left arm, RA = right arm, LL = left leg); (b) when the interventricular septum is depolarized, the surface of the septum is electrically negative compared with the walls of the ventricles, which have not yet become depolarized; the average normal direction of depolarization, or mean electrical axis of the ventricles, is about 59° (RV = right ventricle, LV = left ventricle).

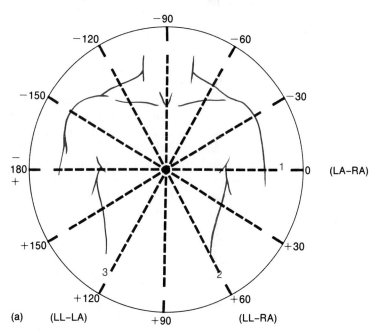

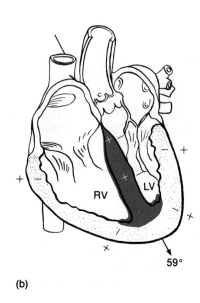

(a)  (LL–LA)  (b)

---

## Procedure

1. Using lead I (with a sensitivity setting of *1*)
   a) Find a QRS complex, and count the number of millimeters (small boxes) that it projects above the top of the baseline. Enter this value in the following space.

   + _____

   b) Count the number of millimeters that the Q and S (or the R, if it is inverted) project below the top of the baseline. Add the sum of these downward deflections and enter this sum in the following space.

   − _____

   c) Algebraically add the two values from parts a) and b) together, and keeping the negative sign if the sum is negative, enter the sum in the laboratory report.

2. Using lead III (with a sensitivity setting of *1*)
   a) Find a QRS complex, and count the number of millimeters (small boxes) that it projects above the top of the baseline. Enter this value in the following space.

   + _____

   b) Count the number of millimeters that the Q and S (or the R, if it is inverted) project below the top of the baseline. Add the sum of these downward deflections and enter this sum in the following space.

   − _____

   c) Algebraically add the two values from parts a) and b) together, and keeping the negative sign if the sum is negative, enter the sum in the laboratory report.

**Figure 5.14.** Sample electrocardiograms of leads I and III used in the example for determination of the mean electrical axis of the heart.

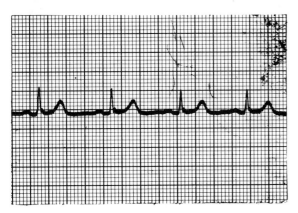

Lead I

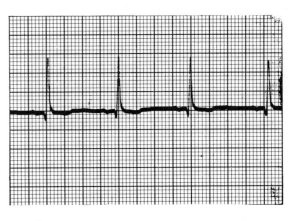

Lead III

3. Using a straightedge, make a line on the grid chart in your laboratory report on the axis of lead I corresponding in position to the sum you obtained in step 1c).

4. Using a straightedge, make a line on the grid chart in your laboratory report on the axis of lead III corresponding in position to the sum you obtained in step 2c).

5. Draw an arrow from the center of the grid chart in your laboratory report through the intersection of the two lines drawn in steps 3) and 4). Extend this arrow to the edge of the grid chart, and record the mean electrical axis of the ventricles.

*Example* (fig. 5.14)

Lead I of sample ECG:

| | |
|---|---:|
| Upward deflection: | +7 mm |
| Downward deflections: | −1 mm |
| | 6 |

Lead III of sample ECG:

| | |
|---|---:|
| Upward deflection: | +14 mm |
| Downward deflections: | − 2 mm |
| | 12 |

A straight line is drawn perpendicular to the axis of lead I and corresponding to position 6 on the scale. Similarly, a straight line is drawn perpendicular to the axis of lead III and corresponding to position 12 on the scale.

An arrow is then drawn from the center of the circle through the intersection of the two lines previously drawn (fig. 5.15). In this example, the mean electrical axis of the ventricles is +71°.

**Figure 5.15.** An example of the method used to determine the mean electrical axis of the heart, using data from leads I and III in the sample ECG provided in figure 5.14. In this example, the mean electrical axis is + 71°.

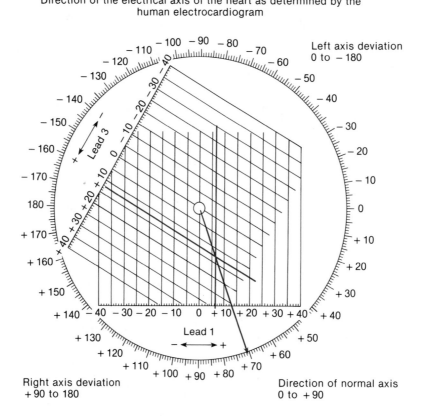

Grid chart

Direction of the electrical axis of the heart as determined by the human electrocardiogram

# Laboratory Report 5.4

Name _____

Date _____

Section _____

## Data from Exercise 5.4

1. Enter the value for the sum of steps 1*a*) and 1*b*) in the space below. Be sure to indicate if it is a positive or negative number.

   _____

2. Enter the value for the sum of steps 2*a*) and 2*b*) in the space below. Be sure to indicate if it is a positive or negative number.

   _____

3. Use the figure below to determine the mean electrical axis of the ventricles from your data, as described in steps 3, 4, and 5 of the procedure.

Grid chart

Direction of the electrical axis of the heart as determined by the human electrocardiogram

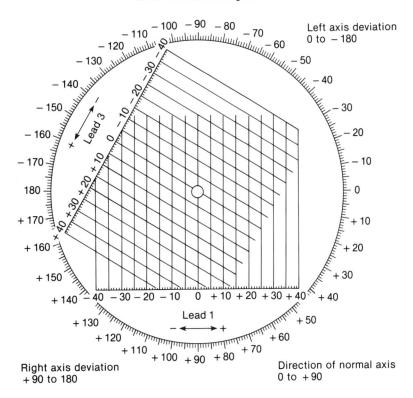

Mean electrical axis of the ventricles: _____

# Questions for Exercise 5.4

1. Explain the electrical events in the heart that produce a QRS wave. Why does the tracing go up from Q to R, and then back to baseline from R to S?

2. Explain how the normal pattern of depolarization is affected by ventricular hypertrophy and by bundle branch block.

# Heart Sounds

Contraction and relaxation of the ventricles is accompanied by pressure changes that cause the one-way heart valves to close. This produces sounds that aid in the diagnosis of structural abnormalities of the heart.

## Objectives

1. Describe the causes of the heart sounds.
2. List some of the causes of abnormal heart sounds.
3. Correlate the heart sounds with the waves of the ECG and the events of the cardiac cycle.

## Materials

1. Stethoscopes
2. Physiograph, high-gain couplers, microphone for heart sounds (Narco)

## A. Auscultation of Heart Sounds with the Stethoscope

The cardiac cycle of contraction (**systole**) and relaxation (**diastole**) can be followed by listening to the heart sounds with a stethoscope. The contraction of the ventricles produces a rise in ventricular pressure, resulting in the vibration of the surrounding structures. It is primarily the vibration of the atrioventricular valves that produces the *first sound* of the heart, usually described phonetically as **lub.** At the end of the contraction phase, the blood in the aorta and pulmonary arteries pushes the one-way semilunar valves shut, and the resulting vibration of these structures produces the *second sound* of the heart, described phonetically as **dub.**

Careful **auscultation** (listening) may reveal two components to each of the two heart sounds. The *splitting* of the heart sounds is more evident during inhalation than it is during exhalation. During inhalation, therefore, the first heart sound may be split into two sounds because of separate closure of the tricuspid and mitral valves. The second heart sound may also be split into two components due to separate closure of the pulmonary and aortic semilunar valves.

## Clinical Significance

Auscultation of the chest is a valuable aid in the diagnosis of a variety of cardiac conditions, including **heart murmurs.** These murmurs may be caused by an irregularity in a valve, a septal defect, or the persistence after birth of the fetal opening (*foramen ovale*) between the right and left atria, resulting in a regurgitation of blood in the reverse direction of normal flow. Abnormal splitting of the first and second heart sounds occurs as a result of a variety of conditions, including heart block, septal defects, aortic stenosis, and hypertension.

### Procedure

1. To best hear the first heart sound, auscultate the *apex* beat of the heart by placing the diaphragm of the stethoscope in the fifth left intercostal space (fig. 5.16).
2. To best hear the second heart sound, place the stethoscope in the second intercostal space to the right or left of the sternum.
3. Compare the heart sounds in the three stethoscope positions described during quiet breathing, slow, deep inhalation, and slow exhalation.

**Figure 5.16.** Positions of a stethoscope and phonocardiograph microphone during auscultation of heart sounds. 2R, the second right intercostal space; 2L, the second left intercostal space; 5L, the fifth left intercostal space (position for apical beat).

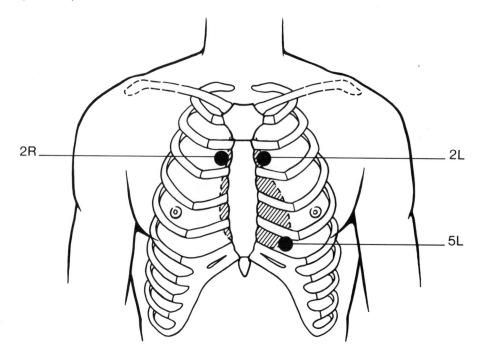

## B. Correlation of the Phonocardiogram with the Electrocardiogram

If the heart sounds are monitored with a device known as a *phonocardiograph* at the same time that the electrical patterns of the heart are monitored with an electrocardiograph, it will be seen that the first heart sound occurs at the end of the QRS complex of the ECG, and the second heart sound occurs at the end of the T wave. The arterial pulse is felt (palpated) in the time interval between the two heart sounds (figs. 5.17 and 5.18).

### Procedure

1. Insert two high-gain couplers into the physiograph. Plug the cable from the ECG lead selector box into the coupler for channel 1, and the cable from the phonocardiograph microphone into the coupler for channel 2.
2. Attach the ECG electrode plates to the subject in the standard limb lead positions, and plug the ECG cable into the lead selector box.

**Figure 5.17.** The correlation of arterial pulse (ap), phonocardiogram sounds (pc), and electrocardiogram (ECG).

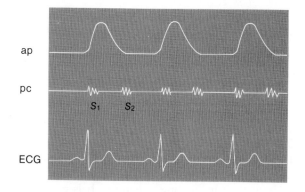

**Figure 5.18.** The correlation of an electrocardiograph (ECG) and a phonocardiograph (PCG). The top tracing shows an ECG, the bottom tracing shows a PCG.

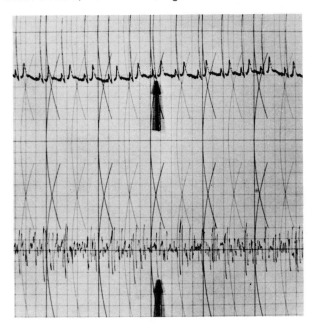

3. For the high-gain coupler in channel 1:
   a) Turn the time constant knob to the *3.2* position.
   b) Turn the gain knob to the *X2* position.
   c) Turn the knob on the ECG lead selector box to the *calibrate* position. Turn the outer sensitivity knob on the amplifier to the *10* position. The inner knob should be turned all the way to the right until it clicks.
   d) Lower the pen lift lever, raise the inkwells, and squeeze the rubber bulbs on the inkwells until ink flows freely. Release the paper advance button, and position the pen for channel 1 so that it writes on the appropriate heavy horizontal line.

4. For the high-gain coupler in channel 2: Adjust the time constant and gain knobs as described in step 3, and position the pen to write on the appropriate heavy horizontal line. The sensitivity knob can be adjusted for the individual subject once recording begins.

5. Move the microphone to the second left intercostal space (fig. 5.16), and repeat the procedure of recording during normal breathing and deep inhalation. Move the microphone to the second right intercostal space, and repeat the procedure again.

6. Tape your recordings or draw facsimiles in the following spaces.

## *Data from Exercise 5.5*

Tape your recordings to (or draw facsimiles in) the table below:

| Microphone Position | Normal Breathing | Deep Inhalation |
|---|---|---|
| Fifth left intercostal space | | |
| Second left intercostal space | | |
| Second right intercostal space | | |

1. Defects of the heart valves can be detected by auscultation but not by electrocardiography. Explain why this is true.

2. What is meant by the splitting of the heart sounds? What causes the heart sounds to be split?

3. Why does the occurrence of the first and second heart sounds correlate with the appearance of the QRS and T waves respectively?

# Measurements of Blood Pressure

Blood exerts a hydrostatic pressure against the walls of arteries that can be measured indirectly, by using a sphygmomanometer and a stethoscope. An arterial blood pressure that is abnormally high or low can be dangerous to health.

## Objectives

1. Describe how the sounds of Korotkoff are produced.
2. Demonstrate the ability to take blood pressure measurements, and explain why measurements of systolic and diastolic pressure correspond to the first and last sounds of Korotkoff.
3. Describe how pulse pressure and mean arterial pressure are calculated.

## Materials

1. Sphygmomanometer
2. Stethoscope

Adequate *perfusion* of the tissues with blood supplies the oxygen and nutrients necessary for normal metabolism. Blood is supplied to the tissue capillaries by the numerous arterioles that branch from a larger artery in such a way that the entire system resembles an *arterial tree*. The blood is pushed through all of the arterial trees in all of the tissues of the body by the maintenance of an adequate arterial blood pressure.

The arterial blood pressure is directly dependent on **cardiac output** (the amount of blood pumped by the heart per minute) and **peripheral resistance** (the resistance to blood flow through the arterioles—which is increased by constriction and decreased by dilation of the arterioles).

The arterial blood pressure is routinely measured in an indirect manner by the use of a device known as a *sphygmomanometer*. This device consists of an inflatable rubber bag connected by rubber hoses to a hand pump and to a pressure gauge (manometer) graduated in millimeters of mercury. The rubber bag is wrapped around

**Figure 5.19.** The use of a sphygmomanometer to measure blood pressure.

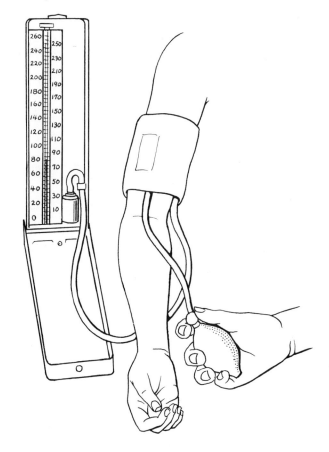

the upper arm and inflated to a pressure greater than the suspected systolic pressure, thus occluding the brachial artery. The examiner auscultates the brachial artery by placing the bell of a stethoscope in the cubital fossa; the pressure in the rubber bag is allowed to fall gradually by opening a screw valve located next to the hand pump (fig. 5.19).

**Figure 5.20.** The five phases of the sounds of Korotkoff (blood pressure measurement).

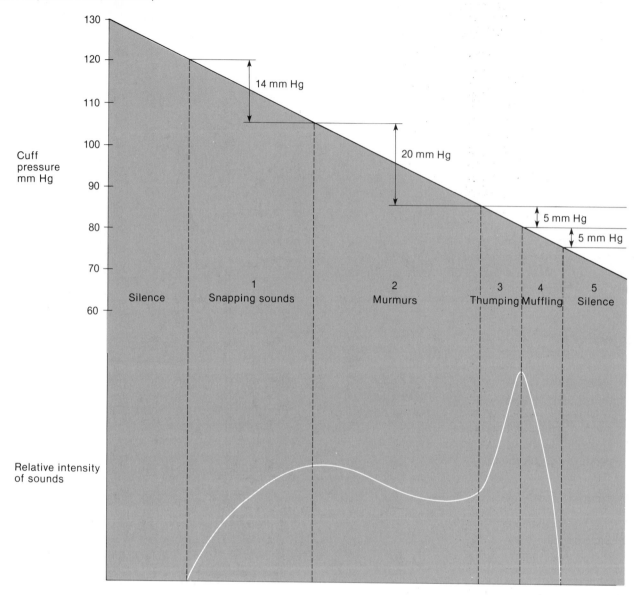

At rest, the blood normally goes through the arteries in a *laminar flow*—that is, the material in the central axial stream moves faster than the material in the peripheral layers, and there is little transverse flow (and thus little mixing) between these axial layers. Under these conditions, the artery is silent when auscultated.

When the sphygmomanometer bag is inflated to a pressure above the systolic pressure, the flow of blood is stopped and the artery is again silent. As the pressure in the bag gradually drops to levels between the systolic and diastolic pressures of the artery, the blood is pushed through the compressed walls of the artery in a *turbulent flow*. Under these conditions, the layers of blood are mixed by eddies that flow at right angles to the axial stream, and the turbulence sets up vibrations in the artery that are heard as sounds in the stethoscope. These sounds are known as the **sounds of Korotkoff,** after the man who first described them.

The sounds of Korotkoff are divided into five phases on the basis of the loudness and quality of the sounds.

Phase 1. A loud, clear *tapping* (or snapping) sound is evident, which increases in intensity as the cuff is deflated. In the example shown in figure 5.20, this phase begins at a cuff pressure of 120 millimeters of mercury (mm Hg) and ends at a pressure of 106 mm Hg.

Phase 2. A succession of *murmurs* can be heard. Sometimes the sounds seem to disappear during this time (auscultatory gap). This may be a result of inflating or deflating the cuff too slowly. In the example shown in figure 5.20, this phase begins at a cuff pressure of 106 mm Hg and ends at a pressure of 86 mm Hg.

Phase 3. A loud, *thumping* sound, similiar to phase 1 but less clear, replaces the murmurs. In the example shown in figure 5.20, this phase begins at a cuff pressure of 86 mm Hg and ends at a pressure of 81 mm Hg.

Phase 4. A *muffled* sound abruptly replaces the thumping sounds of phase 3. In the example shown in figure 5.20, this phase begins at a cuff pressure of 81 mm Hg and ends at a pressure of 76 mm Hg.

Phase 5. All sounds disappear. This phase is absent in some people.

The cuff pressure at which the first sound is heard (that is, the beginning of phase 1) is taken as the **systolic pressure.** The cuff pressure at which the sound becomes muffled (the beginning of phase 4) and the pressure at which the sound disappears (the beginning of phase 5) are taken as measurements of the **diastolic pressure.** Although the phase 5 measurement is closer to the true diastolic pressure than the phase 4 measurement, the beginning of phase 4 is easier to detect and the results are more reproducible. It is often recommended that both measurements of diastolic pressure be recorded. In the example shown in figure 5.20, the pressure would be indicated as 120/81/76. Frequently, however, the blood pressure would simply be recorded in this example as 120/76.

## Clinical Significance

A normal blood pressure measurement for a given individual depends on the person's age, sex, heredity, and environment. When these factors are taken into account, blood pressure measurements that are chronically elevated may indicate a state deleterious to the health of the person. This condition is called **hypertension** and is a major contributing factor in heart disease and stroke.

Hypertension may be divided into two general categories. *Primary hypertension,* which comprises 95% of all cases, refers to hypertension of unknown etiology. This category is, in turn, divided into benign hypertension (also known as *essential hypertension*) and malignant hypertension. When the pathological processes that produce the hypertension are known, it is referred to as *secondary hypertension.*

## Procedure

1. With the subject in a sitting position, rest the right or left arm on a table at the level of the heart, and wrap the cuff of the sphygmomanometer around the arm about 2.5 cm above the elbow.

2. Palpate the brachial artery in the antecubital space, and place the stethoscope where the pulse is felt. Close the screw valve, and pump the pressure in the cuff up to about 20 mm Hg above the point where sounds disappear, or to about 20 mm Hg above the point where the radial pulse can no longer be felt.

3. Open the screw valve to allow the pressure in the cuff to fall at a rate of about 2 or 3 mm Hg per second.

4. Record the systolic pressure (beginning of phase 1) and the two measurements of diastolic pressure (beginning of phases 4 and 5). Enter these values in your laboratory report, and compare your pressure with the range of normal values listed in table 5.1.

5. Calculate the subject's pulse pressure (systolic minus diastolic pressure). Enter this value in your laboratory report.

6. Calculate the subject's mean arterial pressure. This is equal to the diastolic pressure plus 1/3 of the pulse pressure. Enter this in the laboratory report.

7. Repeat these measurements on the same subject in a reclining position (arms at sides), and a few minutes later, repeat it with the subject in a standing position (arms down).

**Table 5.1** Normal arterial blood pressure at different ages.

| Age | Systolic | | Diastolic | | Age | Systolic | | Diastolic | |
|---|---|---|---|---|---|---|---|---|---|
| | Men | Women | Men | Women | | Men | Women | Men | Women |
| 1 day ............... | 70 | | | | 16 years ........... | 118 | 116 | 73 | 72 |
| 3 days ............. | 72 | | | | 17 years ........... | 121 | 116 | 74 | 72 |
| 9 days ............. | 73 | | | | 18 years ........... | 120 | 116 | 74 | 72 |
| 3 weeks ........... | 77 | | | | 19 years ........... | 122 | 115 | 75 | 71 |
| 3 months ......... | 86 | | | | 20–24 years ..... | 123 | 116 | 76 | 72 |
| 6–12 months .... | 89 | 93 | 60 | 62 | 25–29 years ..... | 125 | 117 | 78 | 74 |
| 1 year ............... | 96 | 95 | 66 | 65 | 30–34 years ..... | 126 | 120 | 79 | 75 |
| 2 years ............ | 99 | 92 | 64 | 60 | 35–39 years ..... | 127 | 124 | 80 | 78 |
| 3 years ............ | 100 | 100 | 67 | 64 | 40–44 years ..... | 129 | 127 | 81 | 80 |
| 4 years ............ | 99 | 99 | 65 | 66 | 45–49 years ..... | 130 | 131 | 82 | 82 |
| 5 years ............ | 92 | 92 | 62 | 62 | 50–54 years ..... | 135 | 137 | 83 | 84 |
| 6 years ............ | 94 | 94 | 64 | 64 | 55–59 years ..... | 138 | 139 | 84 | 84 |
| 7 years ............ | 97 | 97 | 65 | 66 | 60–64 years ..... | 142 | 144 | 85 | 85 |
| 8 years ............ | 100 | 100 | 67 | 68 | 65–69 years ..... | 143 | 154 | 83 | 85 |
| 9 years ............ | 101 | 101 | 68 | 69 | 70–74 years ..... | 145 | 159 | 82 | 85 |
| 10 years .......... | 103 | 103 | 69 | 70 | 75–79 years ..... | 146 | 158 | 81 | 84 |
| 11 years .......... | 104 | 104 | 70 | 71 | 80–84 years ..... | 145 | 157 | 82 | 83 |
| 12 years .......... | 106 | 106 | 71 | 72 | 85–89 years ..... | 145 | 154 | 79 | 82 |
| 13 years .......... | 108 | 108 | 72 | 73 | 90–94 years ..... | 145 | 150 | 78 | 79 |
| 14 years .......... | 110 | 110 | 73 | 74 | 95–106 years ... | 145 | 149 | 78 | 81 |
| 15 years .......... | 112 | 112 | 75 | 76 | | | | | |

From Diem, K., and Lentner, C., Eds., *Documenta Geigy Scientific Tables,* 7th ed., J. R. Geigy S. A., Basle, Switzerland, 1970. With permission.

# Laboratory Report 5.6

Name _____

Date _____

Section _____

## Data from Exercise 5.6

Enter your data in the table below:

|  | Sitting | Reclining | Standing |
|---|---|---|---|
| Systolic pressure |  |  |  |
| Diastolic pressure |  |  |  |
| Pulse pressure |  |  |  |
| Mean arterial pressure |  |  |  |

## Questions for Exercise 5.6

1. When blood pressure measurements are taken, the first sound of Korotkoff occurs when the cuff pressure equals the _____ , and the second sound occurs when the cuff pressure equals the _____ .

2. Suppose a person's blood pressure is 165/110.

    (a) What is his systolic pressure? _____

    (b) What is his diastolic pressure? _____

    (c) What is his pulse pressure? _____

    (d) What is his mean arterial pressure? _____

3. What condition does the person in question 2 have? Explain the dangers of this condition.

4. What causes the sounds of Korotkoff? Why can't you normally hear them in the brachial artery before you inflate the cuff?

5. What effect does arm position have on the measurement of blood pressure? Explain.

# Cardiovascular System and Physical Fitness

Physical fitness is dependent on adaptations of the cardiovascular system that include increased stroke volume, decreased resting cardiac rate, and changed cardiovascular responses to exercise. Controlled exercise can be used to assess physical fitness and also to detect heart disease.

## Objectives

1. Describe the relationship between age and the maximum cardiac rate.
2. Describe the cardiovascular changes that occur when a person becomes physically fit.
3. Explain how controlled exercise may be used to detect heart disease.

## Materials

1. Sphygmomanometer
2. Stethoscope
3. Chair or stair or platform 18 inches high

Although the **maximum cardiac rate** (beats per minute) is the same in people of the same age group, those who are physically fit have a higher *stroke volume* (milliliters per beat) than more sedentary individuals. A person who is in poor physical condition, therefore, reaches his or her maximum cardiac rate at a lower work level than a person of comparable age who is in better shape. Maximum cardiac rates are listed in table 5.2. Persons who are in good physical condition can deliver more oxygen to their muscles (have a higher *aerobic capacity*) before reaching maximum cardiac rate than can those in poorer condition.

**Table 5.2** Maximum cardiac rates.

| Age | Maximum Cardiac Rate |
|---|---|
| 20–29 | 190 beats/min |
| 30–39 | 160 beats/min |
| 40–49 | 150 beats/min |
| 50–59 | 140 beats/min |
| 60 and above | 130 beats/min |

The physically fit thus have a slower rate of increase of the cardiac rate with exercise and a faster return to the resting cardiac rate after exercise. Physical fitness, therefore, involves not only muscular development but also the ability of the cardiovascular system to adapt to sudden changes in demand.

## Clinical Significance

Exercise tests have proved extremely useful in the diagnosis of heart disease, particularly *myocardial ischemia* (inadequate blood flow to the heart). People who appear to be normal and who have normal electrocardiograms at rest may develop *angina pectoris* and abnormal ECGs after exercise. In these tests, a standardized exercise procedure is performed (e.g., the Harvard one-step, the Master's two-step, the treadmill, or the bicycle ergometer) for a length of time predetermined to yield a fraction (such as 90%) of the maximum cardiac rate for the patient's age. At the end of the test, irregularities in the ECG are noted, such as depressed or elevated S-T segments, which are indicative of myocardial ischemia.

## Procedure

1. Measure your reclining pulse by placing your fingertips (not the thumb) on the radial artery in the ventrolateral region of the wrist.[9] Count the number of pulses in 30 seconds, and multiply by 2. Score points as indicated.

---

9. The procedure for this exercise is from E. C. Schneider, "A Cardiovascular Rating as a Measure of Physical Fatigue and Efficiency." *JAMA* 74 (1920): 1507. Copyright 1920, American Medical Association.

**Reclining Pulse**

| Rate | Points |
|------|--------|
| 50–60 | 3 |
| 61–70 | 3 |
| 71–80 | 2 |
| 81–90 | 1 |
| 90–100 | 0 |
| 101–110 | −1 |

Score: _____

2. After the reclining pulse has been measured, stand up and measure the pulse rate immediately upon standing.

**Standing Pulse Rate**

| Rate | Points |
|------|--------|
| 60–70 | 3 |
| 71–80 | 3 |
| 81–90 | 2 |
| 91–100 | 1 |
| 101–110 | 1 |
| 111–120 | 0 |
| 121–130 | 0 |
| 131–140 | −1 |

Score: _____

3. Subtract the pulse rate measured in step 1 from the pulse rate measured in step 2 to get the pulse rate increase on standing.

**Pulse Rate Increase on Standing**

| Reclining Pulse | 0–10 Beats | 11–18 Beats | 19–26 Beats | 27–34 Beats | 35–43 Beats |
|------|------|------|------|------|------|
| 50–60 | 3 | 3 | 2 | 1 | 0 |
| 61–70 | 3 | 2 | 1 | 0 | −1 |
| 71–80 | 3 | 2 | 0 | −1 | −2 |
| 81–90 | 2 | 1 | −1 | −2 | −3 |
| 90–100 | 1 | 0 | −2 | −3 | −3 |
| 101–110 | 0 | −1 | −3 | −3 | −3 |

Score: _____

4. Place your right foot on a chair or stair 18 inches high. Raise your body so that your left foot comes to rest by your right foot. Return your left foot to the original position. Repeat this exercise five times, allowing 3 seconds for each step up. Immediately after the completion of this exercise, measure the pulse for 15 seconds and multiply by 4. Record this pulse rate.

Pulse: _____

Measure the pulse as described for 30, 60, 90, and 120 seconds after completion of the exercise. Record the time that it takes for the pulse to return to normal standing level (step 2). Score points as indicated.

**Return of Pulse to Standing Normal after Exercise**

| Seconds | Points |
|---------|--------|
| 0–30 | 4 |
| 31–60 | 3 |
| 61–90 | 2 |
| 91–120 | 1 |
| After 120 | 0 |

Score: _____

5. Subtract your normal standing pulse rate (step 2) from your pulse rate immediately after exercise (step 4).

**Pulse Rate Increase Immediately after Exercise**

| Standing Pulse | 0–10 Beats | 11–20 Beats | 21–30 Beats | 31–40 Beats | 41+ Beats |
|------|------|------|------|------|------|
| 60–70 | 3 | 3 | 2 | 1 | 0 |
| 71–80 | 3 | 2 | 1 | 0 | −1 |
| 81–90 | 3 | 2 | 1 | −1 | −2 |
| 91–100 | 2 | 1 | 0 | −2 | −3 |
| 101–110 | 1 | 0 | −1 | −3 | −3 |
| 111–120 | 1 | −1 | −2 | −3 | −3 |
| 121–130 | 0 | −2 | −3 | −3 | −3 |
| 131–140 | 0 | −3 | −3 | −3 | −3 |

Score: _____

6. Calculate the change in systolic blood pressure as you go from a reclining to a standing position (refer to data in exercise 5.6, or take new measurements).

**Change in Systolic Pressure from Reclining to Standing**

| Change (mm Hg) | Points |
|----------------|--------|
| Rise of 8 or more | 3 |
| Rise of 2–7 | 2 |
| No rise | 1 |
| Fall of 2–5 | 0 |
| Fall of 6 or more | −1 |

Score: _____

7. Determine your total score for all the tests and evaluate this score on the following basis. Enter your score and rating in the laboratory report.

| Excellent | 18–17 |
|-----------|-------|
| Good | 16–14 |
| Fair | 13–8 |
| Poor | 7 or less |

# Laboratory Report 5.7

## Data for Exercise 5.7

Write your total score in the space below, and indicate if this score is excellent, good, fair, or poor according to the rating scale in the procedure.

Total Score: _____

Rating: _____

## Questions for Exercise 5.7

1. Does a person's aerobic capacity change with age? Explain.

2. What factors improve the delivery of oxygen to muscles in a person who is physically fit?

3. How does the blood pressure and pulse rate increase after exercise compare in people who are and are not physically fit?

4. What are the consequences of an inadequate delivery of oxygen to the heart? How does exercise help in the diagnosis of heart disease?

# Respiration and Metabolism

The term *metabolism* refers collectively to all the chemical reactions that occur in the body. Those reactions that build larger molecules out of smaller ones (*biosynthesis*) are generally condensation reactions and require input of energy (are *endergonic*). These reactions are collectively termed **anabolism.** Reactions that break larger molecules down into smaller ones (by hydrolysis) release energy (are *exergonic*) and are collectively termed **catabolism.**

The energy required for anabolic reactions is provided by the hydrolysis of *adenosine triphosphate* (*ATP*). This catabolic reaction produces *adenosine diphosphate* (*ADP*) and inorganic *phosphate* ($PO_4^=$). (See reaction *a.*)

The energy released by the hydrolysis of ATP is used to power all the anabolic reactions in the cell. ATP is frequently referred to as the *universal energy carrier* of the cell. Since ATP is continuously hydrolyzed, it must also be continuously resynthesized by the condensation of ADP with phosphate. (See reaction *b.*)

The energy required for this anabolic reaction is provided by a sequence of catabolic reactions known as **cellular respiration.** In this process, monosaccharides, amino acids, and fatty acids are broken down in a series of hydrolytic steps to smaller molecules, with the accompanying release of energy. For the sake of simplicity, only the fate of glucose as the initial reactant will be considered, and we will eliminate the intermediate steps, showing only the final products of respiration.

---

a. $ATP + H_2O \longrightarrow ADP + PO_4^= + energy$

b. $ADP + PO_4^= + energy \longrightarrow ATP + H_2O$

c. $Glucose + O_2 + 38\ ADP + 38\ PO_4^= \longrightarrow CO_2 + H_2O + 38\ ATP$

d. $Glucose + 2\ ADP + 2\ PO_4^= \longrightarrow lactic\ acid + 2\ ATP$

---

In the presence of oxygen, glucose is broken down to carbon dioxide and water, and the energy released is used to form ATP. Since oxygen is required for this process, it is called *aerobic respiration.* (See reaction *c.*)

Since the cells continuously hydrolyze ATP for energy, they need a continuous source of glucose and oxygen for aerobic respiration. If oxygen is not delivered to the cells in sufficient quantities, they will be forced to switch to an alternative energy-producing process—*anaerobic respiration.*

In anaerobic respiration, glucose is broken down in the absence of oxygen to lactic acid, and two molecules of ATP are formed. (See reaction *d.*)

Aerobic respiration, which can produce thirty-eight molecules of ATP per molecule of glucose, is obviously more economical than anaerobic respiration, which produces two molecules of ATP per molecule of glucose. Moreover, the aerobic pathway is also favored by the fact that the accumulation of lactic acid is toxic to the body.

Oxygen is delivered to the cells of the body by the hemoglobin within the red blood cells (erythrocytes). Proper delivery of oxygen to the tissues depends on a number of factors, including the (1) diffusion of oxygen from the red blood cells to the body cells; (2) unloading of oxygen from the hemoglobin within the red blood cells in the tissue capillaries; (3) loading of hemoglobin with oxygen in the capillaries of the lungs; (4) diffusion of oxygen from the alveoli of the lungs to the red blood cells within the pulmonary capillaries; and (5) removal of "old" air, which is poor in oxygen, and replacement with "new" air, which is rich in oxygen, within the alveoli of the lungs. This process is called **ventilation.**

The factors affecting the delivery of oxygen to the tissues of the body can thus be grouped into two general categories: (1) the uptake, transport, and delivery of oxygen by hemoglobin—simply summarized as **oxygen transport**—and (2) ventilation.

# 6.1 Measurements of Pulmonary Function

Spirometry can be used to measure lung volumes and capacities and to measure ventilation as a function of time. Such measurements are clinically useful in the diagnosis of restrictive and obstructive pulmonary disorders.

## Objectives

1. Identify the muscles involved in inspiration and expiration, and explain the mechanics of breathing.
2. Define the different lung volumes and capacities, and determine the amounts of these measurements in a spirogram.
3. Describe and perform the forced expiratory volume and maximum breathing capacity tests, and determine these measurements in a spirogram.
4. Explain how pulmonary function tests are used in the diagnosis of restrictive and obstructive pulmonary disorders.

## Materials

1. Spirometer (Collins 9-liter respirometer)
2. Disposable mouthpieces and nose clamp

*Spirometry* refers to the measurement of lung volumes and capacities. A Collins respirometer will be used for this purpose (fig. 6.1). As the subject exhales into a mouthpiece, the oxygen bell rises, causing a pen to move downward on a moving chart (kymograph). Since this is a closed system, soda lime is provided to remove $CO_2$ from the exhaled air. As the subject inhales, the oxygen bell moves downward, causing the pen to move upward on the moving chart. The *y* axis of the chart is graduated in milliliters, and the *x* axis is graduated in millimeters. Since the speed with which the chart moves is known, a graph of milliliters of air moved into and out of the lungs in a given time interval can be obtained.

Spirometry enables one to easily visualize, define, and measure many important aspects of pulmonary function (fig. 6.2).

The **total lung capacity** (TLC) is the amount of gas in the lungs after a maximum (forced) inhalation.

The **vital capacity** (VC) is the maximum amount of gas that can be exhaled after a maximum inhalation.

The **tidal volume** (TV) is the volume of gas inspired or expired during each normal (unforced) ventilation cycle.

The **inspiratory capacity** (IC) is the maximum amount of gas that can be inhaled after a normal (unforced) exhalation.

The **inspiratory reserve volume** (IRV) is the maximum amount of gas that can be forcefully inhaled after a normal inhalation.

The **expiratory reserve volume** (ERV) is the maximum amount of gas that can be forcefully exhaled after a normal exhalation.

The **functional residual capacity** (FRC) is the amount of gas left in the lungs after a normal (unforced) exhalation.

The **residual volume** (RV) is the amount of gas left in the lungs after a maximum (forced) exhalation.

The movement of air into and out of the lungs (ventilation) results from a pressure difference between the pulmonary air and the atmosphere. This pressure difference is created by a change in the volume of the thoracic cavity, since according to *Boyle's law,* the pressure of a gas is inversely proportional to its volume. An increase in thoracic volume results in a decrease in intrapulmonary pressure. Air is therefore pushed into the lungs by the greater pressure of the atmosphere (inhalation). When the thoracic volume decreases, the intrapulmonary pressure rises above the atmospheric pressure, pushing air out of the lungs (exhalation).

**Figure 6.1.** The Collins 9-liter respirometer.

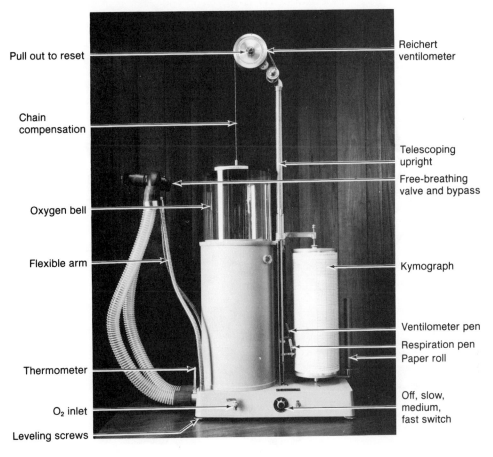

Pull out to reset

Chain compensation

Oxygen bell

Flexible arm

Thermometer

$O_2$ inlet

Leveling screws

Reichert ventilometer

Telescoping upright

Free-breathing valve and bypass

Kymograph

Ventilometer pen

Respiration pen
Paper roll

Off, slow, medium, fast switch

**Figure 6.2.** Lung volumes and capacities as measured by spirometry.

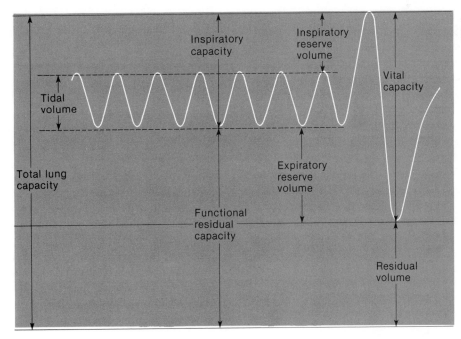

Inspiratory capacity

Inspiratory reserve volume

Tidal volume

Vital capacity

Total lung capacity

Expiratory reserve volume

Functional residual capacity

Residual volume

**Figure 6.3.** The thoracic cavity and the muscles of respiration.

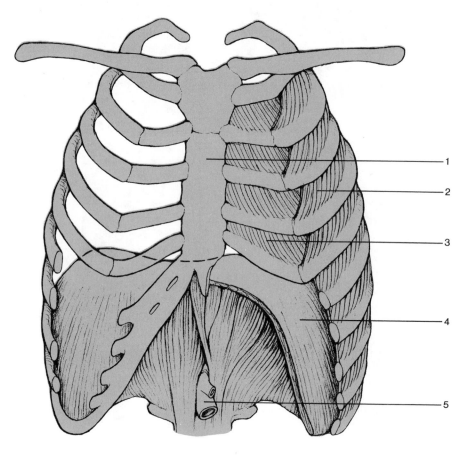

1. Sternum
2. External intercostals
3. Internal intercostals
4. Diaphragm
5. Aorta

In normal (unforced) ventilation, the thoracic volume is regulated by the action of the *diaphragm* and the *external intercostal muscles* (fig. 6.3). When the diaphragm is at rest, it forms a convex floor to the thoracic cavity. During inhalation, the diaphragm contracts and pulls itself into a more flattened form. This lowers the floor of the thorax and increases the thoracic volume (and, incidentally, pushes down on the viscera, causing the abdomen to protrude during inhalation). At the same time, the contraction of the external intercostal muscles increases the volume of the thorax by rotating the ribs upward and outward. At the end of inhalation, the diaphragm and external intercostal muscles relax, causing the thorax to resume its original volume and the air inside the lungs to be exhaled. The amount of air inhaled or exhaled in this manner is the tidal volume.

Inhalation can become difficult if the air passages are obstructed or if the lungs lose their normal elasticity. In these cases, the affected person relies increasingly on muscles not usually used in normal (tidal) ventilation— the *scalenus, sternocleidomastoid,* and *pectoralis major.* These muscles are also used in healthy people during forced inhalation to obtain the inspiratory reserve volume.

During forced exhalation, the *internal intercostal muscles* contract, depressing the rib cage, and the *abdominal muscles* contract, pushing the viscera against the diaphragm. The push of the viscera increases the convexity of the diaphragm and decreases the thoracic volume to a lower level than that achieved in normal exhalation. The amount of air exhaled by contraction of both groups of muscles is the expiratory reserve volume.

Even after a maximum forced exhalation, there is still some air left in the lungs. This residual volume of air makes it easier to inflate the lungs during the next inhalation and oxygenates the blood between ventilation cycles.

# A. Measurement of Simple Lung Volumes and Capacities

## Procedure

1. Raise and lower the oxygen bell (fig. 6.1) several times to get fresh air into the spirometer. Notice that as the bell moves up and down, one of the pens moves a corresponding distance down and up on a shaft. By adjusting the height of the oxygen bell, position this pen so that it will begin writing in the middle of the chart paper. This pen (the ventilometer pen) usually has black ink; the other (respiration) pen usually has red ink and will not be used for this exercise. (It can be rocked away from the paper.)

2. With the free-breathing valve set to the *open* position, place the mouthpiece in the buccal cavity (as in breathing through a snorkel), and go through several ventilation cycles to become accustomed to the apparatus. (When the free-breathing valve is open, you will breathe room air.) If a disposable cardboard mouthpiece is used, be particularly careful to prevent air leakage from the corners of the mouth. Breathing through the nostrils is prevented by means of a nose clamp or by pinching the nose tightly with the thumb and forefinger.

3. Turn the respirometer to the *slow* position (32 mm/min.), and close the free-breathing valve so that the oxygen bell and the pen go up and down with each ventilation cycle.

4. Breathe in a normal, relaxed manner for 1–2 minutes. The breaths should appear relatively uniform, and the slope should go upward (see fig. 6.4). A downward slope indicates that there is an air leak; in this event, tighten the grip of the mouth on the mouthpiece and the nose clamp on the nose, and begin again.

**Note:** *At this speed (32 mm/min.), the distance between vertical lines on the chart is traversed in 1 minute.*

This procedure measures tidal volume—the amount of air inhaled or exhaled in each resting ventilation cycle.

5. When the tidal volume procedure has been completed, perform a test for vital capacity— the maximum amount of air that can be exhaled after a maximum inhalation. At the end of a normal exhalation, inhale as much as possible, then exhale to the fullest possible extent. At the completion of this exercise, the chart should resemble the one shown in figure 6.4.

6. Remove the chart from the kymograph drum. Notice that the chart is marked horizontally in milliliters.

**Note:** *Since the temperature and pressure of the respirometer are different from those existing in the body, the volume that the air occupies in the respirometer will be subject to changes in ambient (room) conditions. To standardize the volumes measured in spirometry, we multiply these measured volumes by a correction factor known as the BTPS factor (body temperature, atmospheric pressure, saturated with water vapor). Since the BTPS factor is very close to 1.1 at normal room temperatures, we will use this figure in the calculations.*

*Calculations*

1. Obtain the measured tidal volume from the chart by subtracting the milliliters corresponding to the trough from the milliliters corresponding to the peak of a typical resting ventilation cycle.

*Example (from fig. 6.5)*

Step 1     3700 ml (inhalation)
       $-3250$ ml (exhalation)
           450 ml

Step 2     450 ml (measured tidal volume)
       $\times$  1.1   (BTPS factor)
           495 ml

Enter the corrected, measured tidal volume (TV) in the Measured column of the table in your laboratory report.

2. Obtain the measured inspiratory capacity from the chart. To do this, subtract the milliliters corresponding to the last normal exhalation before performing the vital capacity maneuver from the milliliters corresponding to the maximum inhalation peak.

**Figure 6.4.** A spirometry chart of tidal volume, inspiratory capacity, expiratory reserve volume, and vital capacity.

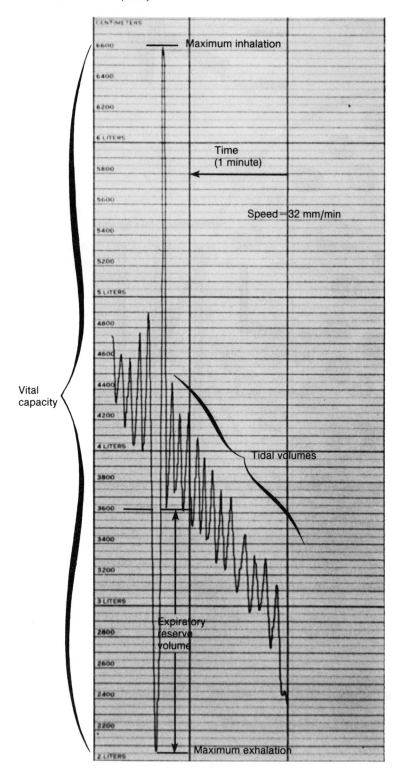

**Figure 6.5.** A close-up of tidal volume measurements on a spirometry chart.

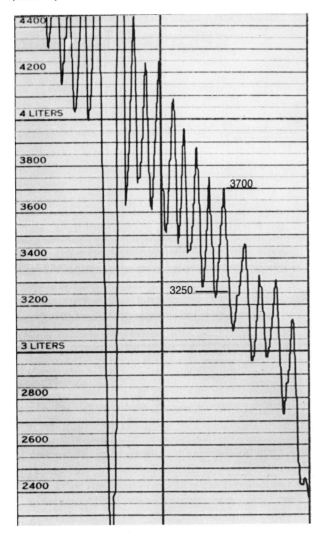

**Figure 6.6.** A close-up of the inspiratory capacity measurement on a spirometry chart.

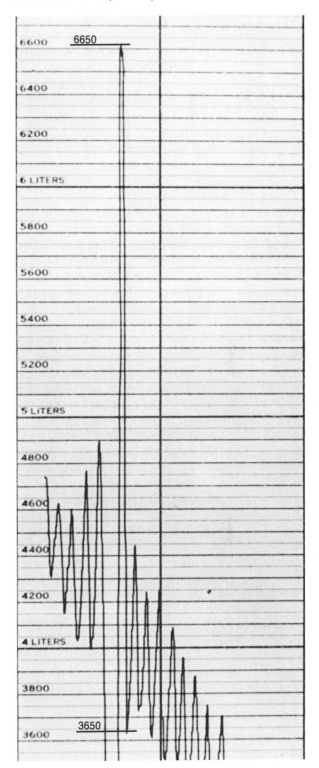

*Example (from fig. 6.6)*

Step 1    6650 ml (maximum inhalation)
      −3650 ml (normal exhalation)
        3000 ml

Step 2    3000 ml (measured inspiratory capacity)
      × 1.1    (BTPS factor)
        3300 ml

Enter the corrected, measured inspiratory capacity (IC) in the Measured column of the table in your laboratory report.

3. Obtain the measured expiratory reserve volume by subtracting the milliliters corresponding to the trough for maximum exhalation from the milliliters corresponding to the last normal exhalation before the vital capacity maneuver (the same value used for step 2).

*Example (from fig. 6.7)*

Step 1    3650 ml (normal exhalation)
        −2050 ml (maximum exhalation)
         1600 ml

Step 2    1600 ml (measured expir. reserve volume)
       × 1.1   (BTPS factor)
       1760 ml

Enter the corrected expiratory reserve volume (ERV) in the Measured column of the table in your laboratory report.

4. Obtain the measured vital capacity. This can be done in either of two ways: (1) simply add the corrected inspiratory capacity (from step 2) and the corrected expiratory reserve volume (step 3); since each of these values has already been corrected to BTPS, an additional correction step is not necessary; (2) subtract the milliliters corresponding to maximum exhalation from the milliliters corresponding to maximum inhalation. However, this value must then be multiplied by the BTPS factor.

*Example*

Method 1    3300 ml (corrected inspiratory capacity)
         +1760 ml (corrected expir. reserve volume)
         5060 ml (corrected vital capacity)

Method 2    6650 ml (maximum inhalation)
         −2050 ml (maximum exhalation)
         4600 ml

         4600 ml (measured vital capacity)
       × 1.1   (BTPS factor)
       5060 ml (corrected capacity)

Enter the corrected vital capacity (VC) in the Measured column of the table in your laboratory report.

5. Obtain the predicted vital capacity for the subject's sex, age, and height by referring to tables 6.3 and 6.4 (see pages 216–17). The height in centimeters can be most conveniently obtained by reference to the height conversion scale in figure 6.10 (see page 214).

*Example*

Sex: male
Age: 34
Height: 174 cm
Predicted vital capacity: 4140 ml

Enter the subject's predicted vital capacity from the tables of normal values in the Predicted column in your laboratory report.

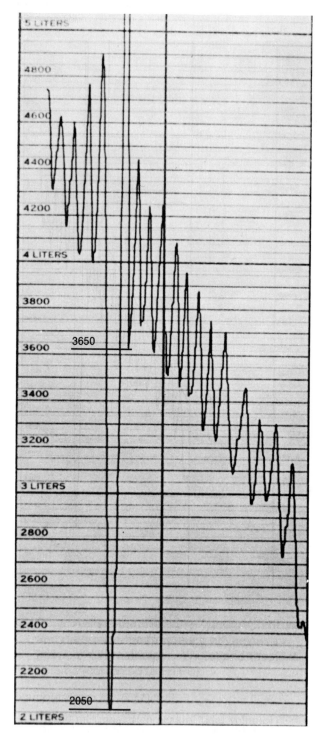

**Figure 6.7.**   A close-up of the expiratory reserve volume measurement on a spirometry chart.

6. To obtain an estimate of the predicted residual volume and the predicted total lung capacity, refer to table 6.1.

**Note:**   *These values cannot be measured by spirometry because residual volume cannot be exhaled; total lung capacity equals the vital capacity plus residual volume.*

**Table 6.1** Factors for obtaining the predicted residual volume and total lung capacity.

| Age | Residual Volume: Vital Capacity × Factor | Total Lung Capacity: Vital Capacity × Factor |
|---|---|---|
| 16–34 | 0.250 | 1.250 |
| 35–49 | 0.305 | 1.305 |
| 50–69 | 0.445 | 1.445 |

7. Obtain the percent predicted value for all the measurements in the following way:

$$\text{Percent predicted} = \frac{\text{corrected measured value}}{\text{predicted value}} \times 100\%$$

*Example*

Measured vital capacity = 5060 ml
(corrected to BTPS)

Predicted vital capacity = 4140 ml
(from table 6.3 or 6.4)

$$\% \text{ predicted} = \frac{5060 \text{ ml}}{4140 \text{ ml}} \times 100\%$$

$$= 122\%$$

Enter the percent predicted values in the appropriate places in the table in your laboratory report.

---

Measurements of vital capacity that are consistently below 80 percent of the predicted value on repeated tests suggest the presence of restrictive lung disease, such as emphysema.

---

## B. Measurement of Forced Expiratory Volume and Maximum Breathing Capacity

The ability to ventilate the lungs in a given time interval is often of greater diagnostic value than measurements of simple lung volumes and capacities. Two often used measurements that consider *time* intervals are the *forced expiratory volume* (FEV), otherwise known as the timed vital capacity, and the *maximum breathing capacity* (MBC).

In the forced expiratory volume test, the subject performs a vital capacity maneuver (inhales maximally and then exhales maximally), while the operator of the respirometer sets the kymograph speed at its fastest setting (1920 mm/min.). This fast speed stretches out the exhalation tracing, because the distance between vertical lines is now traversed in 1 second. By referring to the chart, one can thus calculate the percent of the total vital capacity that is exhaled in the first second ($FEV_{1.0}$), second second ($FEV_{2.0}$), and third second ($FEV_{3.0}$). A sample record of the forced expiratory volume is shown in figure 6.8.

In the maximum breathing capacity test, the subject inhales and exhales as forcefully and as rapidly as possible in an attempt to move the maximum amount of air through the lungs in a 12-second interval (this is later corrected to the amount of air moved per minute). A sample recording of maximum breathing capacity is shown in figure 6.9.

### Pulmonary Disorders

Chronic pulmonary dysfunctions can be divided into two general categories: **obstructive disorders** and **restrictive disorders.** These two categories can be differentiated in part by the use of the spirometry tests performed in this exercise.

The flow of air through a tube is proportional to the fourth power of its radius. A small obstruction in the pulmonary airways thus results in a greatly magnified resistance to airflow. Obstructive disorders of the bronchioles, for example, are characteristic of *emphysema, bronchitis,* and *asthma.* This bronchiolar obstruction can result from inflammation and edema, smooth muscle constriction, or bronchiolar secretion. These conditions make it difficult for the sufferer to move air rapidly into and out of the lungs. In restrictive disorders there is actual damage to the lung tissue resulting in an abnormal vital capacity test. However, if the disease is purely restrictive (as in *pulmonary fibrosis*), the airways may be clear, resulting in a normal forced expiratory volume test (that is, the vital capacity is reduced, but it can be quickly exhaled). This is not true of emphysema, which is both a restrictive and an obstructive disease.

In obstructive disorders, the bronchioles may be weakened to such a degree that they collapse before all the air is emptied from the lungs during exhalation. This condition, known as **air trapping,** is revealed by an increase in the functional residual capacity.

In emphysema (caused primarily by cigarette smoking and aggravated by air pollution), the number of alveoli in the lungs is reduced. This results in an abnormally low vital capacity, which is evidence of restrictive disease. However, since the alveolar tissue normally exerts an elastic support that helps to keep the thin-walled bronchioles open during exhalation, the loss of alveoli in emphysema also results in a reduction in the elastic support of the bronchioles. Because of this, the bronchioles may narrow (increasing the resistance to airflow) and even collapse during exhalation. This gives an obstructive component to the disease, resulting in abnormal forced expiratory volume and maximum breathing capacity tests.

The $FEV_{1.0}$ test detects increased airway resistance, as occurs in asthma, bronchitis, and emphysema. This test is also used extensively as a preoperative procedure to predict the response of a patient to general anesthesia and the length of time the patient must be kept on a respirator postoperatively. The $FEV_{1.0}$ test is also valuable in research designed to determine the effects of air pollutants—such as cigarette smoke and ozone—on pulmonary function.

**Figure 6.8.** A recording of the forced expiratory volume (FEV) or timed vital capacity test.

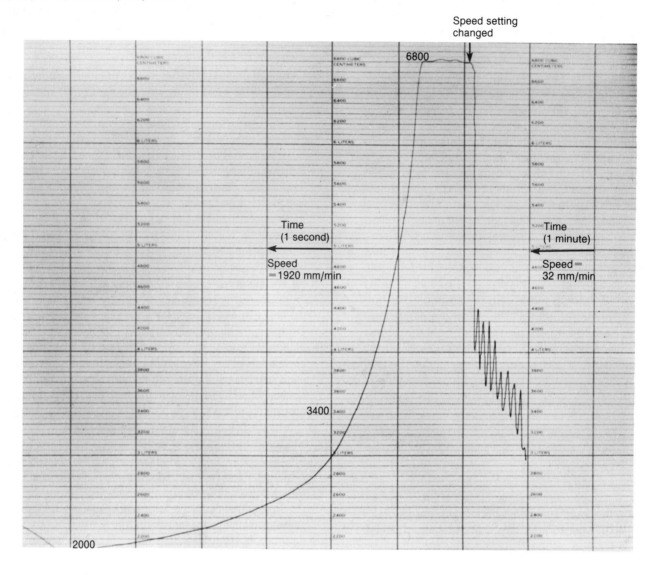

## Procedure

1. The subject breathes normally into the respirometer with the kymograph set to 32 mm/min.
2. After a normal (unforced) exhalation, the operator instructs the subject to take a deep, forceful inhalation. The subject is instructed to hold this inhalation momentarily.
3. The operator sets the kymograph at the fast speed (1920 mm/min.), and instructs the subject to exhale as rapidly and as forcefully as possible.

**Note:** *At a speed of 1920 mm/min., the distance between two vertical lines on the chart is equal to 1 second.*

4. The kymograph speed is again set at 32 mm/min., and the subject breathes normally for several ventilation cycles.
5. The respiration pen (red ink) is pushed against the chart, and the kymograph speed is set at 160 mm/min.

**Note:** *At a speed of 160 mm/min., the distance between two vertical lines on the chart is equal to 12 seconds.*

6. The subject is instructed to inhale and exhale as rapidly and as forcefully as possible for 12 seconds.
7. At the end of this period of forced breathing, the free-breathing valve is opened, and the subject is allowed to resume normal ventilation.

8. Since a certain amount of learning is involved in the execution of these maneuvers, best results are obtained if the subject is allowed to repeat steps 2–7 a second time.
9. At the end of these procedures, the respirometer is turned off, and the kymograph chart is examined.

*Calculations: Forced Expiratory Volume (FEV₁.₀)*

1. Measure the vital capacity from the chart by subtracting the exhalation trough (which is flat, because no more air could be expelled) from the inhalation peak (which is also flat, because the subject's breath is held). You do not have to multiply this value by the BTPS factor.

*Example (from fig. 6.8)*

$$\begin{array}{r} 6800 \text{ ml (maximum inhalation)} \\ -\underline{2000 \text{ ml (maximum exhalation)}} \\ 4800 \text{ ml (vital capacity)} \end{array}$$

Enter the uncorrected vital capacity in the following space:

_____ ml

2. Measure the amount of air exhaled in the first second by subtracting the milliliters corresponding to the exhalation line after 1 second from the milliliters of the inhalation peak. Remember that the distance between vertical lines is passed in 1 second. If the subject does not begin to exhale exactly on a vertical line, you must measure with a ruler 3.2 cm from the beginning of exhalation. (This is the distance between vertical lines and is equivalent to 1 second at this chart speed.)

*Example (from fig. 6.8)*

$$\begin{array}{r} 6800 \text{ ml (maximum inhalation)} \\ -\underline{3400 \text{ ml (exhalation line after 1 second)}} \\ 3400 \text{ ml (amount exhaled in first second)} \end{array}$$

Enter the amount exhaled in the first second in the following space:

_____ ml

3. Calculate the percent of the vital capacity exhaled in the first second (the FEV₁.₀).

*Example*

$$\text{FEV}_{1.0} = \frac{3400 \text{ ml (from step 2)}}{4800 \text{ ml (from step 1)}} \times 100\%$$

$$= 70.8\%$$

Enter the FEV₁.₀ in the laboratory report. Refer to table 6.2, and enter the predicted percentage for the FEV₁.₀ in the laboratory report.

**Table 6.2** Percent of vital capacity exhaled during first second.

| Age | Percent of VC |
| --- | --- |
| 18–29 | 82–80 |
| 30–39 | 78–77 |
| 40–44 | 75.5 |
| 45–49 | 74.5 |
| 50–54 | 73.5 |
| 55–64 | 72–70 |

From Edward Gaensler and George W. Wright, *Arch. Environ. Health* 12 (1966): 146. Courtesy of the American Medical Association.

*Calculations: Maximum Breathing Capacity*

1. Examine the recording made by the respiration (red ink) pen. Notice that this pen goes up with inhalation but does not go down with exhalation (unlike the other pen). This creates a staircase pattern. The rise of each stair is clearly less than the movements of the oxygen bell and of the other (ventilometer) pen. In fact, the rise of the maximum breathing capacity staircase has been reduced by a factor of 25 (the gear ratio between the two pens; see fig. 6.9).

2. Using a straightedge, draw a line that connects either the bottoms or the tops of the stairs. Determine the rise of this line over a 12-second interval by subtracting the milliliters where this line intersects the vertical chart line at the bottom of the staircase from the milliliters where this line intersects the next vertical chart line at the top of the staircase. (Remember that the vertical lines are 12 seconds apart at a chart speed of 160 mm/min.). Multiply your result by the BTPS factor.

*Example (from fig. 6.9)*

$$\begin{array}{r} 3400 \text{ ml (at the end of 12 seconds)} \\ -\underline{2350 \text{ ml (at the beginning of 12 seconds)}} \\ 1050 \text{ ml (rise over 12-second interval)} \end{array}$$

$$1050 \text{ ml} \times 1.1 \text{ (BTPS factor)} = 1155 \text{ ml}$$

3. Change your answer from milliliters per 12 seconds to milliliters per minute by multiplying the value obtained in step 2 by a factor of 5. Correct this figure for the gear ratio reduction by multiplying by a factor of 25. Finally, change your answer from milliliters per minute to liters per minute by dividing by a factor of 1000.

Measurements of Pulmonary Function    213

**Figure 6.9.** (a) a recording of a ventilometer pen (top) and a respiration pen (bottom) during the maximum breathing capacity test; (b) a close-up of a respiration pen recording during the maximum breathing capacity test (note staircase effect).

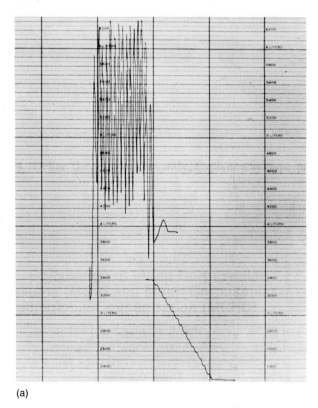

(a)

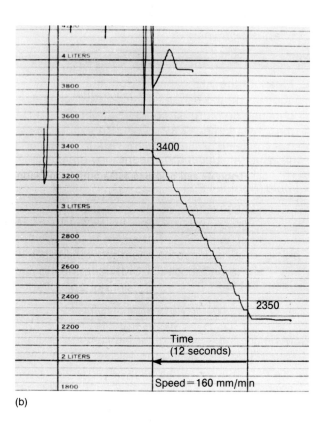

(b)

*Example (from fig. 6.9)*

$$1155 \text{ ml}/12 \text{ sec (from step 2)}$$
$$\times \quad 5$$
$$\overline{5775 \text{ ml/min}}$$

$$5775$$
$$\times \quad 25 \text{ (gear ratio)}$$
$$\overline{144375 \text{ ml/min}}$$

$$\frac{144375 \text{ ml}}{\text{min}} \times \frac{1 \text{ liter}}{1000 \text{ ml}} = 144.375 \text{ L/min}$$

Enter the subject's corrected maximum breathing capacity in the laboratory report.

4. To obtain the *predicted maximum breathing capacity,* we first must obtain the subject's body surface area from the Dubois body surface chart (fig. 6.10). Use a straightedge to connect the subject's height (left scale) with the subject's weight (right scale). Read the body surface area from the intersection of this line with the middle scale.

*Example*

$$\text{Height} = 5'9'' \text{ (175 cm)}$$
$$\text{Weight} = 155 \text{ lbs (70 kg)}$$
$$\text{Body surface area} = 1.86 \text{ square meters (m}^2)$$

Enter the subject's body surface area in the following space:

_____ m²

5. Use table 6.5 (for females) or 6.6 (for males) to determine the maximum breathing capacity that would be predicted for the subject's age.

*Example*

$$\text{Male, age 34, body surface area} = 1.86 \text{ m}^2$$

$$\text{Predicted maximum breathing capacity} = 128 \text{ L/min}$$

Enter the subject's predicted maximum breathing capacity in the following space:

_____ L/min

**Figure 6.10.** Dubois body surface chart. To find the body surface of a patient, locate the height in inches (or centimeters) on scale 1 and the weight in pounds (or kilograms) on scale 3, and place a straightedge (ruler) between these two points that will intersect scale 2 at the patient's surface area.

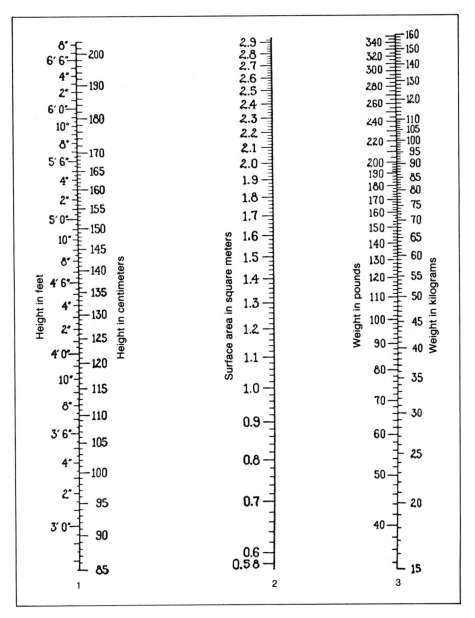

6. Determine the *percent predicted* value; this is the measured maximum breathing capacity divided by the predicted maximum breathing capacity multiplied by 100%.

*Example*

$$\frac{144 \text{ L/min (measured, from step 3)}}{128 \text{ L/min (predicted, from step 5)}} \times 100\%$$

$$= 112.5\%$$

Enter the subject's percent predicted value in the laboratory report.

> Measurements of maximum breathing capacity that are consistently below 80 percent of the predicted value suggest the presence of either an obstructive or a restrictive pulmonary disorder.

**Table 6.3** Predicted vital capacities, females (milliliters).

| Age | 146 | 148 | 150 | 152 | 154 | 156 | 158 | 160 | 162 | 164 | 166 | 168 | 170 | 172 | 174 | 176 | 178 | 180 | 182 | 184 | 186 | 188 | 190 | 192 | 194 |
|---|---|---|---|---|---|---|---|---|---|---|---|---|---|---|---|---|---|---|---|---|---|---|---|---|---|
| 16 | 2950 | 2990 | 3030 | 3070 | 3110 | 3150 | 3190 | 3230 | 3270 | 3310 | 3350 | 3390 | 3430 | 3470 | 3510 | 3550 | 3590 | 3630 | 3670 | 3715 | 3755 | 3800 | 3840 | 3880 | 3920 |
| 17 | 2935 | 2975 | 3015 | 3055 | 3095 | 3135 | 3175 | 3215 | 3255 | 3295 | 3335 | 3375 | 3415 | 3455 | 3495 | 3535 | 3575 | 3615 | 3655 | 3695 | 3740 | 3780 | 3820 | 3860 | 3900 |
| 18 | 2920 | 2960 | 3000 | 3040 | 3080 | 3120 | 3160 | 3200 | 3240 | 3280 | 3320 | 3360 | 3400 | 3440 | 3480 | 3520 | 3560 | 3600 | 3640 | 3680 | 3720 | 3760 | 3800 | 3840 | 3880 |
| 20 | 2890 | 2930 | 2970 | 3010 | 3050 | 3090 | 3130 | 3170 | 3210 | 3250 | 3290 | 3330 | 3370 | 3410 | 3450 | 3490 | 3525 | 3565 | 3605 | 3645 | 3695 | 3720 | 3760 | 3800 | 3840 |
| 22 | 2860 | 2900 | 2940 | 2980 | 3020 | 3060 | 3095 | 3135 | 3175 | 3215 | 3255 | 3290 | 3330 | 3370 | 3410 | 3450 | 3490 | 3530 | 3570 | 3610 | 3650 | 3685 | 3725 | 3765 | 3800 |
| 24 | 2830 | 2870 | 2910 | 2950 | 2985 | 3025 | 3065 | 3100 | 3140 | 3180 | 3220 | 3260 | 3300 | 3335 | 3375 | 3415 | 3455 | 3490 | 3530 | 3570 | 3610 | 3650 | 3685 | 3725 | 3765 |
| 26 | 2800 | 2840 | 2880 | 2920 | 2960 | 3000 | 3035 | 3070 | 3110 | 3150 | 3190 | 3230 | 3265 | 3300 | 3340 | 3380 | 3420 | 3455 | 3495 | 3530 | 3570 | 3610 | 3650 | 3685 | 3725 |
| 28 | 2775 | 2810 | 2850 | 2890 | 2930 | 2965 | 3000 | 3040 | 3070 | 3115 | 3155 | 3190 | 3230 | 3270 | 3305 | 3345 | 3380 | 3420 | 3460 | 3495 | 3535 | 3570 | 3610 | 3650 | 3685 |
| 30 | 2745 | 2780 | 2820 | 2860 | 2895 | 2935 | 2970 | 3010 | 3045 | 3085 | 3120 | 3160 | 3195 | 3235 | 3270 | 3310 | 3345 | 3385 | 3420 | 3460 | 3495 | 3535 | 3570 | 3610 | 3645 |
| 32 | 2715 | 2750 | 2790 | 2825 | 2865 | 2900 | 2940 | 2975 | 3015 | 3050 | 3090 | 3125 | 3160 | 3200 | 3235 | 3275 | 3310 | 3350 | 3385 | 3425 | 3460 | 3495 | 3535 | 3570 | 3610 |
| 34 | 2685 | 2725 | 2760 | 2795 | 2835 | 2870 | 2910 | 2945 | 2980 | 3020 | 3055 | 3090 | 3130 | 3165 | 3200 | 3240 | 3275 | 3310 | 3350 | 3385 | 3425 | 3460 | 3495 | 3535 | 3570 |
| 36 | 2655 | 2695 | 2730 | 2765 | 2805 | 2840 | 2875 | 2910 | 2950 | 2985 | 3020 | 3060 | 3095 | 3130 | 3165 | 3205 | 3240 | 3275 | 3310 | 3350 | 3385 | 3420 | 3460 | 3495 | 3530 |
| 38 | 2630 | 2665 | 2700 | 2735 | 2770 | 2810 | 2845 | 2880 | 2915 | 2950 | 2990 | 3025 | 3060 | 3095 | 3130 | 3170 | 3205 | 3240 | 3275 | 3310 | 3350 | 3385 | 3420 | 3455 | 3490 |
| 40 | 2600 | 2635 | 2670 | 2705 | 2740 | 2775 | 2810 | 2850 | 2885 | 2920 | 2955 | 2990 | 3025 | 3060 | 3095 | 3135 | 3170 | 3205 | 3240 | 3275 | 3310 | 3345 | 3380 | 3420 | 3455 |
| 42 | 2570 | 2605 | 2640 | 2675 | 2710 | 2745 | 2780 | 2815 | 2850 | 2885 | 2920 | 2955 | 2990 | 3025 | 3060 | 3100 | 3135 | 3170 | 3205 | 3240 | 3275 | 3310 | 3345 | 3380 | 3415 |
| 44 | 2540 | 2575 | 2610 | 2645 | 2680 | 2715 | 2750 | 2785 | 2820 | 2855 | 2890 | 2925 | 2960 | 2995 | 3030 | 3060 | 3095 | 3130 | 3165 | 3200 | 3235 | 3270 | 3305 | 3340 | 3375 |
| 46 | 2510 | 2545 | 2580 | 2615 | 2650 | 2685 | 2715 | 2750 | 2785 | 2820 | 2855 | 2890 | 2925 | 2960 | 2995 | 3030 | 3060 | 3095 | 3130 | 3165 | 3200 | 3235 | 3270 | 3305 | 3340 |
| 48 | 2480 | 2515 | 2550 | 2585 | 2620 | 2650 | 2685 | 2715 | 2750 | 2785 | 2820 | 2855 | 2890 | 2925 | 2960 | 2995 | 3030 | 3060 | 3095 | 3130 | 3160 | 3195 | 3230 | 3265 | 3300 |
| 50 | 2455 | 2485 | 2520 | 2555 | 2590 | 2625 | 2655 | 2690 | 2720 | 2755 | 2785 | 2820 | 2855 | 2890 | 2925 | 2955 | 2990 | 3025 | 3060 | 3090 | 3125 | 3155 | 3190 | 3225 | 3260 |
| 52 | 2425 | 2455 | 2490 | 2525 | 2555 | 2590 | 2625 | 2655 | 2690 | 2720 | 2755 | 2790 | 2820 | 2855 | 2890 | 2925 | 2955 | 2990 | 3020 | 3055 | 3090 | 3125 | 3155 | 3190 | 3220 |
| 54 | 2395 | 2425 | 2460 | 2495 | 2530 | 2560 | 2590 | 2625 | 2655 | 2690 | 2720 | 2755 | 2790 | 2820 | 2855 | 2885 | 2920 | 2950 | 2985 | 3020 | 3050 | 3085 | 3115 | 3150 | 3180 |
| 56 | 2365 | 2400 | 2430 | 2460 | 2495 | 2525 | 2560 | 2590 | 2625 | 2655 | 2690 | 2720 | 2755 | 2790 | 2820 | 2855 | 2885 | 2920 | 2950 | 2980 | 3015 | 3045 | 3080 | 3110 | 3145 |
| 58 | 2335 | 2370 | 2400 | 2430 | 2460 | 2495 | 2525 | 2560 | 2590 | 2625 | 2655 | 2690 | 2720 | 2750 | 2785 | 2815 | 2850 | 2880 | 2920 | 2945 | 2975 | 3010 | 3040 | 3075 | 3105 |
| 60 | 2305 | 2340 | 2370 | 2400 | 2430 | 2460 | 2495 | 2525 | 2560 | 2590 | 2625 | 2655 | 2685 | 2720 | 2750 | 2780 | 2810 | 2845 | 2875 | 2915 | 2940 | 2970 | 3000 | 3035 | 3065 |
| 62 | 2280 | 2310 | 2340 | 2370 | 2405 | 2435 | 2465 | 2495 | 2525 | 2560 | 2590 | 2620 | 2655 | 2685 | 2715 | 2745 | 2775 | 2810 | 2840 | 2870 | 2900 | 2935 | 2965 | 2995 | 3025 |
| 64 | 2250 | 2280 | 2310 | 2340 | 2370 | 2400 | 2430 | 2465 | 2495 | 2525 | 2555 | 2585 | 2620 | 2650 | 2680 | 2710 | 2740 | 2770 | 2805 | 2835 | 2865 | 2895 | 2925 | 2955 | 2990 |
| 66 | 2220 | 2250 | 2280 | 2310 | 2340 | 2370 | 2400 | 2430 | 2460 | 2490 | 2525 | 2555 | 2585 | 2615 | 2645 | 2675 | 2705 | 2735 | 2765 | 2800 | 2825 | 2860 | 2890 | 2920 | 2950 |
| 68 | 2190 | 2220 | 2250 | 2280 | 2310 | 2340 | 2370 | 2400 | 2430 | 2460 | 2490 | 2520 | 2550 | 2580 | 2610 | 2640 | 2670 | 2700 | 2730 | 2760 | 2795 | 2820 | 2850 | 2880 | 2910 |
| 70 | 2160 | 2190 | 2220 | 2250 | 2280 | 2310 | 2340 | 2370 | 2400 | 2425 | 2455 | 2485 | 2515 | 2545 | 2575 | 2605 | 2635 | 2665 | 2695 | 2725 | 2755 | 2780 | 2810 | 2840 | 2870 |
| 72 | 2130 | 2160 | 2190 | 2220 | 2250 | 2280 | 2310 | 2335 | 2365 | 2395 | 2425 | 2455 | 2480 | 2510 | 2540 | 2570 | 2600 | 2630 | 2660 | 2685 | 2715 | 2745 | 2775 | 2805 | 2830 |
| 74 | 2100 | 2130 | 2160 | 2190 | 2220 | 2245 | 2275 | 2305 | 2335 | 2360 | 2390 | 2420 | 2450 | 2475 | 2505 | 2535 | 2565 | 2590 | 2620 | 2650 | 2680 | 2710 | 2740 | 2765 | 2795 |

Reprinted from Warren E. Collins, Inc., Braintree, MA.

**Table 6.4** Predicted vital capacities, males (milliliters).

| Age | | | | | | | | | | | | | Height in Centimeters | | | | | | | | | | | | |
|---|---|---|---|---|---|---|---|---|---|---|---|---|---|---|---|---|---|---|---|---|---|---|---|---|---|
| | 146 | 148 | 150 | 152 | 154 | 156 | 158 | 160 | 162 | 164 | 166 | 168 | 170 | 172 | 174 | 176 | 178 | 180 | 182 | 184 | 186 | 188 | 190 | 192 | 194 |
| 16 | 3765 | 3820 | 3870 | 3920 | 3975 | 4025 | 4075 | 4130 | 4180 | 4230 | 4285 | 4335 | 4385 | 4440 | 4490 | 4540 | 4590 | 4645 | 4695 | 4745 | 4800 | 4850 | 4900 | 4955 | 5005 |
| 18 | 3740 | 3790 | 3840 | 3890 | 3940 | 3995 | 4045 | 4095 | 4145 | 4200 | 4250 | 4300 | 4350 | 4405 | 4455 | 4505 | 4555 | 4610 | 4660 | 4710 | 4760 | 4815 | 4865 | 4915 | 4965 |
| 20 | 3710 | 3760 | 3810 | 3860 | 3910 | 3960 | 4015 | 4065 | 4115 | 4165 | 4215 | 4265 | 4320 | 4370 | 4420 | 4470 | 4520 | 4570 | 4625 | 4675 | 4725 | 4775 | 4825 | 4875 | 4930 |
| 22 | 3680 | 3730 | 3780 | 3830 | 3880 | 3930 | 3980 | 4030 | 4080 | 4135 | 4185 | 4235 | 4285 | 4335 | 4385 | 4435 | 4485 | 4535 | 4585 | 4635 | 4685 | 4735 | 4790 | 4840 | 4890 |
| 24 | 3635 | 3685 | 3735 | 3785 | 3835 | 3885 | 3935 | 3985 | 4035 | 4085 | 4135 | 4185 | 4235 | 4285 | 4330 | 4380 | 4430 | 4480 | 4530 | 4580 | 4630 | 4680 | 4730 | 4780 | 4830 |
| 26 | 3605 | 3655 | 3705 | 3755 | 3805 | 3855 | 3905 | 3955 | 4000 | 4050 | 4100 | 4150 | 4200 | 4250 | 4300 | 4350 | 4395 | 4445 | 4495 | 4545 | 4595 | 4645 | 4695 | 4740 | 4790 |
| 28 | 3575 | 3625 | 3675 | 3725 | 3775 | 3820 | 3870 | 3920 | 3970 | 4020 | 4070 | 4115 | 4165 | 4215 | 4265 | 4310 | 4360 | 4410 | 4460 | 4510 | 4555 | 4605 | 4655 | 4705 | 4755 |
| 30 | 3550 | 3595 | 3645 | 3695 | 3740 | 3790 | 3840 | 3890 | 3935 | 3985 | 4035 | 4080 | 4130 | 4180 | 4230 | 4275 | 4325 | 4375 | 4425 | 4470 | 4520 | 4570 | 4615 | 4665 | 4715 |
| 32 | 3520 | 3565 | 3615 | 3665 | 3710 | 3760 | 3810 | 3855 | 3905 | 3950 | 4000 | 4050 | 4095 | 4145 | 4195 | 4240 | 4290 | 4340 | 4385 | 4435 | 4485 | 4530 | 4580 | 4625 | 4675 |
| 34 | 3475 | 3525 | 3570 | 3620 | 3665 | 3715 | 3760 | 3810 | 3855 | 3905 | 3950 | 4000 | 4045 | 4095 | 4140 | 4190 | 4225 | 4285 | 4330 | 4380 | 4425 | 4475 | 4520 | 4570 | 4615 |
| 36 | 3445 | 3495 | 3540 | 3585 | 3635 | 3680 | 3730 | 3775 | 3825 | 3870 | 3920 | 3965 | 4010 | 4060 | 4105 | 4155 | 4200 | 4250 | 4295 | 4340 | 4390 | 4435 | 4485 | 4530 | 4580 |
| 38 | 3415 | 3465 | 3510 | 3555 | 3605 | 3650 | 3695 | 3745 | 3790 | 3840 | 3885 | 3930 | 3980 | 4025 | 4070 | 4120 | 4165 | 4210 | 4260 | 4305 | 4350 | 4400 | 4445 | 4495 | 4540 |
| 40 | 3385 | 3435 | 3480 | 3525 | 3575 | 3620 | 3665 | 3710 | 3760 | 3805 | 3850 | 3900 | 3945 | 3990 | 4035 | 4085 | 4130 | 4175 | 4220 | 4270 | 4315 | 4360 | 4410 | 4455 | 4500 |
| 42 | 3360 | 3405 | 3450 | 3495 | 3540 | 3590 | 3635 | 3680 | 3725 | 3770 | 3820 | 3865 | 3910 | 3955 | 4000 | 4050 | 4095 | 4140 | 4185 | 4230 | 4280 | 4325 | 4370 | 4415 | 4460 |
| 44 | 3315 | 3360 | 3405 | 3450 | 3495 | 3540 | 3585 | 3630 | 3675 | 3725 | 3770 | 3815 | 3860 | 3905 | 3950 | 3995 | 4040 | 4085 | 4130 | 4175 | 4220 | 4270 | 4315 | 4360 | 4405 |
| 46 | 3285 | 3330 | 3375 | 3420 | 3465 | 3510 | 3555 | 3600 | 3645 | 3690 | 3735 | 3780 | 3825 | 3870 | 3915 | 3960 | 4005 | 4050 | 4095 | 4140 | 4185 | 4230 | 4275 | 4320 | 4365 |
| 48 | 3255 | 3300 | 3345 | 3390 | 3435 | 3480 | 3525 | 3570 | 3615 | 3655 | 3700 | 3745 | 3790 | 3835 | 3880 | 3925 | 3970 | 4015 | 4060 | 4105 | 4150 | 4190 | 4235 | 4280 | 4325 |
| 50 | 3210 | 3255 | 3300 | 3345 | 3390 | 3430 | 3475 | 3520 | 3565 | 3610 | 3650 | 3695 | 3740 | 3785 | 3830 | 3870 | 3915 | 3960 | 4005 | 4050 | 4090 | 4135 | 4180 | 4225 | 4270 |
| 52 | 3185 | 3225 | 3270 | 3315 | 3355 | 3400 | 3445 | 3490 | 3530 | 3575 | 3620 | 3660 | 3705 | 3750 | 3795 | 3835 | 3880 | 3925 | 3970 | 4010 | 4055 | 4100 | 4140 | 4185 | 4230 |
| 54 | 3155 | 3195 | 3240 | 3285 | 3325 | 3370 | 3415 | 3455 | 3500 | 3540 | 3585 | 3630 | 3670 | 3715 | 3760 | 3800 | 3845 | 3890 | 3930 | 3975 | 4020 | 4060 | 4105 | 4145 | 4190 |
| 56 | 3125 | 3165 | 3210 | 3255 | 3295 | 3340 | 3380 | 3425 | 3465 | 3510 | 3550 | 3595 | 3640 | 3680 | 3725 | 3765 | 3810 | 3850 | 3895 | 3940 | 3980 | 4025 | 4065 | 4110 | 4150 |
| 58 | 3080 | 3125 | 3165 | 3210 | 3250 | 3290 | 3335 | 3375 | 3420 | 3460 | 3500 | 3545 | 3585 | 3630 | 3670 | 3715 | 3755 | 3800 | 3840 | 3880 | 3925 | 3965 | 4010 | 4050 | 4095 |
| 60 | 3050 | 3095 | 3135 | 3175 | 3220 | 3260 | 3300 | 3345 | 3385 | 3430 | 3470 | 3500 | 3555 | 3595 | 3635 | 3680 | 3720 | 3760 | 3805 | 3845 | 3885 | 3930 | 3970 | 4015 | 4055 |
| 62 | 3020 | 3060 | 3110 | 3150 | 3190 | 3230 | 3270 | 3310 | 3350 | 3390 | 3440 | 3480 | 3520 | 3560 | 3600 | 3640 | 3680 | 3730 | 3770 | 3810 | 3850 | 3890 | 3930 | 3970 | 4020 |
| 64 | 2990 | 3030 | 3080 | 3120 | 3160 | 3200 | 3240 | 3280 | 3320 | 3360 | 3400 | 3440 | 3490 | 3530 | 3570 | 3610 | 3650 | 3690 | 3730 | 3770 | 3810 | 3850 | 3900 | 3940 | 3980 |
| 66 | 2950 | 2990 | 3030 | 3070 | 3110 | 3150 | 3190 | 3230 | 3270 | 3310 | 3350 | 3390 | 3430 | 3470 | 3510 | 3550 | 3600 | 3640 | 3680 | 3720 | 3760 | 3800 | 3840 | 3880 | 3920 |
| 68 | 2920 | 2960 | 3000 | 3040 | 3080 | 3120 | 3160 | 3200 | 3240 | 3280 | 3320 | 3360 | 3400 | 3440 | 3480 | 3520 | 3560 | 3600 | 3640 | 3680 | 3720 | 3760 | 3800 | 3840 | 3880 |
| 70 | 2890 | 2930 | 2970 | 3010 | 3050 | 3090 | 3130 | 3170 | 3210 | 3250 | 3290 | 3330 | 3370 | 3410 | 3450 | 3480 | 3520 | 3560 | 3600 | 3640 | 3680 | 3720 | 3760 | 3800 | 3840 |
| 72 | 2860 | 2900 | 2940 | 2980 | 3020 | 3060 | 3100 | 3140 | 3180 | 3210 | 3250 | 3290 | 3330 | 3370 | 3410 | 3450 | 3490 | 3530 | 3570 | 3610 | 3650 | 3680 | 3720 | 3760 | 3800 |
| 74 | 2820 | 2860 | 2900 | 2930 | 2970 | 3010 | 3050 | 3090 | 3130 | 3170 | 3200 | 3240 | 3280 | 3320 | 3360 | 3400 | 3440 | 3470 | 3510 | 3550 | 3590 | 3630 | 3670 | 3710 | 3740 |

Reprinted from Warren E. Collins, Inc., Braintree, MA.

# Table 6.5 Predicted maximal breathing capacity, females (liters per minute).

| Age | 1.40 | 1.42 | 1.44 | 1.46 | 1.48 | 1.50 | 1.52 | 1.54 | 1.56 | 1.58 | 1.60 | 1.62 | 1.64 | 1.66 | 1.68 | 1.70 | 1.72 | 1.74 |
|-----|------|------|------|------|------|------|------|------|------|------|------|------|------|------|------|------|------|------|
| | | | | | | | | Body Surface Area | | | | | | | | | | |
| 16 | 89 | 91 | 92 | 93 | 94 | 96 | 97 | 98 | 100 | 101 | 102 | 103 | 105 | 106 | 107 | 108 | 110 | 111 |
| 18 | 88 | 89 | 91 | 92 | 93 | 94 | 96 | 97 | 98 | 99 | 101 | 102 | 103 | 104 | 106 | 107 | 108 | 109 |
| 20 | 87 | 88 | 89 | 90 | 92 | 93 | 94 | 95 | 97 | 98 | 99 | 100 | 102 | 103 | 104 | 105 | 106 | 108 |
| 22 | 85 | 87 | 88 | 89 | 90 | 92 | 93 | 94 | 95 | 96 | 98 | 99 | 100 | 101 | 102 | 104 | 105 | 106 |
| 24 | 84 | 85 | 86 | 88 | 89 | 90 | 91 | 92 | 94 | 95 | 96 | 97 | 98 | 100 | 101 | 102 | 103 | 104 |
| 26 | 83 | 84 | 85 | 86 | 87 | 89 | 90 | 91 | 92 | 93 | 94 | 96 | 97 | 98 | 99 | 100 | 101 | 103 |
| 28 | 81 | 83 | 84 | 85 | 86 | 87 | 88 | 89 | 91 | 92 | 93 | 94 | 95 | 96 | 98 | 99 | 100 | 101 |
| 30 | 80 | 81 | 82 | 84 | 85 | 86 | 87 | 88 | 89 | 90 | 92 | 93 | 94 | 95 | 96 | 97 | 98 | 100 |
| 32 | 79 | 80 | 81 | 82 | 83 | 84 | 85 | 87 | 88 | 89 | 90 | 91 | 92 | 93 | 94 | 96 | 97 | 98 |
| 34 | 77 | 79 | 80 | 81 | 82 | 83 | 84 | 85 | 86 | 87 | 88 | 90 | 91 | 92 | 93 | 94 | 95 | 96 |
| 36 | 76 | 77 | 78 | 79 | 80 | 81 | 83 | 84 | 85 | 86 | 87 | 88 | 89 | 90 | 91 | 92 | 93 | 94 |
| 38 | 75 | 76 | 77 | 78 | 79 | 80 | 81 | 82 | 83 | 84 | 85 | 86 | 87 | 88 | 90 | 91 | 92 | 93 |
| 40 | 73 | 74 | 75 | 77 | 78 | 79 | 80 | 81 | 82 | 83 | 84 | 85 | 86 | 87 | 88 | 89 | 90 | 91 |
| 42 | 72 | 73 | 74 | 75 | 76 | 77 | 78 | 79 | 80 | 81 | 82 | 83 | 84 | 85 | 86 | 87 | 88 | 89 |
| 44 | 71 | 72 | 73 | 74 | 75 | 76 | 77 | 78 | 79 | 80 | 81 | 82 | 83 | 84 | 85 | 86 | 87 | 88 |
| 46 | 69 | 70 | 71 | 72 | 73 | 74 | 75 | 76 | 77 | 78 | 79 | 80 | 81 | 82 | 83 | 84 | 85 | 86 |
| 48 | 68 | 69 | 70 | 71 | 72 | 73 | 74 | 75 | 76 | 76 | 77 | 78 | 79 | 80 | 81 | 82 | 83 | 84 |
| 50 | 67 | 67 | 68 | 69 | 70 | 71 | 72 | 73 | 74 | 75 | 76 | 77 | 78 | 79 | 80 | 81 | 82 | 83 |
| 52 | 65 | 66 | 67 | 68 | 69 | 70 | 71 | 72 | 73 | 73 | 74 | 75 | 76 | 77 | 78 | 79 | 80 | 81 |
| 54 | 64 | 65 | 66 | 67 | 68 | 69 | 69 | 70 | 71 | 72 | 73 | 74 | 75 | 76 | 77 | 78 | 79 | 80 |
| 56 | 63 | 63 | 64 | 65 | 66 | 67 | 68 | 69 | 70 | 71 | 72 | 72 | 73 | 74 | 75 | 76 | 77 | 78 |
| 58 | 61 | 62 | 63 | 64 | 65 | 66 | 66 | 67 | 68 | 69 | 70 | 71 | 72 | 73 | 73 | 74 | 75 | 76 |
| 60 | 60 | 61 | 61 | 62 | 63 | 64 | 65 | 66 | 67 | 67 | 68 | 69 | 70 | 71 | 72 | 73 | 73 | 74 |
| 62 | 59 | 59 | 60 | 61 | 62 | 63 | 64 | 64 | 65 | 66 | 67 | 68 | 69 | 69 | 70 | 71 | 72 | 73 |
| 64 | 57 | 58 | 59 | 60 | 61 | 61 | 62 | 63 | 64 | 65 | 65 | 66 | 67 | 68 | 69 | 70 | 70 | 71 |
| 66 | 56 | 57 | 58 | 58 | 59 | 60 | 61 | 62 | 62 | 63 | 64 | 65 | 66 | 66 | 67 | 68 | 69 | 70 |
| 68 | 55 | 55 | 56 | 57 | 58 | 59 | 59 | 60 | 61 | 62 | 62 | 63 | 64 | 65 | 66 | 66 | 67 | 68 |
| 70 | 53 | 54 | 55 | 56 | 56 | 57 | 58 | 59 | 59 | 60 | 61 | 62 | 62 | 63 | 64 | 65 | 66 | 66 |
| 72 | 52 | 53 | 54 | 54 | 55 | 56 | 57 | 57 | 58 | 59 | 60 | 60 | 61 | 62 | 62 | 63 | 64 | 65 |
| 74 | 51 | 51 | 52 | 53 | 54 | 54 | 55 | 56 | 56 | 57 | 58 | 59 | 59 | 60 | 61 | 62 | 62 | 63 |
| 76 | 49 | 50 | 51 | 51 | 52 | 53 | 54 | 54 | 55 | 56 | 56 | 57 | 58 | 58 | 59 | 60 | 61 | 61 |
| 78 | 48 | 49 | 49 | 50 | 51 | 51 | 52 | 53 | 54 | 54 | 55 | 56 | 56 | 57 | 58 | 58 | 59 | 60 |
| 80 | 47 | 47 | 48 | 49 | 49 | 50 | 51 | 51 | 52 | 53 | 53 | 54 | 55 | 55 | 56 | 57 | 57 | 58 |

Reprinted from Warren E. Collins, Inc., Braintree, MA.

**Table 6.5** *continued*

### Body Surface Area

| 1.76 | 1.78 | 1.80 | 1.82 | 1.84 | 1.86 | 1.88 | 1.90 | 1.92 | 1.94 | 1.96 | 1.98 | 2.00 | 2.02 | 2.04 | 2.06 | 2.08 | 2.10 |
|---|---|---|---|---|---|---|---|---|---|---|---|---|---|---|---|---|---|
| 112 | 114 | 115 | 116 | 117 | 119 | 120 | 121 | 122 | 124 | 125 | 126 | 128 | 129 | 130 | 132 | 133 | 134 |
| 111 | 112 | 113 | 114 | 116 | 117 | 118 | 120 | 121 | 122 | 123 | 125 | 126 | 127 | 128 | 130 | 131 | 132 |
| 109 | 110 | 111 | 113 | 114 | 115 | 116 | 118 | 119 | 120 | 121 | 123 | 124 | 125 | 126 | 128 | 129 | 130 |
| 107 | 109 | 110 | 111 | 112 | 113 | 115 | 116 | 117 | 118 | 120 | 121 | 122 | 123 | 124 | 126 | 127 | 128 |
| 106 | 107 | 108 | 109 | 110 | 112 | 113 | 114 | 115 | 116 | 118 | 119 | 120 | 121 | 122 | 124 | 125 | 126 |
| 104 | 105 | 106 | 107 | 109 | 110 | 111 | 112 | 113 | 114 | 116 | 117 | 118 | 119 | 120 | 122 | 123 | 124 |
| 102 | 103 | 105 | 106 | 107 | 108 | 109 | 110 | 112 | 113 | 114 | 115 | 116 | 117 | 119 | 120 | 121 | 122 |
| 101 | 102 | 103 | 104 | 105 | 106 | 108 | 109 | 110 | 111 | 112 | 113 | 114 | 116 | 117 | 118 | 119 | 120 |
| 99 | 100 | 101 | 102 | 103 | 104 | 106 | 107 | 108 | 109 | 110 | 111 | 112 | 114 | 115 | 116 | 117 | 118 |
| 97 | 98 | 100 | 101 | 102 | 103 | 104 | 105 | 106 | 107 | 108 | 109 | 111 | 112 | 113 | 114 | 115 | 116 |
| 96 | 97 | 98 | 99 | 100 | 101 | 102 | 103 | 104 | 105 | 106 | 108 | 109 | 110 | 111 | 112 | 113 | 114 |
| 94 | 95 | 96 | 97 | 98 | 99 | 100 | 101 | 102 | 103 | 104 | 106 | 107 | 108 | 109 | 110 | 111 | 112 |
| 92 | 93 | 94 | 95 | 96 | 97 | 99 | 100 | 101 | 102 | 103 | 104 | 105 | 106 | 107 | 108 | 109 | 110 |
| 90 | 91 | 93 | 94 | 95 | 96 | 97 | 98 | 99 | 100 | 101 | 102 | 103 | 104 | 105 | 106 | 107 | 108 |
| 89 | 90 | 91 | 92 | 93 | 94 | 95 | 96 | 97 | 98 | 99 | 100 | 101 | 102 | 103 | 104 | 105 | 106 |
| 87 | 88 | 89 | 90 | 91 | 92 | 93 | 94 | 95 | 96 | 97 | 98 | 99 | 100 | 101 | 102 | 103 | 104 |
| 85 | 86 | 87 | 88 | 89 | 90 | 91 | 92 | 93 | 94 | 95 | 96 | 97 | 98 | 99 | 100 | 101 | 102 |
| 84 | 85 | 86 | 87 | 88 | 89 | 90 | 90 | 91 | 92 | 93 | 94 | 95 | 96 | 97 | 98 | 99 | 100 |
| 82 | 83 | 84 | 85 | 86 | 86 | 87 | 88 | 89 | 90 | 91 | 92 | 93 | 94 | 95 | 96 | 97 | 98 |
| 80 | 81 | 82 | 83 | 84 | 85 | 86 | 87 | 88 | 89 | 90 | 90 | 91 | 92 | 93 | 94 | 95 | 96 |
| 79 | 80 | 80 | 81 | 82 | 83 | 84 | 85 | 86 | 87 | 88 | 89 | 89 | 90 | 91 | 92 | 93 | 94 |
| 77 | 78 | 79 | 80 | 80 | 81 | 82 | 83 | 84 | 85 | 86 | 87 | 87 | 88 | 89 | 90 | 91 | 92 |
| 75 | 76 | 77 | 78 | 79 | 79 | 80 | 81 | 82 | 83 | 84 | 85 | 85 | 86 | 87 | 88 | 89 | 90 |
| 74 | 74 | 75 | 76 | 77 | 78 | 79 | 79 | 80 | 81 | 82 | 83 | 84 | 84 | 85 | 86 | 87 | 88 |
| 72 | 73 | 74 | 74 | 75 | 76 | 77 | 78 | 79 | 79 | 80 | 81 | 82 | 83 | 83 | 84 | 85 | 86 |
| 70 | 71 | 72 | 73 | 74 | 74 | 75 | 76 | 77 | 78 | 78 | 79 | 80 | 81 | 82 | 82 | 83 | 84 |
| 69 | 70 | 70 | 71 | 72 | 73 | 73 | 74 | 75 | 76 | 76 | 77 | 78 | 79 | 80 | 80 | 81 | 82 |
| 67 | 68 | 69 | 69 | 70 | 71 | 72 | 72 | 73 | 74 | 75 | 75 | 76 | 77 | 78 | 78 | 79 | 80 |
| 65 | 66 | 67 | 68 | 68 | 69 | 70 | 71 | 71 | 72 | 73 | 74 | 74 | 75 | 76 | 77 | 77 | 78 |
| 64 | 64 | 65 | 66 | 67 | 67 | 68 | 69 | 70 | 70 | 71 | 72 | 72 | 73 | 74 | 75 | 75 | 76 |
| 62 | 63 | 63 | 64 | 65 | 65 | 66 | 67 | 68 | 68 | 69 | 70 | 70 | 71 | 72 | 73 | 73 | 74 |
| 60 | 61 | 62 | 62 | 63 | 64 | 64 | 65 | 66 | 67 | 67 | 68 | 69 | 69 | 70 | 71 | 71 | 72 |
| 59 | 59 | 60 | 61 | 61 | 62 | 63 | 63 | 64 | 65 | 65 | 66 | 67 | 67 | 68 | 69 | 69 | 70 |

# Table 6.6 Predicted maximal breathing capacity, males (liters per minute).

| Age | 1.40 | 1.42 | 1.44 | 1.46 | 1.48 | 1.50 | 1.52 | 1.54 | 1.56 | 1.58 | 1.60 | 1.62 | 1.64 | 1.66 | 1.68 | 1.70 | 1.72 | 1.74 |
|---|---|---|---|---|---|---|---|---|---|---|---|---|---|---|---|---|---|---|
| | | | | | | | | Body Surface Area | | | | | | | | | | |
| 16 | 110 | 111 | 113 | 114 | 116 | 118 | 119 | 121 | 122 | 124 | 125 | 127 | 129 | 130 | 132 | 133 | 135 | 136 |
| 18 | 108 | 110 | 111 | 113 | 115 | 116 | 118 | 119 | 121 | 122 | 124 | 125 | 127 | 128 | 130 | 132 | 133 | 135 |
| 20 | 107 | 108 | 110 | 111 | 113 | 114 | 116 | 118 | 119 | 121 | 122 | 124 | 125 | 127 | 128 | 130 | 131 | 133 |
| 22 | 105 | 107 | 108 | 110 | 111 | 113 | 114 | 116 | 117 | 119 | 120 | 122 | 123 | 125 | 126 | 128 | 129 | 131 |
| 24 | 104 | 105 | 107 | 108 | 110 | 111 | 113 | 114 | 116 | 117 | 119 | 120 | 122 | 123 | 125 | 126 | 128 | 129 |
| 26 | 102 | 104 | 105 | 107 | 108 | 110 | 111 | 112 | 114 | 115 | 117 | 118 | 120 | 121 | 123 | 124 | 126 | 127 |
| 28 | 101 | 102 | 104 | 105 | 107 | 108 | 109 | 111 | 112 | 114 | 115 | 117 | 118 | 120 | 121 | 122 | 124 | 125 |
| 30 | 99 | 101 | 102 | 104 | 105 | 107 | 108 | 109 | 111 | 112 | 114 | 115 | 116 | 118 | 119 | 121 | 122 | 124 |
| 32 | 98 | 99 | 101 | 102 | 104 | 105 | 106 | 108 | 109 | 111 | 112 | 113 | 115 | 116 | 118 | 119 | 120 | 122 |
| 34 | 96 | 98 | 99 | 101 | 102 | 103 | 105 | 106 | 107 | 109 | 110 | 112 | 113 | 114 | 116 | 117 | 119 | 120 |
| 36 | 95 | 96 | 98 | 99 | 100 | 102 | 103 | 104 | 106 | 107 | 108 | 110 | 111 | 113 | 114 | 115 | 117 | 118 |
| 38 | 93 | 95 | 96 | 97 | 99 | 100 | 101 | 103 | 104 | 105 | 107 | 108 | 109 | 111 | 112 | 113 | 115 | 116 |
| 40 | 92 | 93 | 95 | 96 | 97 | 99 | 100 | 101 | 102 | 104 | 105 | 106 | 108 | 109 | 110 | 112 | 113 | 114 |
| 42 | 91 | 92 | 93 | 94 | 96 | 97 | 98 | 99 | 100 | 102 | 103 | 105 | 106 | 107 | 109 | 110 | 111 | 113 |
| 44 | 89 | 90 | 92 | 93 | 94 | 95 | 97 | 98 | 99 | 100 | 102 | 103 | 104 | 106 | 107 | 108 | 109 | 111 |
| 46 | 88 | 89 | 90 | 91 | 93 | 94 | 95 | 96 | 98 | 99 | 100 | 101 | 103 | 104 | 105 | 106 | 108 | 109 |
| 48 | 86 | 87 | 88 | 90 | 91 | 92 | 93 | 95 | 96 | 97 | 98 | 100 | 101 | 102 | 103 | 105 | 106 | 107 |
| 50 | 85 | 86 | 87 | 88 | 89 | 91 | 92 | 93 | 94 | 95 | 97 | 98 | 99 | 100 | 101 | 103 | 104 | 105 |
| 52 | 83 | 84 | 85 | 86 | 88 | 89 | 90 | 91 | 92 | 94 | 95 | 96 | 97 | 98 | 99 | 100 | 102 | 103 |
| 54 | 82 | 84 | 85 | 86 | 87 | 88 | 89 | 90 | 91 | 92 | 93 | 94 | 96 | 97 | 98 | 99 | 100 | 101 |
| 56 | 80 | 81 | 82 | 84 | 85 | 86 | 87 | 88 | 89 | 91 | 92 | 93 | 94 | 95 | 96 | 97 | 99 | 100 |
| 58 | 79 | 80 | 81 | 82 | 83 | 84 | 85 | 87 | 88 | 89 | 90 | 91 | 92 | 93 | 94 | 96 | 97 | 98 |
| 60 | 77 | 78 | 79 | 80 | 82 | 83 | 84 | 85 | 86 | 87 | 88 | 89 | 90 | 91 | 93 | 94 | 95 | 96 |
| 62 | 76 | 77 | 78 | 79 | 80 | 81 | 82 | 83 | 84 | 85 | 86 | 87 | 89 | 90 | 91 | 92 | 93 | 94 |
| 64 | 74 | 75 | 76 | 77 | 78 | 80 | 81 | 82 | 83 | 84 | 85 | 86 | 87 | 88 | 89 | 90 | 91 | 92 |
| 66 | 73 | 74 | 75 | 76 | 77 | 78 | 79 | 80 | 81 | 82 | 83 | 84 | 85 | 86 | 87 | 88 | 89 | 90 |
| 68 | 71 | 72 | 73 | 74 | 75 | 76 | 77 | 78 | 79 | 80 | 81 | 82 | 83 | 84 | 85 | 86 | 87 | 88 |
| 70 | 70 | 71 | 72 | 73 | 74 | 75 | 76 | 77 | 78 | 79 | 80 | 81 | 82 | 83 | 84 | 85 | 86 | 87 |
| 72 | 68 | 69 | 70 | 71 | 72 | 73 | 74 | 75 | 76 | 77 | 78 | 79 | 80 | 81 | 82 | 83 | 84 | 85 |
| 74 | 67 | 68 | 69 | 70 | 71 | 72 | 73 | 73 | 74 | 75 | 76 | 77 | 78 | 79 | 80 | 81 | 82 | 83 |
| 76 | 65 | 66 | 67 | 68 | 69 | 70 | 71 | 72 | 73 | 74 | 75 | 76 | 77 | 78 | 78 | 79 | 80 | 81 |

Reprinted from Warren E. Collins, Inc., Braintree, MA.

**Table 6.6** *continued*

## Body Surface Area

| 1.76 | 1.78 | 1.80 | 1.82 | 1.84 | 1.86 | 1.88 | 1.90 | 1.92 | 1.94 | 1.96 | 1.98 | 2.00 | 2.02 | 2.04 | 2.06 | 2.08 | 2.10 |
|------|------|------|------|------|------|------|------|------|------|------|------|------|------|------|------|------|------|
| 138 | 140 | 141 | 143 | 144 | 146 | 147 | 149 | 151 | 152 | 154 | 155 | 157 | 158 | 160 | 162 | 163 | 165 |
| 136 | 138 | 139 | 141 | 143 | 144 | 146 | 147 | 149 | 150 | 152 | 153 | 155 | 156 | 158 | 159 | 161 | 163 |
| 135 | 136 | 137 | 138 | 140 | 142 | 143 | 145 | 146 | 148 | 150 | 151 | 153 | 154 | 156 | 157 | 159 | 160 |
| 132 | 134 | 135 | 137 | 138 | 140 | 141 | 143 | 144 | 146 | 147 | 149 | 150 | 152 | 153 | 155 | 156 | 158 |
| 131 | 132 | 134 | 135 | 137 | 138 | 139 | 141 | 142 | 144 | 145 | 147 | 148 | 150 | 151 | 153 | 154 | 156 |
| 128 | 130 | 131 | 133 | 134 | 136 | 137 | 139 | 140 | 142 | 143 | 145 | 146 | 147 | 149 | 150 | 152 | 153 |
| 127 | 128 | 130 | 131 | 132 | 134 | 135 | 137 | 138 | 140 | 141 | 143 | 144 | 145 | 147 | 148 | 150 | 151 |
| 125 | 126 | 128 | 129 | 131 | 132 | 133 | 135 | 136 | 138 | 139 | 141 | 142 | 143 | 145 | 146 | 148 | 149 |
| 123 | 125 | 126 | 127 | 129 | 130 | 132 | 133 | 134 | 136 | 137 | 139 | 140 | 141 | 143 | 144 | 146 | 147 |
| 121 | 123 | 124 | 125 | 127 | 128 | 130 | 131 | 132 | 134 | 135 | 136 | 138 | 139 | 141 | 142 | 143 | 145 |
| 119 | 121 | 122 | 123 | 125 | 126 | 127 | 129 | 130 | 131 | 133 | 134 | 136 | 137 | 138 | 140 | 141 | 142 |
| 117 | 119 | 120 | 121 | 123 | 124 | 125 | 127 | 128 | 129 | 131 | 132 | 133 | 135 | 136 | 137 | 139 | 140 |
| 116 | 117 | 118 | 120 | 121 | 122 | 124 | 125 | 126 | 127 | 129 | 130 | 131 | 133 | 134 | 135 | 137 | 138 |
| 114 | 115 | 116 | 118 | 119 | 120 | 122 | 123 | 124 | 126 | 127 | 128 | 129 | 131 | 132 | 133 | 135 | 136 |
| 112 | 113 | 114 | 116 | 117 | 118 | 120 | 121 | 122 | 123 | 125 | 126 | 127 | 128 | 130 | 131 | 132 | 134 |
| 110 | 111 | 113 | 114 | 115 | 116 | 118 | 119 | 120 | 121 | 123 | 124 | 125 | 126 | 128 | 129 | 130 | 131 |
| 108 | 109 | 111 | 112 | 113 | 114 | 116 | 117 | 118 | 119 | 121 | 122 | 123 | 124 | 125 | 127 | 128 | 129 |
| 106 | 108 | 109 | 110 | 111 | 112 | 114 | 115 | 116 | 117 | 118 | 120 | 121 | 122 | 123 | 124 | 126 | 127 |
| 104 | 105 | 107 | 108 | 109 | 110 | 111 | 112 | 114 | 115 | 116 | 117 | 118 | 120 | 121 | 122 | 123 | 124 |
| 103 | 104 | 105 | 106 | 107 | 108 | 110 | 111 | 112 | 113 | 114 | 115 | 117 | 118 | 119 | 120 | 121 | 122 |
| 101 | 102 | 103 | 104 | 105 | 107 | 108 | 109 | 110 | 111 | 112 | 113 | 115 | 116 | 117 | 118 | 119 | 120 |
| 99 | 100 | 101 | 102 | 103 | 105 | 106 | 107 | 108 | 109 | 110 | 111 | 112 | 114 | 115 | 116 | 117 | 118 |
| 97 | 98 | 99 | 100 | 101 | 102 | 104 | 105 | 106 | 107 | 108 | 109 | 110 | 111 | 112 | 114 | 115 | 116 |
| 95 | 96 | 97 | 98 | 99 | 100 | 102 | 103 | 104 | 105 | 106 | 107 | 108 | 109 | 110 | 111 | 112 | 113 |
| 93 | 94 | 95 | 96 | 98 | 99 | 100 | 101 | 102 | 103 | 104 | 105 | 106 | 107 | 108 | 109 | 110 | 111 |
| 91 | 92 | 93 | 94 | 95 | 97 | 98 | 99 | 100 | 101 | 102 | 103 | 104 | 105 | 106 | 107 | 108 | 109 |
| 89 | 90 | 91 | 92 | 93 | 94 | 96 | 97 | 98 | 99 | 100 | 101 | 102 | 103 | 104 | 105 | 106 | 107 |
| 88 | 89 | 90 | 91 | 92 | 93 | 94 | 95 | 96 | 97 | 98 | 99 | 100 | 101 | 102 | 103 | 104 | 105 |
| 86 | 87 | 88 | 89 | 90 | 91 | 92 | 93 | 94 | 95 | 96 | 97 | 98 | 99 | 100 | 101 | 102 | 102 |
| 84 | 85 | 86 | 87 | 88 | 89 | 90 | 91 | 92 | 92 | 93 | 94 | 95 | 96 | 97 | 98 | 99 | 100 |
| 82 | 83 | 84 | 85 | 86 | 87 | 88 | 89 | 90 | 91 | 92 | 92 | 93 | 94 | 95 | 96 | 97 | 98 |

# Laboratory Report 6.1

Name _____

Date _____

Section _____

## Data from Exercise 6.1

### A. Measurement of Simple Lung Volumes and Capacities

Enter your data (corrected to BTPS) under the *Measured* column, and enter your calculated *Percent Predicted,* in the table below:

| | Measured | Predicted | Percent Predicted |
|---|---|---|---|
| TV | | 500 ml (avg. normal) | |
| IC | | 2800 ml (avg. normal) | |
| ERV | | 1200 ml (avg. normal) | |
| VC | | (from tables) | |
| RV | leave blank | (VC × factor) | leave blank |
| TLC | leave blank | (VC × factor) | leave blank |

### B. Measurement of Forced Expiratory Volume and Maximum Breathing Capacity

1. Enter your measured and predicted $FEV_{1.0}$ in the spaces below:

   Measured = _____ %      Predicted range = _____ %

2. Enter your measured and predicted maximum breathing capacity in the spaces below:

   Measured = _____ L/min      Percent predicted = _____ %

3. Compare your values to the normal ranges, and enter your conclusions in the space below:

## Questions for Exercise 6.1

1. Identify the following lung volumes and capacities:

   (a) maximum amount of air that can be expired after a maximum expiration _____

   (b) maximum amount of air that can be inspired after a normal inspiration _____

   (c) maximum amount of air that can be inspired after a normal expiration _____

   (d) the amount of air left in the lungs after a maximum expiration _____

Calculate the following values for the spirogram shown below (correct values to BTPS):

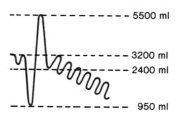

2. Tidal volume _____

3. Inspiratory capacity _____

4. Expiratory reserve volume _____

5. Vital capacity _____

6. Calculate the $FEV_{1.0}$ value for the spirogram shown below:

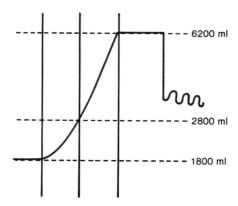

$FEV_{1.0}$ _____ %

7. Pulmonary disorders in which the alveoli are normal but there is an abnormally high resistance to airflow are categorized as _____ disorders.

8. An example of one of the above disorders is _____ .

9. One pulmonary test for the above disorder is the _____ .

10. Does your chest expand because your lungs inflate, or do your lungs inflate because your chest expands? Explain.

11. Distinguish between obstructive and restrictive pulmonary diseases. How does spirometry aid in their diagnosis?

# Total Minute Volume and Oxygen Consumption: Effect of Exercise

Total minute volume measures the rate and depth of breathing; the rate of oxygen consumption is a measure of the metabolic rate. These measurements are related by the fact that the total minute volume is adjusted to keep pace with changes in the metabolic rate.

## Objectives

1. Define the term *total minute volume,* and explain how it is obtained.
2. Describe how the rate of oxygen consumption is measured, and explain how this measurement is related to the metabolic rate.
3. Describe the relationship between the total minute volume and the rate of oxygen consumption, and explain how and why these measurements are changed during exercise.
4. Explain why oxygen consumption and total minute volume remain high for a time after exercise has ceased.

## Materials

1. Spirometer (Collins 9-liter respirometer)
2. Disposable mouthpieces

The volume of air exhaled in a minute of resting breathing is known as the **total minute volume** and equal to the product of tidal volume (milliliters per breath) and the frequency of breathing (breaths per minute). Only about two-thirds of this volume actually reaches the alveoli (this is known as the *alveolar minute volume*). The remaining one-third stays within the dead space of the lungs.

**Gas exchange** occurs in the alveoli of the lungs; oxygen diffuses from the alveolar air into the blood, and carbon dioxide diffuses from the blood into the alveolar air. The blood leaving the lungs is thus enriched in oxygen and depleted in carbon dioxide. When the blood reaches the tissue capillaries, oxygen diffuses from the blood into the tissues, where it can be used by the cells in *aerobic respiration.* Carbon dioxide, which is a waste product of aerobic respiration, diffuses from the tissues into the capillary blood.

Since oxygen is consumed by the body's cells in aerobic respiration, the amount of air that is trapped within the oxygen bell of the respirometer decreases as the subject breathes through the mouthpiece. (The exhaled carbon dioxide is eliminated by soda lime within the respirometer.) Thus, oxygen consumption results in an *upward slope* of the tidal volume measurements, so that the amount of oxygen consumed can be determined by the difference between milliliter levels before and after one minute of resting ventilation (fig. 6.11).

The rate at which oxygen is consumed and carbon dioxide is produced by the body cells during aerobic respiration is related to the **metabolic rate** of the person. When the individual is relaxed and comfortable and has not eaten for twelve to fifteen hours, the metabolic rate is lowest. This is referred to as the *basal metabolic rate (BMR).* Under these conditions, the metabolic rate is set primarily by the activity of the thyroid gland; in the past, measurements of BMR were used to assess thyroid function.

When a person exercises, however, the metabolic rate increases greatly (the metabolism of muscles can increase as much as sixtyfold during strenuous exercise). As a result, oxygen is consumed and carbon dioxide produced at much more rapid rates than during resting conditions. The respiratory system keeps pace with this increased demand by increasing the total minute volume.

The *respiratory centers* in the medulla oblongata and pons areas of the brain stem regulate breathing via motor nerves to the respiratory muscles. The activity of the respiratory centers, however, is itself influenced by those chemical changes in the blood that are affected by breathing. Specifically, a rise in blood $CO_2$ or a fall in blood pH (which may result from increased carbonic acid formation) stimulates **chemoreceptors** in the *aortic* and *carotid bodies* and in the *medulla oblongata*, which in turn activate the brain stem respiratory centers through sensory neurons. Changes in blood oxygen levels do not usually serve as a cue that regulates breathing, although a significant fall in blood oxygen will stimulate increased ventilation.

It is currently believed that the increase in total minute volume that occurs during exercise is due in part to an increase in $CO_2$ production, although concentrations of arterial $CO_2$ during exercise are not usually increased. Sensory feedback from the exercising muscles may also contribute to the *hyperpnea* (increased breathing) of exercise.

Oxygen consumption and the total minute volume remain elevated immediately after exercise. This extra oxygen consumption (over resting levels) following exercise is called the *oxygen debt* and is used to oxidize lactic acid produced by anaerobic respiration of the muscles and to support an increased metabolism of the warmed muscles.

## Clinical Significance

*Hypoventilation* occurs when the alveoli are inadequately ventilated (reduced alveolar minute volume). This may be due to a reduction in the total minute volume, where either the tidal volume or the frequency of breathing is depressed, or to a pathological increase in lung dead space. The latter may be caused by any condition that affects lung tissue (e.g., emphysema) or by inadequate blood flow to the alveoli (an abnormal *ventilation/perfusion ratio*), where even alveoli that are adequately ventilated are incapable of oxygenating the blood. The amount of oxygen delivered to the muscles by the cardiopulmonary system during maximum exercise is a measure of physical conditioning or aerobic capacity.

### Procedure

1. Set the Collins respirometer to a speed of 32 mm/min. (At this speed the distance between two vertical lines is traversed in 1 minute.) Position the mouthpiece securely in the mouth, with the lips pursed tightly against it, and clamp the nostrils closed.
2. Under resting conditions, breathe into the respirometer in a normal fashion for one minute (that is, perform the procedure for measuring tidal volume—see exercise 6.1).

**Note:** *The tidal volume measurements must have an upward slope, indicating that oxygen is being consumed within the air trapped in the oxygen bell. If the slope is downward, there is air leaking into the system, usually through the corners of the mouth or the nose. In this event, reposition the mouthpiece, check the nose clamp, and begin the measurements again.*

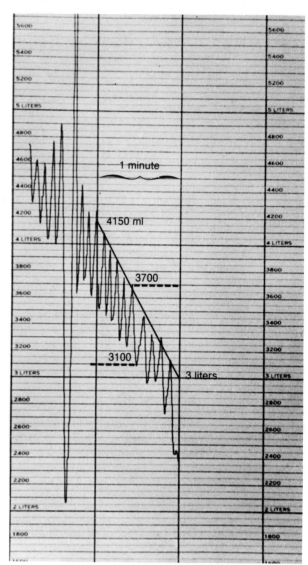

**Figure 6.11.** A spirogram showing tidal volume and vital capacity measurements. Note the rising slope of the tidal volume measurements, which indicates oxygen consumption.

3. Remove the chart from the kymograph drum, and determine the frequency of ventilation (number of breaths per minute) and the tidal volume (corrected to BTPS).

*Example (from fig. 6.11)*

    3700 ml (inhalation peak of tidal volume)
  − 3100 ml (exhalation trough of tidal volume)
    600 ml (uncorrected tidal volume)

      600 ml
  ×   1.1     (BTPS factor)
      660 ml (corrected tidal volume)

From figure 6.11, frequency = 10 breaths/min

Enter the subject's corrected tidal volume in the following space:

_____ ml

Enter the subject's frequency of ventilation in the following space:

_____ breaths/min

> The average frequency is 14 breaths per minute.

4. Determine the subject's *total minute volume* at rest by multiplying the frequency of ventilation by the tidal volume. Enter this value in the data table in your laboratory report.

*Example (from fig. 6.11)*

660 ml/breath × 10 breaths/min
= 6600 ml/min total minute volume

> The average total minute volume is 6750 ml/min.

5. Using a straightedge, draw a line that averages either the peaks or the troughs of the tidal volume measurements. Determine the *oxygen consumption per minute* by subtracting the milliliters where this straight line intersects two vertical chart lines at the beginning and end of 1 minute.

*Example (from fig. 6.11)*

Using a line that averages the peaks:

$$\begin{aligned} 4150 \text{ ml (at end of 1 minute)} \\ \underline{-3000 \text{ ml (at beginning of 1 minute)}} \\ 1150 \text{ ml (oxygen consumption)} \end{aligned}$$

Enter the resting oxygen consumption in the data table in your laboratory report.

6. The subject should now perform light exercise, such as five to ten jumping jacks. Then repeat the respirometer measurements and data calculation described in steps 1–5.

**Note:** *If breathing into the respirometer becomes difficult after exercise, the subject should stop the procedure. Results obtained in less than a minute can then be extrapolated to one minute. Alternatively, the bell can be filled with 100% oxygen to prevent the possible occurrence of hypoxia.*

Enter the corrected tidal volume after exercise in the following space:

_____ ml

Enter the frequency of ventilation after exercise in the following space:

_____ breaths/min

Enter the total minute volume and the oxygen consumption per minute after exercise in the data table.

7. Calculate the *percent increase* after exercise for total minute volume and for oxygen consumption. This is the difference between the exercise and resting measurements, divided by the resting measurement and multiplied by 100%. Enter these values in the data table in your laboratory report.

# Laboratory Report 6.2

Name _____

Date _____

Section _____

## Data from Exercise 6.2

1. Enter the total minute volume and rate of oxygen consumption during rest and exercise in the table below.
2. Calculate and enter the percent increases in your measurements after exercise, and enter these values in the table below.

| Measurement | Resting | Exercise | % Increase |
|---|---|---|---|
| Total minute volume | | | |
| Oxygen consumption | | | |

## Questions for Exercise 6.2

1. Why did the rate of oxygen consumption increase as a result of exercise?

2. Why did the total minute volume increase as a result of exercise? (Explain the physiological mechanisms that may be involved.)

3. High total minute volume during exercise is called *hyperpnea*. How does this differ from hyperventilation?

4. Define the term *oxygen debt*. Explain why hyperpnea continues for a time after exercise has stopped.

# Respiration and Acid-Base Balance

Carbon dioxide in plasma can combine with water to produce carbonic acid, which in turn may dissociate to produce protons ($H^+$) and bicarbonate ions ($HCO_3^-$). Ventilation regulates the carbon dioxide concentration of the plasma and thus plays an important role in acid-base balance.

## Objectives

1. Describe the pH scale, and define the terms *acid* and *base*.
2. Explain how carbonic acid and bicarbonate are formed in the blood and the functions they serve.
3. Define the terms *acidosis* and *alkalosis*, and explain how they relate to *hypoventilation* and *hyperventilation*.
4. Explain how ventilation is adjusted to help maintain acid-base balance.

## Materials

1. pH meter, droppers, beakers, straws
2. Buffer, pH = 7 (made from purchased concentrate); concentrated HCl, concentrated NaOH, phenolphthalein solution (saturated)

Ventilation accomplishes two different but related functions: (1) oxygenation of the blood, accomplished by bringing new air into the alveoli during the inhalation phase, and (2) the elimination of carbon dioxide from the blood, accomplished by the diffusion of $CO_2$ from the blood into the alveoli and the extrusion of this $CO_2$-rich air by exhalation. The former function is required to maintain aerobic cell respiration; the latter function is needed to maintain the normal pH of the blood.

**Table 6.7** The pH scale.

|  | $H^+$ Concentration (molar) | pH | $OH^-$ Concentration (molar) |
|---|---|---|---|
| | 1.0 | 0 | $10^{14}$ |
| | 0.1 | 1 | $10^{13}$ |
| | 0.01 | 2 | $10^{12}$ |
| Acids | 0.001 | 3 | $10^{11}$ |
| | 0.0001 | 4 | $10^{10}$ |
| | $10^{-5}$ | 5 | $10^{9}$ |
| | $10^{-6}$ | 6 | $10^{8}$ |
| Neutral | $10^{-7}$ | 7 | $10^{7}$ |
| | $10^{-8}$ | 8 | $10^{6}$ |
| | $10^{-9}$ | 9 | $10^{5}$ |
| | $10^{-10}$ | 10 | 0.0001 |
| Bases | $10^{-11}$ | 11 | 0.001 |
| | $10^{-12}$ | 12 | 0.01 |
| | $10^{-13}$ | 13 | 0.1 |
| | $10^{-14}$ | 14 | 1.0 |

The pH (see appendix 1) indicates the concentration of $H^+$ in a solution and is defined by the following formula:

$$pH = \log \frac{1}{[H^+]}$$

where $[H^+]$ is the concentration of $H^+$ in moles (atomic weight in grams) per liter.

Some water molecules ionize to produce equal amounts of $H^+$ and $OH^-$ (hydroxyl). In pure water, the $H^+$ concentration is $10^{-7}$ moles/L. (Since hydrogen has an atomic weight of 1, this is the same as $10^{-7}$g/L.) This is equal to a pH of 7.0 and is called a *neutral solution*. An *acidic* solution has a higher $H^+$ concentration and a lower pH; a *basic solution* has a lower $H^+$ concentration and a higher pH (table 6.7).

## Table 6.8  The effect of respiration on blood pH.

| $P_{CO_2}$ (mm Hg) | $H_2CO_3$ (mEq/L)[1] | $HCO_3^-$ (mEq/L)[1] | $HCO_3^-/H_2CO_3$ Ratio | Blood pH | Condition |
|---|---|---|---|---|---|
| 20 | 0.6 | 24 | 40/1 | 7.70 | Respiratory alkalosis |
| 30 | 0.9 | 24 | 26.7/1 | 7.53 | Respiratory alkalosis |
| 40 | 1.2 | 24 | 20/1 | 7.40 | Normal |
| 50 | 1.5 | 24 | 16/1 | 7.30 | Respiratory acidosis |
| 60 | 1.8 | 24 | 13.3/1 | 7.22 | Respiratory acidosis |

1. Ion concentrations are commonly measured in milliequivalents (mEq) per liter. This is equal to the millimolar concentration of the ion multiplied by its number of charges.

An *acid* is a molecule that can donate a free $H^+$ to a solution and thus lower its pH. *Carbonic acid* ($H_2CO_3$) is formed from the combination of $CO_2$ and water within the red blood cells. This reaction is catalyzed by an enzyme called *carbonic anhydrase.*

$$CO_2 + H_2O \xrightarrow{\text{carbonic anhydrase}} H_2CO_3$$

Some of the carbonic acid thus formed can dissociate to yield $H^+$ and *bicarbonate* ion ($HCO_3^-$). The $H^+$ derived from carbonic acid and other acids in the blood gives normal arterial blood a pH of $7.40 \pm 0.05$.

$$H_2CO_3 \longrightarrow HCO_3^- + H^+$$

## A. The Ability of Buffers to Stabilize the pH of Solutions

Plasma contains a particular concentration of bicarbonate as a result of the dissociation of carbonic acid. Bicarbonate serves as the major *buffer* of the blood, helping to stabilize the pH of plasma despite the addition of $H^+$ from molecules of lactic acid, fatty acids, ketone bodies, and other metabolic products. The $H^+$ released by these acids is prevented from lowering the blood pH because it is combined with bicarbonate. Although a new acid molecule (carbonic acid) is formed, this reaction prevents a rise in the free $H^+$ concentration.

$$H^+ + HCO_3^- \longrightarrow H_2CO_3$$

Carbonic acid formed in this way can provide a source of new $H^+$ if the blood pH should begin to rise (from a loss of blood $H^+$) beyond normal levels. The carbonic acid/bicarbonate buffer system thus helps to stabilize the blood pH under normal conditions. Disease states, however, may cause a blood pH less than 7.35 or more than 7.45. These conditions are called *acidosis* and *alkalosis,* respectively.

Normally, the rate of ventilation is matched to the rate of $CO_2$ production by the tissues, so that the carbonic acid, bicarbonate, and $H^+$ concentrations in the blood remain in the normal range. If *hypoventilation* occurs, however, the carbonic acid levels will rise above normal and the pH will fall below 7.35. This condition is called **respiratory acidosis.** *Hyperventilation,* conversely, causes an abnormal decrease in carbonic acid and a corresponding rise in blood pH. This condition is called **respiratory alkalosis.** Respiratory acidosis or alkalosis thus occurs when the blood $CO_2$ level (as measured by the partial pressure of $P_{CO_2}$, in millimeters of mercury) is different from the normal value (40 mm Hg) as a result of abnormal breathing patterns (table 6.8).

## Procedure

1. Allow the pH meter to warm up by setting the selector switch to the *standby* position. Be sure that the pH electrodes are immersed in buffer and are not allowed to dry. Check to see that the temperature selector switch is set at the current room temperature.

2. Turn the selector switch to *pH,* and take a reading of the buffer. Use the calibration knob to set the pH meter to the correct pH of the buffer (7.000). Now turn the selector switch back to the *standby* position, and transfer the pH electrodes to a beaker of distilled water. Turn the selector switch to *pH,* and record the pH of distilled water. Return the selector switch to the *standby* position and the electrodes back to the buffer.

3. Add 1 drop of concentrated hydrochloric acid (HCl) to the beaker of distilled water, and mix thoroughly. Transfer the electrodes to this solution, turn the selector switch to the pH position, and record the pH of the solution in your laboratory report.

**Note:** *After recording the pH of a solution, always turn the selector switch to* standby *and rinse the electrodes thoroughly using a squeeze bottle of distilled water. Wipe the electrodes with lint-free paper and return them to the buffer solution. Check the pH of the buffer solution after the cleaning procedure to make sure you have adequately cleaned the electrodes.*

4. Add 1 drop of concentrated NaOH to a fresh beaker of distilled water, and record the pH of the water before and after adding the NaOH.

5. Add 1 drop of concentrated HCl to a beaker containing standard buffer solution (pH = 7.000).
6. Add 1 drop of concentrated NaOH to a fresh beaker of standard buffer solution (pH = 7.000).
7. Add 2–3 drops of concentrated HCl to a beaker of fresh standard buffer solution (pH = 7.000).
8. Add 2–3 drops of concentrated NaOH to a beaker of fresh standard buffer solution (pH = 7.000).

## B. The Effect of Exercise on the Rate of $CO_2$ Production

Increased muscle metabolism during exercise results in an increase in $CO_2$ production. Despite this, the $CO_2$ levels and pH of arterial blood do not normally change during exercise. This is because the increased rate of $CO_2$ production is matched by an increased rate of its elimination through ventilation. The mechanisms responsible for exercise *hyperpnea* (increased breathing) are complex and incompletely understood.

### Clinical Significance

Hypoventilation results in the retention of carbon dioxide and thus in the excessive accumulation of carbonic acid; this produces a fall in blood pH called respiratory acidosis. Hyperventilation results in the excessive elimination of $CO_2$ and thus in low carbonic acid and high pH. This differs from the normal hyperpnea (increased total minute volume) that occurs during exercise, where increased respiration matches increased $CO_2$ production so that the arterial $CO_2$ levels and pH remain in the normal range.

### Procedure

1. Fill a beaker with 200 ml of distilled water, and add 5.0 ml of 0.10$N$ NaOH and a few drops of phenolphthalein indicator. This indicator is pink in alkaline solutions and clear in neutral or acidic solutions. Divide this solution into two beakers.

2. While sitting quietly, exhale through a glass tube or straw into the solution in the first beaker. Note the time it takes to turn the solution from pink to clear, and record this time in your laboratory report.
3. Exercise vigorously for two to five minutes by running up and down stairs or by doing jumping jacks. Exhale through a glass tube or straw into the second beaker, and again note the time it takes to clear the pink solution.

## C. The Role of Carbon Dioxide in the Regulation of Ventilation

The carbon dioxide concentration of the blood reflects a balance between the rate of its production (by aerobic cell respiration) and the rate of its elimination through the lungs. When a person consciously holds his or her breath for a sufficiently long time, the carbon dioxide level rises (and the pH falls) to such an extent that reflex breathing occurs. On the other hand, during hyperventilation, the pH of the blood can rise to the point that the desire to breathe is eliminated until the amount of carbon dioxide in the blood again rises above the critical point.

### Procedure

1. Count the number of breaths you take in one minute of relaxed, unforced breathing.

   Enter this number in your laboratory report.

2. Force yourself to hyperventilate for about 10 sec (stop if you begin to feel dizzy).
3. Immediately after hyperventilation, count the number of breaths you take in a minute of relaxed, unforced breathing.

## *Data from Exercise 6.3*

### A. The Ability of Buffers to Stabilize the pH of Solutions

1. Enter your data in the spaces below:

    pH of Distilled Water: _____          pH of Buffer: 7.000

    pH of Water + 1 drop HCl: _____          pH of Buffer + 1 drop HCl: _____

    pH of Water + 1 drop NaOH: _____          pH of Buffer + 1 drop NaOH: _____

    pH of Buffer + 3 drops HCl: _____

    pH of Buffer + 3 drops NaOH: _____

2. Does your data support the statement that buffers help to stabilize the pH of solutions? Explain

### B. The Effect of Exercise on the Rate of $CO_2$ Production

1. Enter your data in the spaces below:

    Time for color change at rest: _____

    Time for color change after exercise: _____

2. Explain your results in the space below:

## C. The Role of Carbon Dioxide in the Regulation of Ventilation

1. Enter your data in the spaces below:

   Rate of breathing at rest: _____ breaths/minute

   Rate of breathing after hyperventilation: _____ breaths/minute

2. Explain your results in the space below:

# Questions for Exercise 6.3

1. Define the following terms:

   (a) *acid* _____

   _____

   (b) *base* _____

   _____

   (c) *acidosis* _____

   _____

   (d) *alkalosis* _____

   _____

2. A solution with a $H^+$ concentration of $10^{-9}$ molar has a pH of _____ ; its $OH^-$ concentration is

   _____ .

3. Hypoventilation produces respiratory _____ ,

   whereas hyperventilation produces respiratory _____ .

4. Draw equations to show how hypoventilation affects the blood concentration of carbon dioxide, carbonic acid, $H^+$, and bicarbonate.

5. Intravenous infusions of sodium bicarbonate are often given to acidotic patients to correct the acidosis and relieve the strain of rapid breathing. Write an equation and verbally describe the reason why bicarbonate is helpful in this situation.

# Blood: Respiratory, Immune, and Clotting Functions

The blood contains a number of components that serve different physiological functions. The fluid portion of the blood, called **plasma,** provides the major means of distributing chemicals between organs. For example, it transports food molecules absorbed through the intestine, hormones secreted by the endocrine glands, and antibodies produced by certain white blood cells. The plasma also helps to eliminate metabolic wastes by carrying these molecules to the liver (for excretion in the bile), the kidneys (for excretion in the urine), and—in the case of $CO_2$—to the lungs (for excretion in the exhaled air).

There are two major types of blood cells: **red blood cells (erythrocytes)** and **white blood cells (leukocytes).** Red blood cells contribute to the respiratory function of the blood by providing transport for oxygen and (to a lesser degree) carbon dioxide. White blood cells and their products help provide immunity from infection by recognizing and attacking foreign molecules and cells. The blood also contains **platelets,** which are membrane-bound fragments of a bone marrow cell (called a megakaryocyte). Platelets, together with proteins in the plasma, help maintain the integrity of blood vessels by forming clots (fig. 7.1).

**Figure 7.1.** Blood cells become packed at the bottom of the test tube when whole blood is centrifuged, leaving the fluid plasma at the top of the tube. Red blood cells (erythrocytes) are the most abundant of the blood cells. White blood cells (leukocytes) and platelets form only a thin, light-colored "buffy coat" at the interface between the packed red blood cells and the plasma.

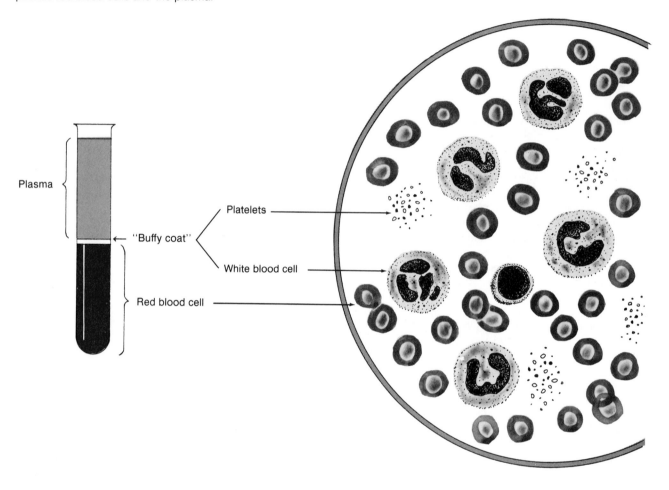

Plasma

"Buffy coat"

Platelets

White blood cell

Red blood cell

# Hemoglobin and Oxygen Transport

Almost all of the oxygen transported by the blood is carried within the red blood cells attached to hemoglobin. Measurements of the oxygen-carrying capacity of blood include the red blood cell count, hemoglobin concentration, and hematocrit. Anemia is indicated when one or more of these measurements is abnormally low.

## Objectives

1. Describe the composition of blood.
2. Describe the composition of hemoglobin, and explain how it participates in oxygen transport.
3. Demonstrate the procedures for taking the red blood cell count and hemoglobin and hematocrit measurements, and list the normal values for these measurements.
4. Explain how measurements of the oxygen-carrying capacity of blood can be used to diagnose anemia and polycythemia.

## Materials

1. Hemocytometer
2. Diluting (Thoma) and Sahli pipettes or Unopettes (Becton-Dickinson) for manual red blood cell count and hemoglobin measurements
3. Heparinized capillary tubes, clay capillary tube sealant (Seal-ease), microcapillary centrifuge, hematocrit reader
4. Microscope
5. Hayem's solution: 0.5 g of mercuric chloride, 5.0 g of sodium sulfate, 1.0 g of sodium chloride in 200 ml of water (not needed if Unopette system is used); cyanomethemoglobin reagent (not needed if Unopette system is used)
6. Sterile lancets and 70% alcohol
7. Colorimeter and cuvettes

Each ventilation cycle delivers a fresh supply of oxygen to the alveoli of the lungs. The oxygen must then be transported by the blood to the body cells to be used for aerobic cellular respiration.

The amount of oxygen that leaves the lungs dissolved in plasma is equal to 0.3 ml of $O_2$ per 100 ml of blood. The amount of oxygen leaving the lungs in whole blood, however, is equal to 20.0 ml of $O_2$ per 100 ml of blood. It is obvious that most of the oxygen must be carried within the cellular elements of the blood.

Most of the oxygen in the blood is carried by hemoglobin molecules within the red blood cells. Each hemoglobin molecule consists of four polypeptide chains (actually two pairs of chains, one pair called the *alpha* chains and one pair called the *beta* chains) and four disc-shaped organic groups called *hemes*. Each heme group contains one central ferrous ion ($Fe^{++}$), which is capable of bonding to one molecule of oxygen. One molecule of hemoglobin can thus combine with four molecules of oxygen.

The hemoglobin within the red blood cells loads up with oxygen in the capillaries of the lungs and unloads oxygen in the tissue capillaries. In both cases, oxygen moves according to its diffusion gradient. Since red blood cells always respire anaerobically, they cannot utilize the oxygen they carry; thus, a maximum diffusion gradient for oxygen is maintained between the red blood cells and the tissues.

The *oxygen-carrying capacity* of the blood is dependent on the total number of red blood cells (and therefore on the total amount of hemoglobin). The total number of red blood cells is dependent on a balance between the rate of red blood cell production and the rate of red blood cell destruction.

The rate of red blood cell production by the bone marrow is regulated by the hormone **erythropoietin,** secreted by the kidneys in response to a fall in blood oxygen. The rate of erythropoietin secretion is, in turn, regulated by the oxygen requirements of the body.

The red blood cells are destroyed by the action of phagocytic cells, which are fixed to the sides of blood channels (sinusoids) by a meshwork (reticulum) of fibers. These fixed phagocytes compose the **reticuloendothelial system** of the spleen, liver, and bone marrow. The reticuloendothelial cells digest the hemoglobin within the old red blood cells (those that are approximately 120 days old) into the component parts of protein, iron, and the heme pigment. The protein goes back into the general amino acid pool of the body, the iron is recycled to the bone marrow, and the heme is changed into a new pigment—**bilirubin.**

Bilirubin is released into the blood by the reticuloendothelial cells, then picked up by the liver, and secreted into the bile as bile pigment. An abnormal increase in the amount of bilirubin in the blood, due to an increased rate of red blood cell destruction, liver dysfunction, or bile duct obstruction, results in the condition known as *jaundice* (yellowing of the skin and sclera of the eyes).

## A. Red Blood Cell Count

The object of this exercise is to determine the number of red blood cells in a cubic millimeter of blood.[11] Since this number is very large, it is more practical to dilute a sample of blood with an isotonic solution, count the number of red blood cells in a fraction of this diluted blood, and then multiply by a correction factor. This procedure is accurate only when (1) the blood diluted is a representative fraction of all the blood in the body, (2) the dilution volumes are accurate, and (3) the sample counted is representative of the total volume of diluted blood.

### Procedure
*Obtaining and Diluting Blood Samples*

1. If a **Thoma pipette** will be used for the procedure (fig. 7.2), pour 2–5 ml of diluting solution (*Hayem's solution*) into a small beaker. If a **Unopette** will be used for this procedure (fig. 7.3), this step is unnecessary, since the reservoir contains a premeasured amount of Hayem's solution.
2. Swing your hand around until your fingers become engorged with blood (hyperemia). Cleanse the tip of your index or third finger with 70% alcohol, and prick it with a sterile lancet.
3. Discard the first drop of blood, and hold your finger downward to collect a large droplet of blood. If a Thoma pipette is used, suck this

---

11. For white blood cell count, see p. 255. For ABO and Rh typing, see p. 357.

**Figure 7.2.** (a) a hemocytometer (for a red and white blood cell count); (b) a Thoma pipette for blood dilution (a white blood cell count); (c) a Thoma pipette for blood dilution (a red blood cell count); (d) a Sahli pipette (for the measurement of blood hemoglobin); a rubber tube with a plastic mouthpiece (not shown) is used for sucking blood and diluent solutions into the pipettes.

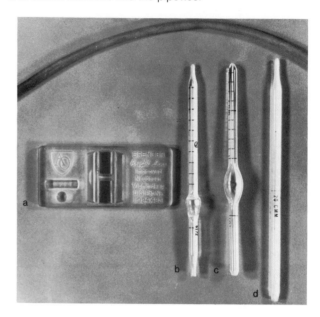

**Figure 7.3.** The Unopette system (Becton-Dickinson), consisting of a reservoir containing the premeasured amount of diluent (left) and a plastic capillary tube within a shield (right) for puncturing the reservoir top and delivering a measured amount of whole blood to the reservoir.

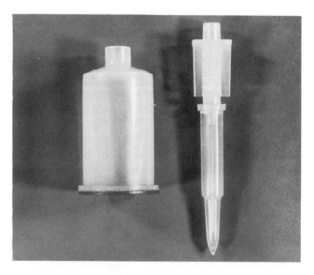

blood into the pipette (using a mouthpiece and rubber hose) to the 0.5 mark (fig. 7.4). If a Unopette is used, remove the shield over the pipette, and simply touch the tip of the pipette to the drop of blood. Allow the pipette to fill by capillary action (fig. 7.5a).

**Figure 7.4.** A method for filling a Thoma pipette with blood for a red blood cell count.

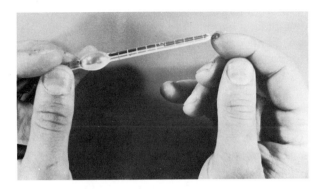

**Figure 7.5.** The Unopette method for measuring a red blood cell count or hemoglobin concentration. (a) the method of filling the plastic capillary pipette with fingertip blood; (b) squeezing of the reservoir to draw blood out of the pipette into diluent within the reservoir.

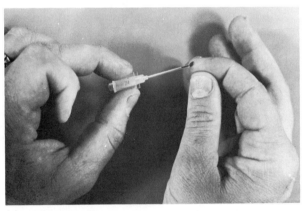

(a)

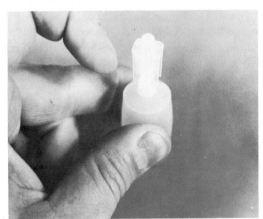

(b)

**Figure 7.6.** A procedure for filling a hemocytometer with diluted blood for a red blood cell count from a Unopette reservoir. Squeezing of the reservoir places a drop of diluted blood at the edge of the cover slip; the drop of blood then moves under the hemocytometer grid by capillary action.

4. If a Thoma pipette is used, gently suck the Hayem's solution into the pipette until the total volume of solution reaches the 101 mark. If a Unopette is used, puncture the top of the reservoir with the pipette shield. Then squeeze the reservoir, and while squeezing, insert the pipette with its content of blood. When you release pressure on the reservoir, the blood will be expelled into the premeasured Hayem's solution within the reservoir (fig. 7.5b).

5. Thoroughly mix the blood with the Hayem's solution for approximately 1 minute.

**Procedure**

*Filling the Hemocytometer and Determining Red Blood Cell Count*

1. Place a cover slip on the hemocytometer so that it covers one of the silvered areas.

2. Discard the first 3 drops of blood from the Thoma pipette or the Unopette. Place the next drop of diluted blood at the edge of the cover slip. If a Unopette is used, the pipette must be removed from the reservoir, turned around, and reinserted into the reservoir. The diluted blood will be drawn underneath the cover slip by capillary action (fig. 7.6).

3. Locate the grid on the hemocytometer using the 10× objective. Change to 45×, and count the total number of red blood cells in the five indicated squares (fig. 7.7).

**Figure 7.7.** The hemocytometer grid. Squares 1–5 are used for red blood cell counts, whereas squares A–D are used for white blood cell counts.

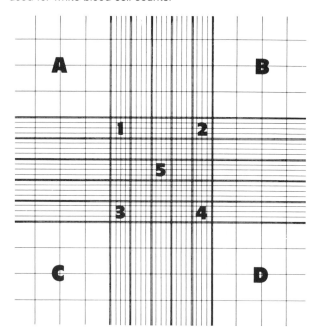

**Note:** *If a red blood cell lies on the upper or left-hand line, include it in your count. Do not include red blood cells in your count that lie on the lower or right-hand lines.*

4. The central grid of twenty-five squares is 1 square millimeter (mm²) in area and 0.10 mm deep. The dilution factor is 1:200. To convert the number of red blood cells that you counted in five squares to the number of red blood cells per cubic millimeter, you must multiply your count by 10,000 (the product of 5 × 10 × 200).

5. Record your count of the red blood cells in the five squares, and calculate the number of red blood cells in a cubic millimeter of your blood. Enter the latter value in the laboratory report.

Red blood cells/5 squares: _____

> The normal red blood cell count for a male is 4.5 million to 6.0 million, and for a female is 4.0 million to 5.5 million red blood cells per cubic millimeter of blood.

## B. Hematocrit

When you centrifuge whole blood, the red blood cells become packed into the bottom of the tube, leaving the plasma at the top. The ratio of the volume of packed red blood cells to the total blood volume is called the *hematocrit*.

## Procedure

1. Prick your finger with a sterile lancet to obtain a drop of blood. Discard the first drop.

2. Obtain a heparinized capillary tube (heparin is an anticoagulant). Notice that one end of the tube is marked with a red band. Touch the end of the capillary tube opposite the marked end to the drop of blood, allowing blood to enter the tube by capillary action and gravity (fig. 7.8). The tube does not have to be completely full (half-full or more is adequate), and air bubbles are not important (these will disappear during centrifugation).

3. Using clay capillary sealant, seal the red-banded end of the capillary tube (this is the fire-polished end) by gently pushing it into Seal-ease and then removing it.

4. Place the sealed capillary tube in a numbered slot on a microcapillary centrifuge, with the plugged end of the capillary tube facing outward and against the rubber gasket. Screw the top plate onto the centrifuge head and centrifuge for 3 minutes. At the end of the centrifugation, determine the hematocrit with the hematocrit reader provided, and enter this in your laboratory report.

> The normal hematocrit for an adult male is 47 ± 7, and for an adult female is 42 ± 5. Hematocrit values are percentages.

## C. Hemoglobin Concentration

Hemoglobin absorbs light in the visible spectrum and hence is a *pigment* (a colored compound). It should therefore be possible to measure the concentration of hemoglobin in a hemolyzed sample of blood by measuring the intensity of its color. This procedure, however, is complicated by the fact that red blood cells contain different types of hemoglobin, and each type absorbs light in a slightly different region of the visible spectrum (i.e., has a slightly different color).

When the oxygen concentration of the blood is high, such as in the capillaries of the lungs, normal deoxyhemoglobin (or **reduced hemoglobin**) combines with oxygen to form the compound **oxyhemoglobin.** When the concentration of oxygen in the blood is low, such as in the tissue capillaries, the oxyhemoglobin dissociates to form reduced hemoglobin and oxygen.

$$\text{Reduced Hemoglobin} + \text{oxygen} \underset{\text{tissues}}{\overset{\text{lungs}}{\rightleftharpoons}} \text{oxyhemoglobin}$$

**Figure 7.8.** A method for filling a capillary tube with fingertip blood.

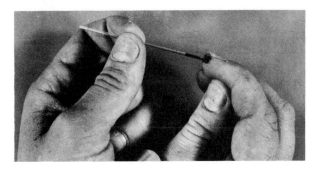

The bright red color of arterial blood is due to the predominance of the oxyhemoglobin pigment, whereas venous blood has the darker hue characteristic of reduced hemoglobin. It should be emphasized, however, that venous blood still contains a large amount of oxyhemoglobin, which functions as an oxygen reserve.

A less common, though clinically important, form of hemoglobin is **carboxyhemoglobin**—a complex of hemoglobin and carbon monoxide. This complex, unlike oxyhemoglobin, does not readily dissociate; hence, the hemoglobin that is bonded to carbon monoxide cannot participate in oxygen transport. The carboxyhemoglobin complex has a bright, cherry red color.

A small percentage of hemoglobin contains iron that is oxidized to the ferric state ($Fe^{+++}$) instead of being in the normal ferrous state ($Fe^{++}$). Hemoglobin in this oxidized state is called **methemoglobin** and is incapable of bonding to either oxygen or carbon monoxide. An increase in the amount of methemoglobin occurs in some genetic diseases or as a result of the action of certain drugs (e.g., nitroglycerin poisoning).

In this exercise, an attempt will be made to measure the concentration of hemoglobin in a solution of hemolyzed blood by measuring the intensity of its color with a spectrophotometer. To do this accurately, we must first convert all the hemoglobin into one form (methemoglobin) and then combine it with cyanide to make it more stable. We can then determine the hemoglobin concentration of the unknown sample by comparing its absorbance with that of a standard hemoglobin solution of known concentration.

## Procedure
*Measurement of Blood Hemoglobin Concentration*

1. If a **Sahli pipette** will be used (fig. 7.2), measure 5.0 ml of cyanomethemoglobin reagent into each of three tubes. If a **Unopette** will be used (fig. 7.3), this step is not necessary, since the reservoir already contains a premeasured volume of cyanomethemoglobin reagent.

**Figure 7.9.** A method for filling a Sahli pipette with blood for the determination of hemoglobin concentration.

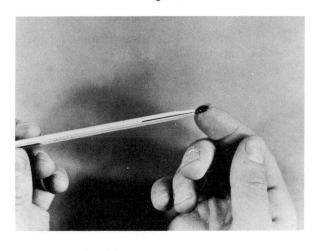

2. Clean your finger with 70% alcohol, and puncture it with a sterile lancet. Discard the first drop of blood. Using either a Sahli pipette or the plastic capillary pipette in the Unopette, fill the pipette with 0.02 ml of blood. Fill the Sahli pipette to the line by gently sucking on the mouthpiece attached to the rubber hose (fig. 7.9). Fill the Unopette by simply touching the tip of the pipette to the drop of blood and allowing the pipette to completely fill by capillary action (fig. 7.5a).

3. If a Sahli pipette is used, blow the blood out of the pipette into the tube containing cyanomethemoglobin solution. Draw the solution up into the pipette, and blow it out several times to wash the walls of the pipette. Mix the solution thoroughly, and let it stand at room temperature for at least 10 minutes. If the Unopette system is used, puncture the top of the reservoir with the pipette shield, squeeze the reservoir, insert the pipette, and release the reservoir (fig. 7.5b). Squeeze and release the reservoir a few more times to completely wash the pipette. Mix and allow it to stand at room temperature for 10 minutes.

4. Some standard hemoglobin solutions come full strength and must be diluted with cyanomethemoglobin reagent to be at the same dilution as the unknown. Use the same procedure as in steps 2 and 3 to make this dilution (using a clean Sahli pipette or a new Unopette).

Some hemoglobin standards are purchased in an already diluted state. These can be used as they come, but you may have to calculate the hemoglobin concentration of blood that would be equivalent to the diluted standard solution.

5. Set the colorimeter at a wavelength of 540 nm, and standardize the instrument using plain cyanomethemoglobin solution as the blank. Record the absorbance values of the unknown and standard.

Absorbance of unknown: _____

Absorbance of standard: _____

6. Calculate the hemoglobin concentration of the unknown using the formula

$$\text{Concentration}_{\text{unknown}} = \frac{\text{Concentration}_{\text{standard}} \times A_{\text{unknown}}}{A_{\text{standard}}}$$

Enter your hemoglobin concentration in the laboratory report.

> The normal hemoglobin concentration of an adult male is 13–16 g/dl, and of an adult female is 12–15 g/dl.

## D. Calculation of Mean Corpuscular Volume (MCV) and Mean Corpuscular Hemoglobin Concentration (MCHC)

An abnormally low hemoglobin, hematocrit, or red blood cell count may indicate a condition known as **anemia.** Anemia may have many different causes, such as iron deficiency, vitamin $B_{12}$ and folic acid deficiencies, bone marrow disease, hemolytic disease (e.g., sickle-cell anemia), loss of blood through hemorrhage, and infections. Diagnosis of the type of anemia present is aided by relating the measurements of hemoglobin, hematocrit, and red blood cell count to derive the **mean corpuscular volume (MCV)** and the **mean corpuscular hemoglobin concentration (MCHC).**

---

### Clinical Significance

Anemia is subdivided into a number of categories on the basis of the MCV and MCHC. *Macrocytic anemia* (MCV greater than 94, MCHC within normal range) may be caused by folic acid deficiency and by pernicious anemia—the inability of the stomach to secrete "intrinsic factor," which is needed for vitamin $B_{12}$ absorption. *Normocytic normochromic anemia* (MCV and MCHC are normal) may be due to acute blood loss, hemolysis, aplastic anemia (damage to the bone marrow), and a variety of chronic diseases. *Microcytic hypochromic anemia* (abnormally low MCV and low MCHC) is the most common type of anemia, caused by inadequate iron in the diet.

---

**Procedure**

1. Calculate the mean corpuscular volume (MCV) according to the following formula:

$$\text{MCV} = \frac{\text{hematocrit} \times 10}{\text{RBC count (in millions per mm}^3 \text{ blood)}}$$

*Example*

$$\text{Hematocrit} = 46$$

$$\text{RBC count} = 5.5 \text{ million}$$

$$\text{MCV} = \frac{46 \times 10}{5.5} = 84$$

Calculate your mean corpuscular volume, and enter it in the laboratory report.

> Average normal adult (male and female) mean corpuscular volume is 82–92.

2. Calculate your mean corpuscular hemoglobin concentration (MCHC) according to the following formula:

$$\text{MCHC} = \frac{\text{hemoglobin (in g/dl)} \times 100}{\text{hematocrit}}$$

*Example*

$$\text{Hematocrit} = 46$$

$$\text{Hemoglobin} = 16 \text{ g/dl}$$

$$\text{MCHC} = \frac{16 \times 100}{46} = 35$$

Calculate your mean corpuscular hemoglobin concentration, and enter it in the laboratory report.

> Average normal adult (male and female) mean corpuscular hemoglobin concentration is 32–36.

# Laboratory Report 7.1

Name _____

Date _____

Section _____

## Data from Exercise 7.1

### A. Red Blood Cell Count

Write your red blood cell count per cubic millimeter of blood in the space below:

_____ /mm³ blood

### B. Hematocrit

Write your hematocrit in the space below:

_____

### C. Hemoglobin Concentration

Enter your hemoglobin concentration in the space below:

_____ g/100 ml blood

### D. MCV and MCHC

Calculate your mean corpuscular volume (MCV) and mean corpuscular hemoglobin concentration (MCHC), and enter these values in the spaces below:

MCV _____

MCHC _____

Compare your values to normal, and write your conclusions in the space below:

## Questions for Exercise 7.1

1. One hemoglobin molecule contains _____ heme groups and can thus combine with _____ molecules of oxygen.

2. The hormone _____ stimulates the bone marrow to produce red blood cells.

3. The hormone in question 2 is produced by the _____ .

4. When red blood cells are destroyed, the heme (minus the iron) is converted into a new pigment called

_____ .

5. Accumulations of the above pigment, due to bile duct obstruction, for example, produce a condition called

   _____ .

6. The ratio of packed red blood cells to the total volume of a blood sample is called the _____ .

7. The molecule formed by the combination of reduced hemoglobin and oxygen is called _____ .

8. A hemoglobin molecule containing oxidized iron ($Fe^{+++}$) is called _____ .

9. The molecule formed by the combination of hemoglobin and carbon monoxide is called _____ .

10. Define the term *anemia*, describe its causes, and explain its dangers.

11. Newborn babies, particularly premature ones, often have a rapid rate of red blood cell destruction and are jaundiced. Explain the relationship between these two observations.

# Oxyhemoglobin Saturation

The iron atoms within the heme groups of hemoglobin may be free, or they may bond to oxygen or carbon monoxide. Each of these different forms of hemoglobin has a slightly different color, or absorption spectrum, which allows the percentage of each type in a mixture to be measured. Knowledge of the percentage composition, or saturation, of deoxyhemoglobin, oxyhemoglobin, and carboxyhemoglobin is needed for the clinical assessment of lung function and of the oxygen transport ability of blood.

## Objectives

1. Define the term *percent saturation.*
2. Describe the clinical significance of the percent oxyhemoglobin measurement.
3. Describe the clinical significance of the percent carboxyhemoglobin measurement.
4. Explain how an absorption spectrum is obtained, and explain how the absorption spectra of the different forms of hemoglobin are used to determine the percent saturation.

## Materials

1. Graduate cylinder, 1 cc syringe
2. Test tube and distilled water
3. Colorimeter and cuvettes
4. Sodium dithionite (hydrosulfite), 1.0 g per 100 ml
5. Alcohol swabs and lancets

The blood's ability to carry oxygen depends not only on the number of red blood cells (and the amount of hemoglobin) present, but also on the proper delivery of oxygen to the blood (ventilation) and the ability of hemoglobin to combine with oxygen (i.e., the affinity of hemoglobin for oxygen). In carbon monoxide poisoning, for example, the ventilation and the hemoglobin level may remain normal while the total amount of oxygen carried by the hemoglobin is reduced. It is thus frequently necessary to know not only the total hemoglobin level but also the relative proportions of each type of hemoglobin.

The relative proportion of each type of hemoglobin is given as its **percent saturation.** The percent oxyhemoglobin saturation, for example, is the proportion of hemoglobin that is bound to oxygen. This value is approximately 97% in normal arterial blood and 75% in normal venous blood.

% oxyhemoglobin saturation

$$= \frac{\text{oxyhemoglobin}}{\text{total blood hemoglobin}} \times 100$$

The determination of percent oxyhemoglobin saturation is a very sensitive means of assessing the adequacy of pulmonary function. Even when pulmonary function is normal, however, the percent oxyhemoglobin saturation can be reduced by carbon monoxide poisoning or methemoglobinemia. When a person's blood contains a carboxyhemoglobin saturation of 6.9%, for example (obtained in one study from cigarette-smoking New York taxicab drivers), the percent oxyhemoglobin saturation is decreased accordingly. Notice that these impairments in oxygen transport *cannot* be detected by a measurement of red blood cell count, hematocrit, or total blood hemoglobin.

The percent saturation of the different types of hemoglobins is measured by comparing the **absorption spectrum** of an unknown sample of blood with the absorption spectra of pure oxyhemoglobin, pure reduced hemoglobin, and pure carboxyhemoglobin.

Since these hemoglobins are different colors, they absorb different amounts of light at each wavelength. A graph of absorbance versus wavelength (where the concentration is constant) is called an *absorption spectrum* (fig. 7.10).

**Figure 7.10.** Absorption spectra of reduced hemoglobin (Hb), oxyhemoglobin (HbO₂), and carboxyhemoglobin (HbCO).

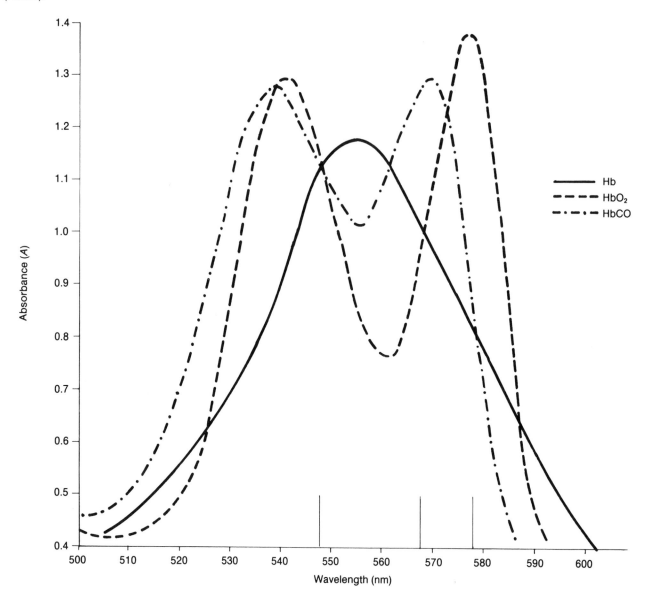

The absorption spectrum of an unknown sample of blood will be a mixture of these three absorption spectra, since it contains all three types of hemoglobins. The relative contribution of each hemoglobin type to the absorption spectrum is proportional to the relative amount of each type in the blood. This analysis, which is obviously complex, is usually performed by a laboratory instrument specifically manufactured for this purpose.

In this exercise, an attempt will be made to construct an absorption spectrum for 100% oxyhemoglobin and 100% reduced hemoglobin. By bubbling air into a flask containing blood until the blood is in equilibrium with the air, 100% oxyhemoglobin may be obtained. This process (called tonometering) essentially duplicates the process that occurs in the capillaries of the lungs. A simpler, though less accurate, method is to obtain a sample of blood from the fingertip, which contains a high percent oxyhemoglobin saturation. The sample of 100% reduced hemoglobin may be obtained by adding sodium hydrosulfite (Na₂S₂O₄) to a second sample of blood. The sodium hydrosulfite (or sodium dithionite) removes oxygen from oxyhemoglobin.

## Clinical Significance

A person may have normal hemoglobin, hematocrit, and red blood cell counts and still not be delivering adequate amounts of oxygen to the body cells. This may be due to inadequate lung function, resulting in poor oxygenation of the blood, or a high concentration of carboxyhemoglobin or methemoglobin. In this event, the hemoglobin cannot become fully saturated with oxygen, and therefore the percent oxyhemoglobin saturation of arterial blood may drop below normal. The effects of this are similar to the effects of anemia, because in both cases the amount of oxygen carried by the blood is reduced. In this sense, carbon monoxide poisoning may be thought of as a functional anemia—the hemoglobin and red blood cell counts are normal—but the red blood cells are not transporting the normal amount of oxygen.

### Procedure

1. Add 8.0 ml of distilled water to a test tube. Obtain a large drop of blood by cleaning the fingertip with 70% alcohol and puncturing it with a sterile lancet, and mix this blood with the distilled water by inverting the test tube over the punctured finger.

2. Transfer half the contents of the test tube (4.0 ml) to a second tube.

3. Add 0.20 ml of 1.0% sodium dithionite solution to the second test tube and mix thoroughly.

**Note:** *The dithionite solution should be freshly prepared just prior to use, and the absorbance values of the two tubes should be determined within 5 minutes of the time the dithionite is added to the second tube.*

4. Transfer the two solutions to two cuvettes. Fill a third cuvette with distilled water, and use it as a blank to standardize the spectrophotometer at 500 nm.

5. Record the absorbances of solutions 1 and 2. Standardize the spectrophotometer at each of the wavelengths indicated, and record the absorbances of the solutions in the laboratory report.

6. Graph the absorption spectra of oxyhemoglobin and reduced hemoglobin on the graph provided in the laboratory report.

## Data from Exercise 7.2

| | Absorbance Oxyhemoglobin | Absorbance Reduced hemoglobin |
|---|---|---|
| 500 nm | | |
| 510 nm | | |
| 520 nm | | |
| 530 nm | | |
| 540 nm | | |
| 550 nm | | |

| | Absorbance Oxyhemoglobin | Absorbance Reduced hemoglobin |
|---|---|---|
| 560 nm | | |
| 570 nm | | |
| 580 nm | | |
| 590 nm | | |
| 600 nm | | |

# Questions for Exercise 7.2

1. The percent oxyhemoglobin saturation of normal arterial blood is _____ .

2. It is not uncommon for a city-dwelling cigarette smoker to have a percent carboxyhemoglobin saturation of about 3%. If this is the case, what would be the percent oxyhemoglobin saturation?

   _____

3. What is the usual percent saturation of venous blood?

   _____

4. Given the information in questions 1 and 3, what percent of the oxyhemoglobin that enters tissue capillaries unloads its oxygen?

   _____

5. The percent oxyhemoglobin saturation of arterial blood samples is commonly measured in babies under treatment for respiratory distress syndrome and in patients under general anesthesia during prolonged surgical procedures. Explain the value of the percent oxyhemoglobin measurements under these circumstances.

6. Describe what happens during carbon monoxide poisoning, and explain the dangers of this condition.

# Total and Differential White Blood Cell Counts

White blood cells—including lymphocytes, monocytes, neutrophils, eosinophils, and basophils—are agents of the immune system. Lymphocytes provide immunity against specific antigens, whereas the other leukocytes are phagocytic. Measures of the total white blood cell count and the relative proportion of each type of white blood cell change in a characteristic way in different disease states.

## Objectives

1. Distinguish between the different types of leukocytes on the basis of the appearance of their nuclei and their cytoplasm.
2. Describe the origin and function of B and T lymphocytes.
3. List the phagocytic white blood cells, and explain their functions in a local inflammation.
4. Perform a total and a differential white blood cell count, and explain how this information aids in the diagnosis of diseases.

## Materials

1. Microscopes
2. Thoma diluting pipettes, lancets, alcohol swabs
3. Methylene blue in 1% acetic acid for total white blood cell count, Wright's stain (or Diff-Quik, Harleco) for differential count
4. Heparinized capillary tubes, glass slides

The white blood cells (leukocytes) are divided into two general categories on the basis of their histological appearance—*granular* (or *polymorphonuclear*) and *nongranular*. Leukocytes in the former category have lobed or segmented nuclei and cytoplasmic granules, whereas leukocytes in the latter category have unlobed nuclei and lack cytoplasmic granules (plate 1).

The granular leukocytes are distinguished by their affinity for stain. The cytoplasmic granules of **eosinophils** stain bright red (the color of eosin stain), and the granules of **basophils** stain dark blue (the color of basic stain). The granules of **neutrophils** have a low affinity for stain, and hence the cytoplasm of these cells appears relatively clear.

The nongranular leukocytes include **lymphocytes** and **monocytes**. Lymphocytes are the smaller of these two cell types and are easily identified by their round nuclei and scant cytoplasm. Monocytes have kidney-bean-shaped nuclei, often with brainlike convolutions, and their cytoplasm has a ground glass appearance. Monocytes may also be identified occasionally by the appearance of short blunt cytoplasmic extensions (pseudopods).

Leukocytes can leave the vascular system and enter the connective tissues of the body by squeezing through capillaries (a process known as *diapedesis*). During an inflammation response, the permeability of the capillaries—and so too the process of diapedesis—is increased by the release of *histamine* from tissue mast cells and basophils. This sequence of events also produces the local edema, redness, and pain associated with inflammation.

Neutrophils and, to a lesser degree, eosinophils destroy the invading pathogens by *phagocytosis*. The battle is then joined by monocytes, which undergo a transformation when they enter the connective tissues and become voracious phagocytic cells, the *tissue macrophages*. The specific immune response may also play a role in local inflammation, since many bacteria must first be "buttered" with antibodies before they can be phagocytosed. The engorged white blood cells form pus in the inflamed area.

The specific immune response is a function of the lymphocytes. Lymphocytes are first produced in the embryonic bone marrow, which then seeds the other lymphopoietic sites—the thymus, lymph nodes, and spleen. The thymus, in turn, sends cells to other locations and apparently regulates the general rate of lymphocyte production at all these sites through the release of a hormone. All lymphocytes may thus be categorized, in terms of their ancestry, as either bone marrow derived (**B cells**) or thymus derived (**T cells**).

Each lymphocyte is capable of attacking a specific antigen, which can bond to a specific *receptor protein* on the outer membrane of the lymphocyte. By means of this bonding, the antigen inadvertently selects the lymphocyte that is capable of attacking it. When bonding of the antigen to its receptor protein occurs, the lymphocyte is stimulated to divide many times until a large population of genetically identical cells (a *clone*) is produced. This **clone selection theory** accounts for the fact that the immune response to second and subsequent exposures to an antigen is greater than the immune response to the initial exposure to an antigen.

When stimulated by antigens (generally bacterial), B lymphocytes develop into *plasma cells* that secrete large amounts of antibody into the plasma. This may result in the destruction of the bacteria in one of two ways: (1) the antibodies coat the bacterial cell, making it more palatable for the phagocytic neutrophils and tissue macrophages; (2) the attachment of antibody to antigen on the bacterial surface activates a system of plasma proteins—*complement*—which produces lysis of the bacterial cell. These two systems work together, since a chemical released from the complement attracts the phagocytic white blood cells and increases capillary permeability. Inflammation can be suppressed by eosinophils, which engulf free antigen-antibody complexes, thus preventing the complement reaction.

T lymphocytes do not secrete antibodies. Instead, they must move into close proximity with their victim cells in order to destroy them. T lymphocytes are thus said to provide **cell-mediated immunity,** which involves the secretion of chemicals called *lymphokines,* released by some T cells. This cell-mediated immunity—against cells infected with viruses, cancer cells, and cells of tissue transplants—is directed against specific antigens on the victim cell surface. The T and B lymphocytes are therefore both specific in their immune attack and indeed cooperate with each other in the immune defense against disease.

## A. Total White Blood Cell Count

In this procedure, a small amount of blood is diluted with a solution that lyses the red blood cells and lightly stains the white blood cells (WBC). The white blood cells are counted in the four large corner squares of a hemocytometer (see exercise 7.1).

Since the dilution factor is 20 and each of the four squares counted has a volume of 0.1 mm³, the number of white blood cells per cubic millimeter of blood can be calculated as follows:

$$WBC/mm^3 = \frac{\# \text{ cells} \times 20}{4 \times 0.1 \text{ mm}^3}$$

or,

$$WBC/mm^3 = \# \text{ cells} \times 50$$

### Procedure

1. Obtain a drop of blood, discard the first drop, and fill the diluting pipette (the one with the white bead) to the 0.5 mark. Avoid air bubbles; if too much blood is drawn into the pipette, it can be removed by touching the tip of the pipette to a filter paper.
2. Draw the diluting fluid to the 11 mark on the pipette.
3. Shake the pipette for 3 minutes.
4. Discard the first four drops, and fill the hemocytometer as described in exercise 7.1.
5. Allow the cells to settle for 1 minute; then using the low-power objective, count the number of white blood cells in the four large corner squares (labeled *A, B, C,* and *D* in fig. 7.7). Count the cells in the upper and left-hand lines, but not the cells touching the lower and right-hand lines.
6. Calculate the number of white blood cells per cubic millimeter of blood, and enter this value in the laboratory report.

The normal white blood cell count is 5,000–10,000 cells per cubic millimeter of blood.

## B. Differential White Blood Cell Count

It is usually necessary to know not only the total number of white blood cells but also the relative abundance of each leukocyte type. This knowledge is obtained by determining the number of each leukocyte type out of a total count of 100 white blood cells.

## Clinical Significance

An increase in the white blood cell count (leukocytosis) may be produced by an increase in any one of the leukocyte types. These include: (1) neutrophil leukocytosis—due to appendicitis, rheumatic fever, smallpox, diabetic acidosis, hemorrhage; (2) lymphocyte leukocytosis—due to infectious mononucleosis and chronic infections, such as syphilis; (3) eosinophil leukocytosis—due to parasitic diseases (such as trichinosis), psoriasis, bronchial asthma, and hay fever; (4) basophil leukocytosis—due to hemolytic anemia, chicken pox, and smallpox; (5) monocyte leukocytosis—due to malaria, Rocky Mountain spotted fever, bacterial endocarditis, and typhoid fever. In certain cases, an increase in the relative abundance of one type of leukocyte may occur in the absence of an increase in the total white blood cell count—for example, lymphocytosis due to pernicious anemia, influenza, infectious hepatitis, German measles, and mumps.

A decrease in the white blood cell count (leukopenia) is usually due to either a decrease in the number of neutrophils or a decrease in the number of eosinophils. A decrease in the number of neutrophils occurs in typhoid fever, measles, infectious hepatitis, rubella, and aplastic anemia. Eosinopenia is produced by an elevated secretion of the corticosteroids, which occurs under various conditions of stress, such as severe infections and shock, and in adrenal hyperfunction (Cushing's syndrome).

## Procedure
*Making a Blood Smear*

1. Fill a heparinized capillary tube at least ⅓ full with blood. This can serve as a reservoir of blood for making a number of slides.
2. Using the capillary tube, apply a small drop of blood on one end of a glass slide that is *absolutely clean* and free of grease (fig. 7.11*a*). Place this slide flat on a laboratory bench.
3. Lower a second glass slide at an angle of 30° to the first slide, so that it is lightly touching the first slide in front of the drop of blood (fig. 7.11*b*).
4. Back the second slide into the drop of blood, maintaining the pressure and angle that allows the blood to spread out along the edge of the second slide (fig. 7.11*b*).
5. Keeping the same angle and pressure, push the second slide across the first in a rapid, smooth motion. The blood should now be spread in a thin film across the first slide. If this is done correctly, the concentration of blood in the smear should diminish toward the distal end, producing a feathered appearance (fig. 7.11*c* and *d*).

**Figure 7.11.** A procedure for making a blood smear for a differential white blood cell count.

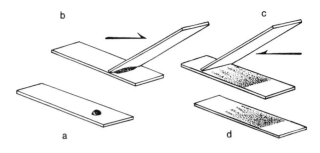

## Procedure
*Staining a Slide Using Wright's Stain*

1. Place the slide on a slide rack, and flood the surface of the slide with Wright's stain. Rock the slide back and forth gently for 1–3 minutes.

**Caution:** *The stain is dissolved in methyl alcohol, which easily evaporates. If any part of the slide should dry during this procedure, the stain will precipitate, ruining the slide.*

2. Drip buffer or distilled water on top of the Wright's stain, being careful not to wash the stain off the slide. Mixing Wright's stain with water is crucial for proper staining; this mixing can be aided by gently blowing on the surface of the stain. Proper staining is indicated by the presence of a metallic sheen on the surface of the stain. The diluted stain should be left on the slide for a full 5 minutes.
3. Wash the stain off the slide with a jet of distilled water from a water bottle, and allow the slide to drain at an angle for a few minutes.
4. Using the oil-immersion objective, count the different types of white blood cells, by starting at one point in the feathered-tip area and systematically scanning the slide until you have counted a total of 100 leukocytes.
5. Keep a running count of the different leukocytes in the table provided on plate 1, and indicate the total of each. Calculate the percent of the overall total of each leukocyte, and enter these percentages in your laboratory report.

## Procedure

*Staining a Slide Using Diff-Quik (Harleco)*

1. Dip the slide in fixative solution (light blue) five times, allowing 1 second per dip.
2. Dip the slide in solution 1 (orange) five times, allowing 1 second per dip.
3. Dip the slide in solution 2 (dark blue) five times, allowing 1 second per dip.
4. Rinse the slide with distilled water, and count the white blood cells under a microscope, using the oil-immersion objective. Keep a running count of each different type of leukocyte in the table provided on plate 1. At the end of the count, calculate the percent of the total count contributed by each type of white blood cell, and enter these values in your laboratory report.

# Laboratory Report **7.3**

Name _____

Date _____

Section _____

## Data from Exercise 7.3

## A. Total White Blood Cell Count

1. Enter your white blood cell count in the space below:

   _____ WBC/mm$^3$

2. Compare your measured values to the normal range, and write your conclusions in the space below:

## B. Differential White Blood Cell Count

1. Add the totals of each type of white blood cell counted to determine your grand total. Use this number to calculate the percent of each type of white blood cell, and enter these values in the table below:

| Leukocyte | Percent |
|-----------|---------|
| Neutrophils | |
| Eosinophils | |
| Basophils | |
| Lymphocytes | |
| Monocytes | |

2. Compare your values to the normal range, and write your conclusions in the space below:

# Questions for Exercise 7.3

1. Identify the leukocyte by the following description:

   (a) polymorphonuclear with poorly staining granules _____

   (b) agranular with round nucleus, relatively little cytoplasm _____

   (c) granules have affinity for red stain _____

   (d) rarest white blood cell _____

2. Antibodies are produced by _____ lymphocytes; cell-mediated immunity is provided by _____ lymphocytes.

3. White blood cells leave capillaries by a process called _____ .

4. The major phagocytic white blood cell is the _____ .

5. How do phagocytic and antibody-secreting white blood cells cooperate in the fight against infection?

6. Compare the origin and function of B and T lymphocytes.

7. What is a clone of lymphocytes? How is this clone produced?

8. Active immunity occurs when a person is exposed to a pathogen whose virulence (ability to cause disease) has been reduced but whose antigenicity is unaltered. How does this form of immunization protect the person during subsequent exposures to the pathogen?

9. Passive immunity occurs when an individual who is exposed to a virulent pathogen is injected with serum containing antibodies (*antiserum*) against that pathogen. Antiserum is usually obtained from an animal that had previously been injected with the same pathogen. What are the advantages and disadvantages of passive versus active immunity?

**Plate 1**  Formed elements of blood.

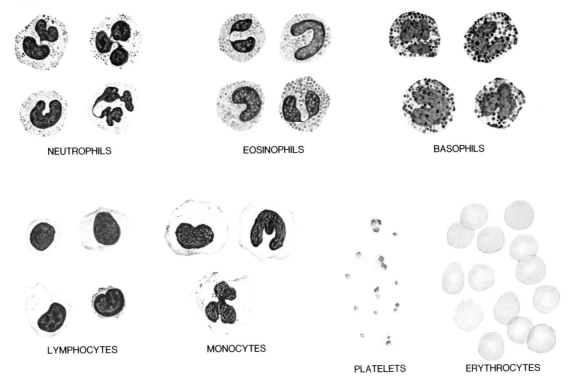

NEUTROPHILS    EOSINOPHILS    BASOPHILS

LYMPHOCYTES    MONOCYTES    PLATELETS    ERYTHROCYTES

The average differential count in the normal adult is as follows:

| Leukocyte | Percentage |
|---|---|
| Neutrophils | 55%–75% |
| Eosinophils | 2%–4% |
| Basophils | 0.5%–1% |
| Lymphocytes | 20%–40% |
| Monocytes | 3%–8% |

| Leukocyte | Cells Counted | Total |
|---|---|---|
| Neutrophils | | |
| Eosinophils | | |
| Basophils | | |
| Lymphocytes | | |
| Monocytes | | |

# Coombs' Test for Antibodies on Red Blood Cells

Human antibodies within the gamma globulin fraction of plasma proteins can serve as antigens when they are injected into a rabbit. The rabbit then produces its own antibodies directed against the human antibodies. These anti-antibodies are used clinically in the Coombs' test to detect the presence of human antibodies on red blood cells.

## Objectives

1. Explain how the antiserum in the Coombs' test is prepared, and describe the nature of this antiserum.
2. Explain how an agglutination reaction in the Coombs' test is produced.
3. Describe the clinical significance of a positive Coombs' test.

## Materials

1. Glass slides, Pasteur (transfer) pipettes
2. Coombs' antiserum (anti-gamma globulin)
3. Washed red blood cells, 50% suspension in isotonic saline

Nearly all the circulating antibodies belong to the **gamma globulin** fraction of plasma proteins. If a rabbit is injected with human gamma globulin, therefore, it will make antibodies against a large number of human antibodies, since these are foreign (and therefore antigenic) to the rabbit. Antiserum against human gamma globulin can subsequently be collected and used in the Coombs' test.

The Coombs' test was devised to detect antibodies on the surface of red blood cells, as might be found, for example, following incompatible transfusions or following the birth of an Rh positive baby to an Rh negative mother (see exercise 10.6). In these cases, the concentration of antibody on the red blood cell membrane may not produce an immediately detectable hemolysis, but may lead to complications after the individual has left the hospital.

Suppose that an individual with antigen $x$ on the red blood cells received an incompatible transfusion that resulted in coating of the red blood cells with a small amount of anti-$x$ antibody. Since this antibody is itself an antigen to one of the antibodies in anti–gamma globulin serum, the addition of this serum to the patient's blood will result in a positive *agglutination reaction,* analogous to the one performed for the determination of blood types (exercise 10.6).

$$\text{RBC} - ag_x - \text{anti-}x --- \text{anti-}\gamma --- \text{anti-}x - ag_x - \text{RBC}$$

Antibody — Globulin — Antibody

To test for the presence of antibody on the surface of the red blood cells, the plasma must be completely washed away, since the free antibodies in the plasma can compete with the bound antibodies on the red blood cells for the anti–gamma globulin. This competition would suppress the agglutination reaction.

## Clinical Significance

Since the Coombs' test detects the presence of gamma globulin (antibodies) on the red blood cells rather than the presence of particular antigens, it can be used to determine if a patient has become exposed to a variety of different antigens. The Coombs' test is thus widely used to double-check the accuracy of blood type cross matching following a transfusion and to determine if an Rh negative mother has become sensitized to the Rh antigen.

**Procedure**

1. A 50% suspension of red blood cells in isotonic saline will be provided. These cells were washed four times in normal saline to remove all plasma proteins.
2. Place 1 drop of the washed suspension of red blood cells on a clean glass slide.
3. Add a drop of anti–gamma globulin (Coombs' antiserum) to the slide.
4. Mix thoroughly with an applicator stick, and examine for agglutination within a 2-minute interval.

## Questions for Exercise 7.4

1. Explain how the Coombs' antiserum is obtained, and describe its specificity for antigens.

2. Describe how an agglutination reaction is produced in a positive Coombs' test.

3. Explain why a person who received an incompatible blood transfusion would have a positive Coombs' test.

# Autoimmunity and the Test for Rheumatoid Factor

Exercise **7.5**

---

Autoimmune diseases are those produced by the body's own immune system. Rheumatoid arthritis is an example of an autoimmune disease.

---

## Objectives

1. Explain how allergic and autoimmune responses differ from normal immune responses.
2. Demonstrate a test for rheumatoid arthritis, and explain why this disease is considered to be autoimmune.

## Materials

1. Glass slide, droppers, wooden mixing sticks
2. Plasma
3. Arthritis screen test (Wampole)

Although the purpose of the immune response is to protect the body against infection, the symptoms of many diseases are produced not by an invading pathogen, but by the immune response itself.

In hypersensitive individuals, certain antigens evoke the production of high levels of antibodies in the IgE class, whereas in normal individuals, lesser amounts of IgE together with antibodies of other classes would be produced. The IgE antibodies attach to the surface of tissue mast cells and basophils. When the same antigen (now called an **allergen**) next appears, it attaches to the antibodies on these cell surfaces, stimulating the release of histamine and other chemicals. These substances stimulate smooth muscle contraction (e.g., around the bronchioles in asthma) and increased capillary permeability, thus producing the symptoms of **allergy.**

When antigen-antibody complexes are free in the plasma, they can become trapped in tissue capillaries, producing inflammation of the affected organ. *Glomerulonephritis,* for example, may be produced in this way. It is thus not the specific antigen, but the immune response to the antigen that produces the disease.

When a tissue is infected with viruses, it can be destroyed by them unless antibodies destroy the cells before the viruses have reached maturity and are able to infect other cells. The disease poliomyelitis can develop in this way. Many viruses, however, do not destroy their host cells but simply produce viral antigens on the cell surface. The lymphocytes, of course, do not know that these antigens are harmless and mount a full immune response, thus destroying the infected cells through the activation of complement. The symptoms of mumps and hepatitis are believed to develop in this way.

Individuals do not normally produce antibodies to their own proteins—that is, the lymphocytes can distinguish *self* from *not self*. This distinction is made shortly after birth, at the time that *immunological competence* is established. The reason for this may be that lymphocytes that are capable of producing antibodies to the person's own molecules are destroyed at this time. Any antigen that appears after this event has occurred is usually foreign and a fit object for an immune response.

When some viruses infect cells, they evoke the appearance of cellular proteins that were not exposed to lymphocytes at the time that immunological competence was established. The immune system responds to these proteins as if they were foreign antigens, and T cells are mobilized to destroy the infected cells. An immune response that is mounted against the body's own proteins is termed **autoimmunity.**

**Rheumatoid arthritis** is believed to have an autoimmune etiology; the inflammation is caused not by an invading virus, but by the immune response to a newly revealed cellular protein. The presence of rheumatoid arthritis is often associated with an elevated concentration of gamma globulin in the plasma. This can be tested by mixing a drop of plasma with antibodies against gamma globulin that have been embedded on latex particles and checking for agglutination. A positive test is not specific for arthritis, however, and may be associated with other conditions, such as bacterial endocarditis, cirrhosis, viral hepatitis, and leukemia.

267

## Clinical Significance

In addition to autoimmune diseases that involve inflammation of the affected organ, some autoimmune diseases result in actual tissue destruction. In *Hashimoto's thyroiditis,* for example, autoantibodies destroy the thyroid gland, and in autoimmune *thrombocytopenia,* antibodies destroy the blood platelets. An interesting exception to this pattern occurs in *Graves' disease,* where autoantibodies act in a manner similar to the pituitary hormone TSH (thyroid-stimulating hormone). These antibodies (called LATS—long acting thyroid stimulator) cause an excessive growth of the thyroid (resulting in a goiter) and excessive secretion of thyroid hormones.

In the case of autoimmune diseases of the thyroid, treatment can involve use of antithyroid drugs and thyroidectomy (surgical removal of the thyroid). Rheumatoid arthritis is most frequently treated with large doses of aspirin, which is anti-inflammatory, and with cortisone, which is both anti-inflammatory and immunosuppressive.

## Procedure

1. Place 1 drop of test plasma on one end of a clean glass slide and 1 drop of positive control serum on the other end of the slide.
2. Add 1 drop of reagent 1 to both the test plasma and the control. Mix thoroughly with an applicator stick.
3. Add 2 drops of reagent 2 to both the test plasma and the control. Mix thoroughly with an applicator stick, spreading the samples over a 1-square-inch area.
4. Rock the slide gently for 3 minutes, and check for agglutination.

1. In allergic responses, antibodies of the _____ class are produced.

2. An antigen that provokes an allergic reaction is called an _____ .

3. Define autoimmune diseases, and citing examples, explain how they can produce organ damage.

4. Explain why aspirin and cortisone are used in the treatment of rheumatoid arthritis.

5. Explain how an autoimmune process can produce the hyperthyroidism of Graves' disease.

# Clotting System

There are two interrelated clotting pathways—the intrinsic system and the extrinsic system. These pathways require the successive activation of plasma clotting factors, and defects in these factors can be detected by means of two clotting time tests.

## Objectives

1. Describe the intrinsic and extrinsic clotting systems.
2. Describe the reasons why bleeding time is prolonged in vitamin K deficiency and in hemophilia.
3. Demonstrate the tests for prothrombin time and for activated partial thromboplastin time, and explain how these tests are used to diagnose bleeding disorders.

## Materials

1. Pipettes (0.10–0.20 ml), small test tubes
2. Constant temperature water bath set at 37° C
3. 0.02 M calcium chloride, activated thromboplastin, activated cephaloplastin (Dade), fresh plasma

Damage to a blood vessel initiates a series of events that, if successful, culminates in **hemostasis** (the arrest of bleeding). The first event is vasoconstriction, which decreases the flow of the blood in the damaged vessel. The next event is the formation of a platelet plug. This response occurs in two steps. In the first step, platelets adhere to the exposed collagen (connective tissue protein) of the damaged vessel and then release adenosine diphosphate (ADP). The second step occurs when the ADP, by making the platelets sticky, causes other platelets to adhere at this site and form a platelet clump. The third event is the sequential activation of clotting factors in the plasma, resulting in the formation of an insoluble fibrous protein, **fibrin,** around the platelet clump. This produces a blood clot.

The formation of fibrin from its precursor, *fibrinogen,* requires the presence of the enzyme *thrombin.*

$$\text{Fibrinogen} \xrightarrow{\text{thrombin}} \text{fibrin}$$

The insoluble fibrin is formed instantly whenever the enzyme thrombin is present, and thus the formation of thrombin must be a carefully regulated event in the body. The formulation of thrombin from its precursor, *prothrombin,* requires the sequential activation of a number of other clotting factors.

When the sequence of events leading to the formation of thrombin is initiated by the release of *tissue thromboplastin* from damaged tissue cells, fibrin is rapidly formed (10–15 seconds). These events constitute the **extrinsic system** of blood clotting, since the sequence is initiated by a factor extrinsic to the blood.

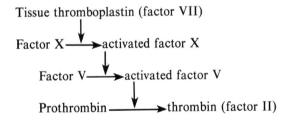

A blood clot may be initiated in the absence of tissue thromboplastin through the activation of *Hageman factor* (factor XII) by contact with glass, crystals, or collagen. This **intrinsic system** of blood clotting is relatively slow (28–45 seconds) compared with the extrinsic system.

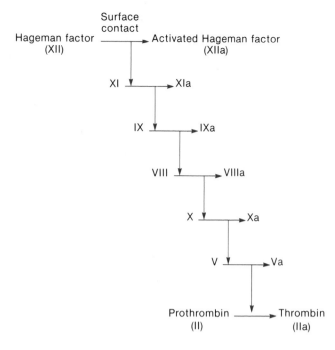

Many people have either an acquired or an inherited inability to form fibrin threads within the normal time interval. This inability may be due to a *vitamin K* deficiency, since this vitamin is necessary for the formation of four of the clotting factors, including prothrombin. Vitamin K deficiency may occur in the newborn because of an inadequate intake of milk, in a person with obstructive jaundice due to inadequate absorption of this vitamin (bile salts facilitate absorption), as a result of antibiotic therapy, and as a result of oral anticoagulants (e.g., dicumarol).

There are many hereditary conditions in which a clotting factor is either missing or defective. The best known of these conditions, classical *hemophilia,* is due to the genetic inability to synthesize normal factor VIII. This condition, as well as *Christmas disease* (defective factor IX), is inherited as a sex-linked recessive trait. Genetic defects inherited as autosomal traits include those associated with factors II, VII, X, XI, and XII.

In this exercise, two screening tests will be performed for defective clotting factors by using plasma in which the formation of thrombin has been inhibited by an anti-co-agulant. The anticoagulant used, either citric acid or oxalic acid, removes $Ca^{++}$ from the plasma. This has an anticoagulant effect because calcium is a necessary co-factor in the activation of a number of the clotting factors. This inhibition can be easily reversed by adding calcium during the clotting tests.

## Clinical Significance

The test for **prothrombin time** is used to determine deficiencies in the *extrinsic clotting system* and is prolonged when either factor V, VII, or X is defective. The test for **activated partial thromboplastin time** (APTT) is used to determine deficiencies in the *intrinsic clotting system* and is sensitive to all defective factors except factor VII (tissue thromboplastin). A person with classical hemophilia (defective factor VIII), therefore, would have a normal prothrombin time but an abnormal APTT. These two tests complement each other and can be used, together with other tests, to determine the exact cause of prolonged clotting time. (See table 7.1.)

## A. Test for Prothrombin Time

### Procedure

1. Pipette 0.10 ml of activated thromboplastin and 0.10 ml of 0.02 $M$ $CaCl_2$ into a test tube. Place the tube in a 37° C water bath, and allow it to warm for at least 1 minute.
2. Warm a sample of plasma in the water bath for at least 1 minute, then forcibly expel 0.10 ml of plasma into the tube containing the thromboplastin-$CaCl_2$ mixture. Start timing at this point.
3. Keep the tube in the water bath, and continuously agitate it for 10 seconds.
4. Remove the tube, quickly wipe it, and hold it in front of a bright light. Tilt the tube gently back and forth, and stop timing when the first fibrin threads appear (the solution will change from a fluid to a semigel). Enter the time in your laboratory report.

The normal prothrombin time is 11 ± 1 seconds.

## B. Test for Activated Partial Thromboplastin Time (APTT)

### Procedure

1. Warm a tube of 0.02 $M$ $CaCl_2$ by placing it in a 37° C water bath.
2. Pipette 0.10 ml of activated cephaloplastin and 0.10 ml of plasma into a test tube, and allow it to incubate at 37° C for 3 minutes.
3. Forcibly expel 0.10 ml of warmed $CaCl_2$ into the cephaloplastin-plasma mixture. Start timing at this point.

| Table 7.1 | Test results for clotting factors. | |
|---|---|---|
| Defective Factor | Prothrombin Time | APTT |
| V | Abnormal | Abnormal |
| VII | Abnormal | Normal |
| VIII | Normal | Abnormal |
| IX | Normal | Abnormal |
| X | Abnormal | Abnormal |
| XI | Normal | Abnormal |
| XII | Normal | Abnormal |

4. Allow the tube to incubate at 37° C for 30 seconds, agitating continuously; then remove the tube, quickly wipe it, and hold it against a bright light while rocking the tube back and forth.
5. Stop timing when the first fibrin threads appear. Enter the time in your laboratory report.

The normal APTT is less than 40 seconds.

## Data from Exercise 7.6

### A. Prothrombin Time

Enter your prothrombin time measurement in the space below:

_____ seconds

### B. Activated Partial Thromboplastin Time (APTT)

1. Enter your APTT measurement in the space below:

   _____ seconds

2. Compare your data to the normal measurements, and write your conclusions in the space below:


## Questions for Exercise 7.6

1. The factor that starts the extrinsic clotting pathway is

   _____ .

2. The factor that converts fibrinogen to fibrin is

   _____ .

3. The five factors that are common to both the intrinsic and extrinsic pathways are the following:

   _____

   _____

   _____

   _____

   _____

4. Heparin is a mucopolysaccharide extracted from beef lung and liver that inhibits the action of thrombin. Why was citric acid or oxalic acid used instead of heparin as an anticoagulant in the clotting tests?

5. Which factor(s) would be defective if a person had a prolonged prothrombin time but a normal partial thromboplastin time? Explain.

6. Why might a person with an abnormally slow clotting time be given vitamin K? Would treatment with vitamin K immediately improve the clotting time? Explain your answer.

# Renal Function and Homeostasis

The kidneys are responsible for the elimination of most of the waste products of metabolism, such as *urea* and *creatinine* (derived from protein catabolism) and *ketone bodies* (derived from fat catabolism). The difficulty of this kidney function is compounded by the fact that the kidney also retains (or *reabsorbs*) molecules that are essential for normal body function, such as *glucose, amino acids,* and *bicarbonate.*

The kidneys are involved in the maintenance of a constant internal environment (homeostasis) of *electrolyte concentrations, fluid balance,* and *acid-base balance.* The fluid volume of the blood is maintained by the reabsorption of 98%–99% of the water that leaves the blood in the initial step of urine formation, while the electrolyte and pH balance of the blood is maintained by the selective reabsorption of such ions as $Na^+$, $K^+$, $Cl^-$, and $HCO_3^-$.

The kidneys contain approximately two million functional units called **nephrons.** Each nephron is composed of two parts: (1) the *glomerulus,* which is a tightly woven, highly permeable capillary bed at the end of an arteriole, and (2) the *renal tubule,* which is a bent and convoluted tube composed of kidney cells (fig. 8.1). The mouth of the renal tubule (Bowman's capsule) envelops the glomerulus. The last part of the renal tubule (the collecting duct) empties its contents into the renal pelvis, which funnels urine to the ureters.

The formation of urine in the nephron can be divided into two stages. (1) The hydrostatic pressure of the blood squeezes fluid out of the capillary wall of the glomerulus, producing an *ultrafiltrate* of blood. Except for proteins, which are usually too large to leave the capillaries, the glomerular filtrate contains the same solute molecules as plasma and is isotonic to plasma. (2) As the glomerular filtrate passes through the renal tubules, the cells of the tubules selectively reabsorb solute molecules and ions. The solution that emerges at the end of the collecting duct (urine) is thus very different in composition and concentration from the solution that enters the tubule (glomerular filtrate).

**Figure 8.1.** Renal nephrons, showing glomeruli and different segments of the nephron tubules.

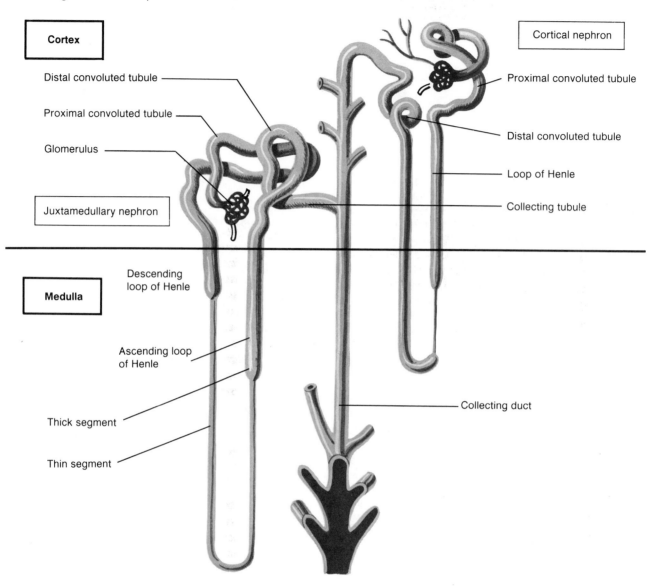

Cortex

Distal convoluted tubule

Proximal convoluted tubule

Glomerulus

Juxtamedullary nephron

Cortical nephron

Proximal convoluted tubule

Distal convoluted tubule

Loop of Henle

Collecting tubule

Medulla

Descending loop of Henle

Ascending loop of Henle

Thick segment

Thin segment

Collecting duct

# Renal Regulation of Fluid and Electrolyte Balance

The volume, solute concentration, and electrolyte content of the urine are adjusted to maintain homeostasis of the blood volume and composition. Loading the blood with water or with salt results in compensatory increases in the urinary excretion of these compounds.

## Objectives

1. Describe the roles of ADH and aldosterone in the regulation of fluid and electrolyte balance.
2. Calculate the milliequivalents per liter concentration of ions.
3. Demonstrate and explain how the kidneys respond to water and salt loading by changes in urinary volume, specific gravity, pH, and electrolyte composition.

## Materials

1. Urine collection cups
2. Urinometers, droppers
3. pH paper (pH range 3–9), potassium chromate (20 g per 100 ml), silver nitrate (2.9 g per 100 ml)
4. NaCl crystals or salt tablets

The reabsorption of fluid and electrolytes is adjusted to meet the needs of the body by the action of *hormones*. The major hormones involved in this process are **antidiuretic hormone (ADH)**, released by the posterior pituitary gland, and **aldosterone,** secreted by the adrenal cortex.

The release of antidiuretic hormone by the posterior pituitary is regulated by osmoreceptors in the hypothalamus. These receptors are stimulated by an increase in the osmotic pressure of the blood, as might occur, for example, in dehydration. The antidiuretic hormone released in response to this stimulus promotes the reabsorption of water from the renal tubules, resulting in (1) the retention of water and therefore a decrease in the osmotic pressure of the blood back to the normal level and (2) the excretion of a small volume of highly concentrated (hypertonic) urine.

The secretion of aldosterone by the adrenal cortex may be stimulated by an increase in blood $K^+$ or a decrease in blood $Na^+$ and blood volume. An increase in blood $K^+$ directly stimulates the adrenal cortex to secrete aldosterone. A decrease in blood $Na^+$ or blood volume indirectly affects aldosterone secretion by stimulating the kidneys to secrete the enzyme *renin* into the blood. The enzyme renin catalyzes the reaction that leads to the formation of a polypeptide known as **angiotensin II.** This substance has two known activities: (1) it stimulates vasoconstriction, thus increasing the blood pressure, and (2) it stimulates the secretion of aldosterone from the adrenal cortex. Aldosterone promotes the reabsorption of $Na^+$ from the glomerular filtrate into the blood, in exchange for $K^+$, which is secreted from the blood into the renal tubules. When $Na^+$ ions are reabsorbed, water follows passively owing to the osmotic gradient that is created.

## Milliequivalents

The concentrations of ions in body fluids are usually given in terms of milliequivalents (mEq) per liter. To understand the meaning and significance of this unit of measurement, we will consider the chloride concentration of the urine.

Suppose that a urine sample had a chloride concentration of 610 mg per 100 ml. How does this number of ions and this number of charges compare with the number of other ions and charges that are present in the urine? To determine this, we must first convert the chloride concentration from milligrams per 100 ml to millimoles per liter.

## Example

The atomic weight of chloride is 35.5. Therefore,

$$\frac{610 \text{ mg of Cl}^-}{100 \text{ ml}} \times \frac{1g}{1000 \text{ mg}} \times \frac{1000 \text{ ml}}{1 \text{ L}} \times \frac{1 \text{ mole}}{35.5 \text{ g}}$$

$$= 0.171 \ M \times \frac{1000mM}{1 \ M}$$

$$= 171mM$$

One mole of chloride has the same number of ions as 1 mole of $Na^+$ or 1 mole of $Ca^{++}$ or 1 mole of $SO_4^=$ or 1 mole of anything else. One mole of $Ca^{++}$, however, has twice the number of charges (*valence*) as 1 mole of $Cl^-$. It requires 2 moles of $Cl^-$, therefore, to neutralize 1 mole of $Ca^{++}$. If this is taken into account by *multiplying the moles by the valence,* the product is termed the **equivalent weight** of an ion. One-thousandth of the equivalent weight dissolved in 1 liter of solution gives a concentration in milliequivalents per liter (mEq/L).

## Example

$$171mM \times 1 \text{ (the valence of } Cl^-)$$

$$= 171 \text{ mEq/L of } Cl^-$$

The major advantage in expressing the concentrations of ions in milliequivalents per liter is that the total concentration of anions can easily be compared with the total concentration of cations. In an average sample of venous plasma, for example, the total anions and the total cations are each equal to 156 mEq/L. Chloride, the major anion, has a plasma concentration of 103 mEq/L. The chloride concentration in the urine is highly variable, ranging from 61 to 310 mEq/L.

## Clinical Significance

Due in large part to the effects of ADH and aldosterone, the kidneys can vary their excretion of water and electrolytes to maintain homeostasis of the blood volume and composition. Abnormally low blood volume can produce *hypotension* (low blood pressure) and may result in *circulatory shock*; abnormally high blood volume contributes to *hypertension*. Renal regulation of $Na^+/K^+$ balance is also critical for health. Changes in blood $Na^+$ cause secondary changes in blood volume. Changes in blood $K^+$ affect the bioelectrical properties of all cells, but the effects on the heart are particularly serious. *Hyperkalemia* (high blood $K^+$) is usually fatal when the $K^+$ concentration rises from 4 mEq/L (normal) to over 10 mEq/L. This may be caused by a variety of conditions, including inadequate aldosterone secretion (Addison's disease) or an excessive intake of potassium.

## Procedure

1. The students void their urine at the beginning of the laboratory session. They will analyze it, using this sample as the control (time zero).
2. The students drink 500 ml of water; some students should take 4.5 g of NaCl (salt tablets are easiest to take), whereas others should not take NaCl.
3. After drinking the solutions described in step 2, the urine is voided every 30 minutes for 2 hours. The urine samples are analyzed as described in step 4.
4. Each of the five urine samples collected are analyzed for pH, specific gravity, and chloride content in the following manner.
   a) *pH.* Determine the pH of the urine samples by dipping a strip of pH paper into the urine and matching the color developed with a color chart. The urine normally has a pH between 5.0 and 7.5.
   b) *Specific gravity.* Determine the specific gravity of the urine samples by floating a urinometer in a cylinder (fig. 8.2) nearly filled with the specimen. Read the specific gravity directly from the scale, making sure that the urinometer is not touching the bottom or the sides of the cylinder. The specific gravity is directly related to the amount of solutes in the urine and ranges from 1.010 to 1.025.
   c) *Chloride concentration.* When $Na^+$ is reabsorbed by the renal tubules, $Cl^-$ follows passively by electrostatic attraction. Determine the chloride concentration in the urine samples by the following method.
   (1) Measure 10 drops of urine into a test tube (1 drop is approximately 0.05 ml).
   (2) Add 1 drop of 20% potassium chromate solution with a second dropper.
   (3) Add 2.9% silver nitrate solution, 1 drop at a time, using a third dropper, while shaking the test tube continuously. Count the minimum number of drops that are just sufficient to change the color of the solution from yellow to brown.

**Figure 8.2.** Instruments for determining the specific gravity of urine. (a) a glass cylinder; (b) a urinometer float.

(4) Determine the chloride concentration of the urine sample. Since each drop of 2.9% silver nitrate added in step 3 is equivalent to 61 mg of $Cl^-$ per 100 ml of urine, simply multiply the number of drops added by 61 to obtain the chloride concentration of the urine in milligrams per 100 ml.

*Example*

If 10 drops of 2.9% silver nitrate were required, $10 \times 61$ mg of $Cl^-/100$ ml $= 610$ mg $Cl^-/100$ ml.

5. Convert the chloride concentration to mEq/L, and enter your data in the appropriate table in the laboratory report.

## Data from Exercise 8.1

Enter your data in the appropriate table below.

1. Ingestion of water only

| Time | Volume (ml) | pH | Specific Gravity | Chloride (mEq/L) |
|------|-------------|-----|------------------|-------------------|
| 0 | | | | |
| 30 | | | | |
| 60 | | | | |
| 90 | | | | |
| 120 | | | | |

2. Ingestion of water and NaCl

| Time | Volume (ml) | pH | Specific Gravity | Chloride (mEq/L) |
|------|-------------|-----|------------------|-------------------|
| 0 | | | | |
| 30 | | | | |
| 60 | | | | |
| 90 | | | | |
| 120 | | | | |

## Questions for Exercise 8.1

1. Name the hormone that stimulates the reabsorption of water and thus helps to produce a decrease in blood osmolality. _____

2. Name the hormone that is secreted in response to stimulation by angiotensin II. _____

3. Calcium is normally present in plasma at a concentration of about 0.1 g/L. Calculate the mEq/L of $Ca^{++}$ in the plasma. (The atomic weight of calcium is 40.)

4. Imagine a dehydrated desert prospector and a champagne-quaffing partygoer, each of whom drinks a liter of water at time zero and void urine over a period of 3 hours. Using their urine samples, compare the probable differences in volume and composition. (*Hint*: alcohol inhibits ADH secretion.)

| | Prospector | Partygoer |
|---|---|---|
| Urine Volume | | |
| Specific Gravity | | |
| $Na^+$, $K^+$, and $Cl^-$ content | | |

5. Explain your answers to question 4.

6. Many clinically used diuretic drugs inhibit $Na^+$ reabsorption in the loop of Henle. Predict the effect these drugs would have on the urinary excretion of $Cl^-$ and $K^+$, and explain your answer.

# Urea Clearance Rate Measurement

Urea and other waste products in the plasma are eliminated by the kidneys through excretion in the urine. The efficiency with which this process is performed for each solute is measured by its renal plasma clearance rate.

## Objectives

1. Describe the chemical nature and physiological significance of urea.
2. Define the renal plasma clearance rate, and explain how it is measured.
3. Perform a renal plasma clearance rate measurement for urea, and explain the physiological significance of this measurement.
4. Explain how the renal plasma clearance rate for a solute is affected by filtration, reabsorption, and secretion.

## Materials

1. Pipettes with mechanical pipettors (or Repipettes), mechanical microliter pipettes (capacity 20 $\mu$l), disposable tips
2. Colorimeter, cuvettes
3. BUN reagents and standard (Sclavo Diagnostics, available through Curtin Matheson Scientific, Inc.)
4. Sterile lancets, 70% alcohol
5. File
6. Microhematocrit centrifuge and heparinized capillary tubes

When amino acids are broken down in the process of cellular respiration or when they are converted to glucose (a process known as *gluconeogenesis*), the amino groups are removed and secreted into the blood in the form of urea. This function is performed by the liver.

$$NH_2 - C - NH_2$$
$$\underset{O}{\overset{\|}{}}$$

Urea

The urea is filtered by the glomerulus and enters the renal tubules. Since it is a waste product of amino acid metabolism, the urea is not selectively reabsorbed by the tubules. However, since cell membranes are highly permeable to the urea, it can move from the renal tubules back into the blood by a process known as *passive reabsorption*.

Because urea is passively reabsorbed after filtration, only 60% of the blood that is filtered by the glomeruli is cleared of urea. Since the average *glomerular filtration rate* (*GFR*) is 125 ml/min (for both kidneys), this amounts to an average of 75 ml/min of plasma that is cleared of urea. This figure is termed the urea **plasma clearance rate.**

The clearance rate of a substance depends on the size of the kidneys and the rate of urine production, as well as the other factors discussed. In this exercise, it will be assumed that the kidneys are of average size and that urine production is equal to or greater than 2.0 ml/min. Under these conditions, the clearance rate of urea can be calculated using the formula

$$\text{Clearance rate} = \frac{U \times V}{P}$$

where $U$ is the concentration of urea in urine, in milligrams per 100 ml, $P$ is the concentration of urea in plasma, in milligrams per 100 ml, and $V$ is the urine excreted in milliliters per minute.

The concentration $U$ of a substance in urine multiplied by the volume $V$ of urine produced per minute gives the milligrams of the substance excreted in the urine per minute. If this figure is divided by the concentration $P$ of the substance in the plasma, the result indicates the volume of plasma (in milliliters per minute) that contained the amount of the excreted substance. This is the amount of plasma per minute that was cleared by passage through the kidneys.

If the substance is filtered from the glomeruli but is not reabsorbed or secreted (as with the substance *inulin*), the renal clearance rate equals the glomerular filtration rate. If a substance is filtered but then reabsorbed into the blood (as with glucose, amino acids, urea, and many other substances), the renal plasma clearance rate must be less than the glomerular filtration rate. (How much less depends on the percent reabsorption.) If a substance enters the renal tubules both by filtration and by active transport from the capillaries into the nephron (a process called *secretion*), the renal plasma clearance rate is greater than the glomerular filtration rate. This is the case with the substance *para-aminohippuric acid (PAH)*, which is almost entirely removed from the blood in a single passage through the kidneys.

## Clinical Significance

The plasma concentration of blood urea nitrogen (BUN) reflects both the rate of urea formation from protein and the rate of urea excretion by filtration through the glomeruli of the kidneys. In the absence of abnormal protein metabolism, therefore, a rise in BUN indicates abnormal kidney function such as nephritis, pyelonephritis, or kidney stones.

Since the renal plasma clearance rate for urea is substantially less than the glomerular filtration rate (GFR) because of passive reabsorption, the urea clearance rate is not a particularly good indicator of kidney function. More useful clinically are the plasma clearance rate of exogenously administered inulin (a large polysaccharide) and endogenous creatinine (a byproduct of creatine, a molecule found primarily in muscle). Since inulin is neither reabsorbed nor secreted by the nephron, its clearance rate equals the GFR. Creatinine is secreted to a slight degree by the renal nephron, so its clearance rate is 20%–25% greater than the true GFR (as defined by the inulin clearance test).

## Procedure
### Collection of Plasma and Urine Samples

1. Empty the urinary bladder, then drink 500 ml of water as quickly as is comfortable.
2. About 20 minutes after drinking the water, obtain a drop of blood from the fingertip using a sterile lancet (first cleanse the fingertip with 70% alcohol). Fill a heparinized capillary tube at least halfway with blood, plug one end, and centrifuge in a microhematocrit centrifuge for 3 minutes (as in performing a hematocrit measurement).
3. Score the capillary tube lightly with a file at the plasma-cell junction, and break the tube at the scored mark. Expel the plasma into a small beaker or test tube.
4. Collect a urine sample 30 minutes after drinking the 500 ml of water. Measure the milliliters of water produced in 30 minutes, divide by 30, and enter the volume per minute of urine produced in the laboratory report.
5. Dilute the urine 1:20 with water. This can be done by adding 19 ml of water to 1 ml of urine, or by adding 1.9 ml of water to 0.10 ml (100 $\mu$l) of urine. Mix the diluted urine solution.

## Procedure
### Measurement of Urea

1. Label 4 test tubes or cuvettes $B$ (blank), $S$ (standard), $P$ (plasma), and $U$ (urine).
2. Pipette 2.5 ml of *Reagent A* into each tube. Then pipette 20 $\mu$l of the following into the indicated tubes:

   *Tube B:*  20 $\mu$l of distilled water
   *Tube S:*  20 $\mu$l of urea standard (28 mg/dl)
   *Tube P:*  20 $\mu$l of plasma from the capillary tube
   *Tube U:*  20 $\mu$l of the 30 minute urine sample that was previously diluted to 1/20 of its original concentration

**Note:** *Since 20 $\mu$l is a very small volume, pipetting must be carefully performed to be accurate. If an automatic microliter pipette is used, depress the plunger several times to wet the disposable tip thoroughly in the solution before withdrawing the 10 $\mu$l sample. When delivering the sample, depress the plunger to the first stop with the disposable tip against the wall of the test tube. Then pause several seconds before depressing the plunger to the second stop. Be sure to mix the test tube well so that you wash the sample from the test tube wall.*

3. Mix and incubate the tubes at room temperature for 10 min.
4. Pipette 2.5 ml of *Reagent B* into each tube and incubate for an additional 10 minutes.
5. Set the colorimeter at 600 nm, standardize with the reagent blank, and record the absorbance values of the standard, plasma, and urine samples in the data table in your laboratory report.
6. Calculate the urea concentration of the plasma (using Beer's Law, as described in exercise 2.1), and enter this value in your laboratory report.
7. Calculate the urea concentration of the diluted urine sample in the same manner as in step 6. Then multiply your answer by the dilution factor of 20, and enter this corrected value of the urea concentration of the urine in your laboratory report.
8. Using your values for the volume of urine produced per minute ($V$), plasma urea concentration ($P$), and urine area concentration ($U$), calculate your renal plasma clearance rate of urea. Enter this value in your laboratory report.

> The normal range of plasma urea is 5–25 mg/dl.

*Example*

Suppose $V$ (from step 6) = 2.0 ml/min

$P$ (from step 11) = 10 mg/dl

$U$ (from step 12) = 375 mg/dl

$$\text{Clearance rate} = \frac{\dfrac{375 \text{ mg}}{\text{dl}} \times \dfrac{2.0 \text{ ml}}{\text{min}}}{\dfrac{10 \text{ mg}}{\text{dl}}}$$

$$= 75 \text{ ml/min.}$$

> The normal range of urea renal plasma clearance rate is 64–99 ml/min.

Name _____

Date _____

Section _____

## Data from Exercise 8.2

1. Enter the volume of urine produced per minute in the space below.

   $V =$ _____ ml/min

2. Enter your absorbance values in the table below.

| Tube | Contents | Absorbance |
|------|----------|------------|
| 2 | Plasma | |
| 3 | Diluted urine | |
| 4 | Standard (28 mg/dl) | |

3. Enter the urea concentration of the

   plasma $(P)$ _____ mg/dl

   urine $(U)$ _____ mg/dl

4. Calculate your renal plasma clearance rate for urea, and enter this value in the space below.

   Clearance Rate = _____ ml/min

## Questions for Exercise 8.2

1. Name a molecule in the plasma which is

   (a) filtered but neither reabsorbed nor secreted _____

   (b) filtered and partially reabsorbed _____

   (c) filtered and completely secreted _____

   (d) filtered and only slightly secreted _____

   (e) not filtered _____

2. Identify the substances that have the following clearance rates:

   (a) The clearance rate is greater than zero but less than the GFR for _____ .

   (b) The clearance rate is equal to the GFR for _____ .

   (c) The clearance rate is slightly greater than the GFR for _____ .

   (d) The clearance rate is equal to the total plasma flow rate to the kidneys for _____ .

3. Define the plasma clearance rate, and explain how it is measured.

4. Explain the mechanism by which each of the following conditions might produce an increase in the plasma concentration of urea: (*a*) increased protein catabolism; (*b*) decreased blood pressure (in circulatory shock); and (*c*) kidney failure.

# Clinical Examination of the Urine

The presence of abnormally large amounts of proteins and casts in the urine indicates glomerular damage. The presence of bacteria and a large number of white blood cells in the sediment indicate urinary tract infection. Abnormal concentrations of glucose, ketone bodies, bilirubin, and other plasma solutes may indicate that these molecules are present in abnormally high concentrations in the plasma.

## Objectives

1. Describe the physiological processes responsible for normal urinary concentrations of protein, glucose, ketone bodies, and bilirubin in the urine.
2. Explain the pathological processes that may produce abnormal urinary concentrations of solutes and the clinical significance of this information.
3. Describe the normal constituents of urine sediment, and explain how the microscopic examination of urine sediment is clinically useful.

## Materials

1. Microscopes
2. Urine collection cups, test tubes, microscope slides, and cover slips
3. Albustix, Clinitest tablets, Ketostix, Hemastix, Ictotest tablets, or Multistix (all from Ames)
4. Sternheimer-Malbin stain
5. Centrifuge and centrifuge tubes
6. Transfer pipettes (droppers)

**Table 8.1**   Appearance of urine and cause.

| Color | Cause |
|---|---|
| Yellow-orange to brownish green | Bilirubin from obstructive jaundice |
| Red to red-brown | Hemoglobinuria |
| Smoky red | Unhemolyzed RBCs from urinary tract |
| Dark wine color | Hemolytic jaundice |
| Brown-black | Melanin pigment from melanoma |
| Dark brown | Liver infections, pernicious anemia, malaria |
| Green | Bacterial infection (*Pseudomonas aeruginosa*) |

A clinical examination of urine may provide evidence of urinary tract infection or kidney disease. Additionally, since urine is derived from plasma, an examination of the urine provides a convenient, nonintrusive means of assessing the composition of plasma and thus of detecting a variety of systemic diseases. A clinical examination of the urine includes an observation of its appearance (table 8.1), tests of its chemical composition, and a microscopic examination of urine sediment.

## Clinical Significance

When the kidneys are inflamed, the permeability of the glomerular capillaries may be increased, resulting in the leakage of proteins into the urine and the appearance of casts in the urine sediment. Since this represents a continuous loss of the solutes that produce the colloid osmotic pressure of plasma, fluid may accumulate in the tissues, resulting in *edema* together with the proteinuria.

The appearance of glucose in the urine suggests the presence of diabetes mellitus. If diabetes is suspected, however, the test for glucose in the urine alone is not sufficient, because a person may have hyperglycemia without glycosuria. This can occur if the plasma glucose concentration at the time of the test is not high enough to exceed the ability of the tubules to completely reabsorb glucose from the filtrate. If this **transport maximum** ($T_m$) for glucose is not exceeded, the urine will be free of glucose. A better test for diabetes is the oral *glucose tolerance test*. In this test the patient drinks a solution containing glucose, and samples of plasma are taken periodically to measure the rate at which the elevated plasma glucose declines to the normal level. A rate of decline that is slower than normal suggests inadequate insulin secretion or action.

## A. Test for Proteinuria

Since proteins are very large molecules (macromolecules), they are not normally present in measurable amounts in the glomerular ultrafiltrate or the urine. The detection of proteins in the urine, therefore, may indicate that the permeability of the glomerulus is abnormally increased. This may be caused by renal infections (glomerulonephritis), or it may be caused by other diseases that have secondarily affected the kidneys, such as diabetes mellitus, jaundice, or hyperthyroidism.

### Procedure

Dip the yellow end of an Albustix[12] strip into a urine sample, and compare the color developed with the chart provided. Enter your observations in the data table in your laboratory report.

## B. Test for Glycosuria

Although glucose is easily filtered in the glomerulus, it is not normally present in the urine, because all of the glucose that is filtered is normally reabsorbed from the renal tubules into the blood. This reabsorption process is *carrier mediated*—that is, the glucose is transported across the wall of the renal tubule by a molecular carrier.

---

12. Albustix strips, Clinitest tablets, Ketostix strips, Hemastix strips, and Ictotest tablets are from Ames Laboratories.

When the glucose concentration of the plasma and of the glomerular ultrafiltrate is within the normal limits (70–110 mg per 100 ml), there is a sufficient number of carrier molecules in the renal tubules to transport all the glucose back into the blood. However, if the blood glucose level exceeds a certain limit (called the **renal plasma threshold** for glucose, about 180 mg per 100 ml), the number of glucose molecules in the glomerular ultrafiltrate will be greater than the number of available carrier molecules, and the untransported glucose will spill over into the urine.

The chief cause of glycosuria is diabetes mellitus, although other conditions, such as hyperthyroidism, hyperpituitarism, and liver disease may also have this effect. Glycosuria, therefore, is not a renal disease but a symptom of other systemic diseases that raise the blood sugar level.

### Procedure

1. Place 10 drops of water and 5 drops of urine in a test tube.
2. Add a Clinitest tablet.
3. Wait 15 seconds, and compare the color developed with a color chart.
4. Record your observations in the data table in your laboratory report.

## C. Test for Ketonuria

When there is carbohydrate deprivation, such as in starvation or high-protein diets, the body relies increasingly on the metabolism of fats for energy. This pattern is also seen in people with the disease diabetes mellitus, where lack of insulin prevents the body cells from utilizing the large amounts of glucose available in the blood. This occurs because insulin is necessary for the transport of glucose from the blood into the body cells.

The metabolism of fat proceeds in a stepwise manner: (1) triglycerides are hydrolyzed to fatty acids and glycerol; (2) fatty acids are converted into smaller intermediate compounds—*acetoacetic acid, beta-hydroxybutyric acid,* and *acetone;* and (3) the intermediate products are utilized in aerobic cellular respiration. When the production of the intermediate products of fatty acid metabolism (collectively known as **ketone bodies**) exceeds the ability of the body to metabolize these compounds, they accumulate in the blood (*ketonemia*) and spill over into the urine (*ketonuria*).

### Procedure

Dip a Ketostix strip into a urine sample, and 15 seconds later, compare the color developed with the color chart. Record your observations in the data table in your laboratory report.

## D. Test for Hemoglobinuria

Hemoglobin may appear in the urine when there is hemolysis in the systemic blood vessels (e.g., in transfusion reactions), rupture of the capillaries of the glomerulus, or hemorrhage in the urinary system. In the latter condition, whole red blood cells may be found in the urine (*hematuria*), although the low osmotic pressure of the urine may cause hemolysis and the release of hemoglobin (hemoglobinuria) from these cells.

**Procedure**

Dip the test end of a Hemastix strip into the urine sample, wait 30 seconds, and compare the color developed with the color chart. Enter your observations in the data table in your laboratory report.

## E. Test for Bilirubinuria

The fixed phagocytic cells of the spleen and bone marrow (*reticuloendothelial system*) destroy old red blood cells and convert the heme groups of hemoglobin into the pigment *bilirubin*. The bilirubin is secreted into the blood and carried to the liver, where it is bonded to (*conjugated* with) glucuronic acid, a derivative of glucose. Some of the conjugated bilirubin is secreted into the blood, and the rest is excreted in the bile as bile pigment that passes into the small intestine.

The blood normally contains a small amount of free and conjugated bilirubin. An abnormally high level of blood bilirubin may result from (1) an increased rate of red blood cell destruction (hemolytic anemia); (2) liver damage, as in hepatitis and cirrhosis; and (3) obstruction of the common bile duct, as might occur because of a gallstone. The increase in blood bilirubin results in jaundice, a condition characterized by a brownish yellow pigmentation of the skin, of the sclera of the eye, and of the mucous membranes.

The kidneys can usually excrete only bilirubin that is conjugated with glucuronic acid. An increase in the urine bilirubin, therefore, may be associated with jaundice due to liver disease or bile duct obstruction, but it is not normally found in jaundice due to hemolytic anemia.

**Procedure**

1. Place 5 drops of urine on a square of the test mat.
2. Place an Ictotest tablet in the center of the mat.
3. Place 2 drops of water on the tablet.
4. Interpret the test as follows.
   a) Negative: Mat has no color or a slight pink to red color.
   b) Positive: Mat turns blue to purple. The speed and intensity of color development is proportional to the amount of bilirubin present.
5. Record your observations in the data table in your laboratory report.

## F. Microscopic Examination of Urine Sediment

Microscopic examination of the urine sediment may reveal the presence of various cells, crystals, bacteria, and casts. Casts are cylindrical structures formed by the precipitation of protein into the renal tubules.

Although a small number of casts are found in normal urine, a large number indicate renal disease such as glomerulonephritis and nephrosis. The casts may be either noncellular or cellular, containing leukocytes, erythrocytes, or epithelial cells (fig. 8.3). The presence of large numbers of erythrocytes, leukocytes, or epithelial cells in the urine is indicative of renal disease.

Although a small number of crystals are present in normal urine, a large number are associated with the tendency to form kidney stones, and a large number of uric acid crystals occur in gout (fig. 8.4).

**Procedure**

1. Fill a conical centrifuge tube ¾ full, and centrifuge at a moderate speed for 5 minutes.
2. Discard the supernatant, and place a drop of Sternheimer-Malbin stain on the sediment. Mix by aspiration with a transfer pipette.
3. Place a drop of the stained sediment on a clean slide, and cover with a cover slip.
4. Scan the slide with the low-power objective under reduced illumination, and identify the components of the sediment.

**Figure 8.3.** Components of urine sediment. (a) red blood cells; (b) white blood cells; (c) renal tubule epithelial cells; (d) bladder epithelial cells; (e) urethral epithelial cells; (f) bacteria; (g) a hyaline cast; (h) a waxy cast.

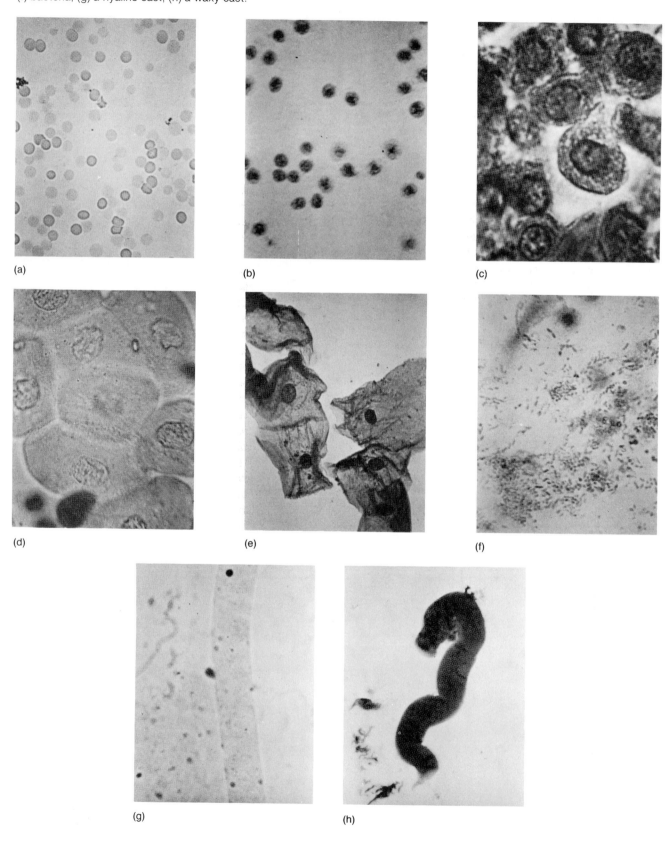

**Figure 8.4.** Crystals found in urine sediment.

Crystals

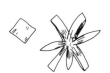    

1.  Uric acid    2.  Calcium oxalate    3.  Hippuric acid    4.  Ammonium–magnesium phosphate

5.  Calcium phosphate    6.  Cystine    7.  Tyrosine    8.  Cholesterol

## Data from Exercise 8.3

Record your data and the interpretations of your data in the table below:

| Urine Test | Result of Exercise (Positive or Negative) | Physiological Reason for Negative Result | Clinical Significance of Positive Result |
|---|---|---|---|
| Proteinuria | | | |
| Glycosuria | | | |
| Ketonuria | | | |
| Hemoglobinuria | | | |
| Bilirubinuria | | | |

# Questions for Exercise 8.3

1. Name a possible cause of each of the following conditions:

    (a) glycosuria _____

    (b) proteinuria _____

    (c) ketonuria _____

    (d) bilirubinuria _____

2. Explain the composition of urinary casts and how casts get into the urine.

3. Is it possible for someone to have an abnormally high plasma glucose concentration and yet not have glycosuria? Explain your answer.

4. Proteinuria and the presence of numerous casts in the urine are often accompanied by edema. What is the relationship between these symptoms?

# The Digestive System

The digestive tract is open to the environment at both ends by means of the mouth and the anus (fig. 9.1). Material that is inside this digestive tract is outside the body in the sense that it can only contact the epithelial cells that line the tract. For this material to reach the inner cells of the body, it must pass through the epithelial cells of the tract (a process known as **absorption**) into the blood. Before nutritive material can be absorbed, however, it must first be broken down by physical processes, such as chewing (mastication), and by enzymatic hydrolysis into its monomers. The process of hydrolyzing food molecules (polymers) into absorbable monomers is known as **digestion.**

The embryonic digestive system consists of a hollow tube, only one cell layer thick. As the embryo develops, different regions of the digestive tract become specialized for different functions. Some cells that line the tract become secretory, forming exocrine glands that secrete mucus, HCl, or particular hydrolytic enzymes characteristic of a certain region of the digestive tract (table 9.1). The liver, which produces bile, and the pancreas, which produces the many digestive enzymes found in

"pancreatic juice," develop as outpouchings (*diverticula*) of the embryonic small intestine and maintain their connections with the intestine by means of the hepatic and pancreatic ducts. Other regions of the small intestine become specialized for absorption through an increase in surface area due to epithelial folds (*villi*) and minute foldings of the epithelial cell membranes (*microvilli*). The digestive tract may be visualized as a disassembly line, where the food is conveyed, by means of muscular movements of the tract (*peristalsis*) and the opening and closing of sphincter muscles, from one stage of processing to the next. Coordination of these processes is achieved by neural reflexes and by hormones secreted by the gastrointestinal tract (table 9.2).

**Figure 9.1.** Organs of the digestive system.

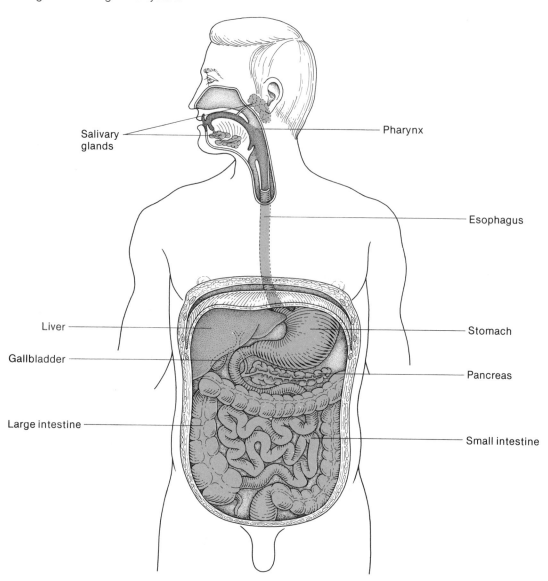

Salivary glands

Pharynx

Esophagus

Liver

Stomach

Gallbladder

Pancreas

Large intestine

Small intestine

**Table 9.1**   Selected enzymes of the digestive tract and their activities.

| Region of Tract | Substrate | Enzyme | Products of Enzyme Action | Optimal pH |
|---|---|---|---|---|
| Mouth | Carbohydrate Starch | Ptyalin (salivary amylase) | Maltose and higher polymers | 6.7 |
| Stomach | Protein | Pepsin | Polypeptides | 1.6–2.4 |
| Small intestine | Carbohydrate | | | |
| | Starch | Pancreatic amylase | Disaccharides | 6.7–7.0 |
| | Maltose | Maltase | Glucose | 5.0–7.0 |
| | Lactose | Lactase | Glucose and galactose | 5.8–6.2 |
| | Sucrose | Sucrase (invertase) | Glucose and fructose | 5.0–7.0 |
| | Protein | Trypsin | Polypeptides | 8.0 |
| | | Chymotrypsin | Dipeptides | 8.0 |
| | | Dipeptidase | Amino acids | 8.0 |
| | Nucleic acids | Nuclease Nucleotidase | Pentose sugar and purine and pyrimidine bases | 8.0 |
| | Lipid | Pancreatic and intestinal lipase | Glycerol and fatty acids | 8.0 |

**Table 9.2**   Summary of the physiological effects of gastrointestinal hormones.

| Secreted by | Hormone | Effects |
|---|---|---|
| Stomach | Gastrin | Stimulates parietal cells to secrete HCl, Stimulates chief cells to secrete pepsinogen, Maintains structure of gastric mucosa |
| Small intestine | Secretin | Stimulates water and bicarbonate secretion in pancreatic juice, Potentiates actions of cholecystokinin on pancreas |
| Small intestine | Cholecystokinin (CCK) | Stimulates contraction of the gallbladder, Stimulates secretion of pancreatic juice enzymes, Potentiates action of secretin on pancreas, Maintains structure of exocrine pancreas (acini) |
| Small intestine | Gastric inhibitory peptide (GIP) | Inhibits gastric emptying, Inhibits gastric acid secretion, Stimulates secretion of insulin from endocrine pancreas (islets of Langerhans) |

# 9.1 Histology of the Gastrointestinal Tract, Liver, and Pancreas

All regions of the gastrointestinal tract have mucosal, submucosal, muscularis, and serosal layers, but some of these layers display different specializations in different regions of the tract. The histological structure of the liver and pancreas provides insights into the functions of these organs.

## Objectives

1. Identify the mucosa, submucosa, muscularis, and serosa of different regions of the gastrointestinal tract.
2. Describe the structure and function of the histological layers of the esophagus, stomach, small intestine, and large intestine.
3. Describe the histologic structure of the liver, and explain the functional significance of this structure.
4. Describe the histologic structure of the pancreas, and distinguish the parts involved in the endocrine and exocrine functions of the pancreas.

## Materials

1. Microscopes
2. Prepared tissue slides of the digestive system

The tubular digestive tract, including the esophagus, stomach, small intestine, and large intestine, consists of four major layers (fig. 9.2). From the innermost layer outward, they are as follows:

1. The **mucosa,** or mucous membrane, consists of an inner epithelium over a thin layer of connective tissue (the *lamina propria*), which is bordered by a ribbon of smooth muscle, the *muscularis mucosa.* The epithelium is stratified squamous in the esophagus and anal canal and simple columnar in the stomach, small intestine, and large intestine.

2. The **submucosa** is connective tissue and therefore has abundant extracellular space for blood vessels, nerves, and mucus-secreting glands. Parasympathetic fibers and ganglia can be seen as the *submucosal (Meissner) plexus* in the submucosa.

3. The **muscularis externa** consists of smooth muscle, which in most of the digestive tract is arranged in an inner circular and outer longitudinal layer. Parasympathetic fibers and ganglia can be seen as the *myenteric (Auerbach) plexus* in this layer.

4. The **serosa** consists of a simple squamous epithelium and connective tissue and is the outermost covering of the digestive tract.

## A. The Esophagus and Stomach

The esophagus is lined with a stratified squamous epithelium. The muscles of the first third of the esophagus, like those of the pharynx and mouth, are striated to provide voluntary control of swallowing. The middle third contains a mixture of striated and smooth muscle, and the last third of the esophagus contains only involuntary smooth muscle (fig. 9.3).

The submucosa of the stomach contains large folds, or *rugae,* which can be seen with the unaided eye. Microscopic examination of the mucosa shows that it is also folded. The openings of these folds into the stomach lumen are called gastric pits. The cells that line the folds of mucosa are secretory and form the **gastric glands** (figs. 9.4 and 9.5).

The gastric glands include (1) *goblet cells,* which secrete mucus, (2) *parietal cells,* which secrete hydrochloric acid (HCl), (3) *chief cells,* which secrete pepsinogen (the inactive precursor of pepsin, a protein-digesting enzyme), (4) *argentaffin cells,* which secrete serotonin and histamine, and (5) *G cells,* which secrete the hormone gastrin into the blood. The gastric mucosa also secretes a polypeptide called *intrinsic factor,* which aids in the absorption of vitamin $B_{12}$ in the intestine.

**Figure 9.2.** A schematic illustration of the layers and structures seen in a cross section of the intestine.

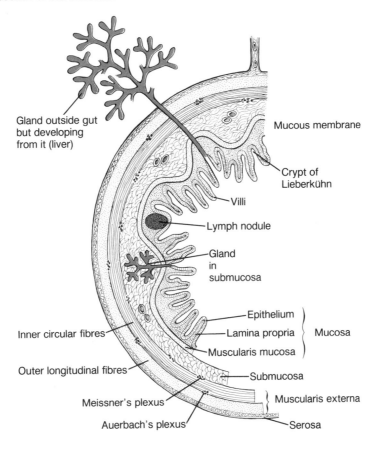

Gland outside gut but developing from it (liver)

Mucous membrane

Crypt of Lieberkühn

Villi

Lymph nodule

Gland in submucosa

Epithelium  }
Lamina propria  } Mucosa
Muscularis mucosa  }

Inner circular fibres

Outer longitudinal fibres

Submucosa

Meissner's plexus

Muscularis externa

Auerbach's plexus

Serosa

**Figure 9.3.** The microscopic appearance of the esophagus.

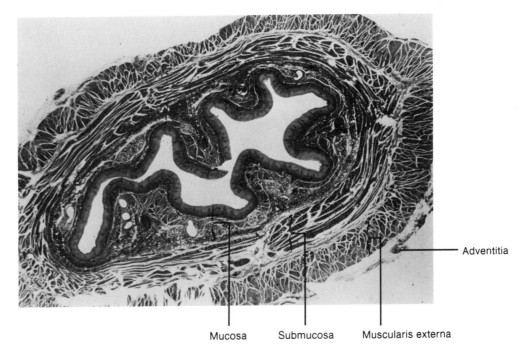

Adventitia

Mucosa          Submucosa          Muscularis externa

Histology of the Gastrointestinal Tract, Liver, and Pancreas          303

**Figure 9.4.** The microscopic structure of the stomach.

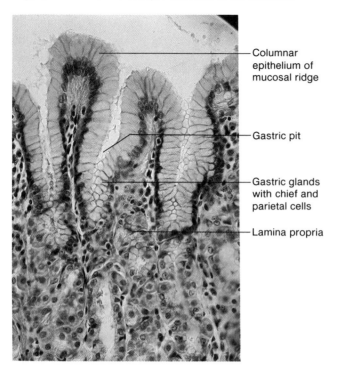

Columnar epithelium of mucosal ridge

Gastric pit

Gastric glands with chief and parietal cells

Lamina propria

## Procedure

1. Observe a cross section of the esophagus under 100× (using the 10× objective lens), and note the four major layers.

2. Hold a slide containing a stomach section up to a light source, and observe a fold, or ruga. Now place the slide on a microscope, and under 100×, observe the gastric pits and glands in the mucosa, the submucosa, and the muscularis externa.

3. Using the high-dry objective lens (45×), observe the gastric glands in the mucosa under a total magnification of 450×. Identify goblet cells near the surface of the gastric pits. These mucus-secreting cells are numerous and clear in appearance. Near the base of the glands, identify parietal cells (with red-staining cytoplasm) and chief cells (with blue-staining cytoplasm). Argentaffin and G cells cannot be easily identified without specially stained slides.

## B. The Small and Large Intestines

The small intestine is approximately 21 feet long and divided into three regions. The first 12 inches are called the **duodenum;** of the remaining length, the next two-fifths are known as the **jejunum** and the last three-fifths the **ileum.**

**Figure 9.5.** A schematic illustration of the gastric mucosa, showing gastric pits and glands.

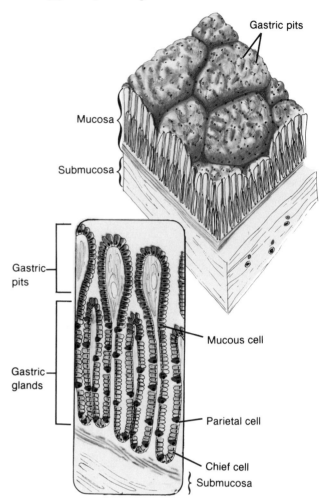

Gastric pits

Mucosa

Submucosa

Gastric pits

Gastric glands

Mucous cell

Parietal cell

Chief cell

Submucosa

The mucosa and submucosa of the small intestine form large folds called the *plicae circulares.* The surface area of the mucosa is further increased by microscopic folds that form fingerlike projections called *villi* (fig. 9.6). Each villus is covered with a simple columnar epithelium around a core of connective tissue (the lamina propria). The apical surface (facing the lumen) of each epithelial cell has a slightly blurred, "brush border," appearance because of numerous projections of its cell membrane in the form of *microvilli.* Microvilli can only be clearly seen with an electron microscope. The microvilli, villi, and plicae circulares increase the surface area of the small intestine tremendously, thus maximizing the rate at which the products of digestion can be absorbed by transport through the epithelium into the blood. Various digestive enzymes—called **brush border enzymes**—are fixed to the cell membranes of the microvilli and act together with enzymes in pancreatic juice to catalyze hydrolysis reactions of food molecules.

**Figure 9.6.** The microscopic structure of the duodenum.

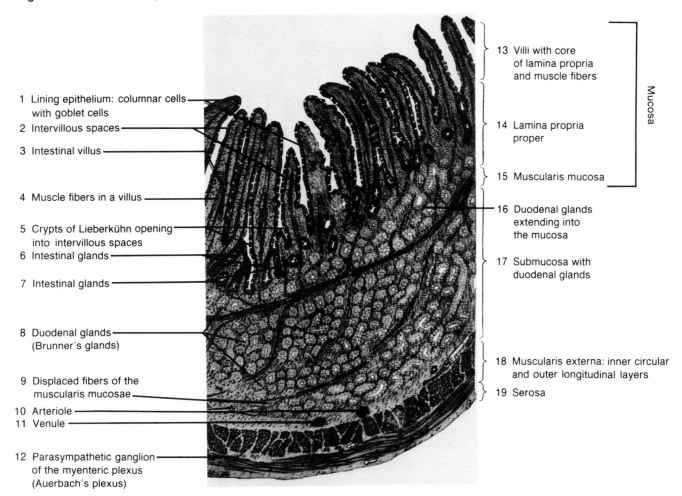

1 Lining epithelium: columnar cells with goblet cells
2 Intervillous spaces
3 Intestinal villus

4 Muscle fibers in a villus

5 Crypts of Lieberkühn opening into intervillous spaces
6 Intestinal glands

7 Intestinal glands

8 Duodenal glands (Brunner's glands)

9 Displaced fibers of the muscularis mucosae
10 Arteriole
11 Venule

12 Parasympathetic ganglion of the myenteric plexus (Auerbach's plexus)

13 Villi with core of lamina propria and muscle fibers

14 Lamina propria proper

15 Muscularis mucosa

Mucosa

16 Duodenal glands extending into the mucosa

17 Submucosa with duodenal glands

18 Muscularis externa: inner circular and outer longitudinal layers

19 Serosa

The epithelium at the base of the villi invaginates to form pouches called *crypts of Lieberkühn*. Although these appear somewhat similar to the gastric glands of the stomach, the crypts do not secrete enzymes. Instead, it appears that the cells within the crypts undergo mitotic division and push upward to replace those cells that are continuously lost from the tips of the villi. Within the submucosa of the duodenum are mucus-secreting *Brunner's glands* (fig. 9.6).

Waste products from the small intestine pass into the *colon* of the large intestine where water, sodium, and potassium are absorbed. The mucosa of the large intestine contains crypts of Lieberkühn but not villi, and thus its surface has a flat appearance. As with the small intestine, numerous lymphocytes can be seen in the lamina propria, and large lymphatic nodules appear at the junction of the mucosa and submucosa. Lymphatic nodules are clearly evident in a section of the appendix (fig. 9.7), which is a short outpouching from the cecum.

## Procedure

1. Use the lowest power available on the microscope to observe the layers of a section of small intestine. Identify the villi, submucosa, and muscularis externa.
2. Observe the villi using the 45× objective lens. Identify the goblet cells in the epithelium and the numerous lymphocytes (small, blue-staining cells) in the lamina propria within each villus. Also within the lamina propria, observe the *central lacteal*—a lymphatic vessel that transports absorbed fat from the intestine.
3. Observe a slide of the large intestine using the 10× objective lens, and note the absence of villi and the appearance of lymphatic nodules.

**Figure 9.7.** The microscopic appearance of a cross section of the human appendix, showing numerous lymphatic nodules.

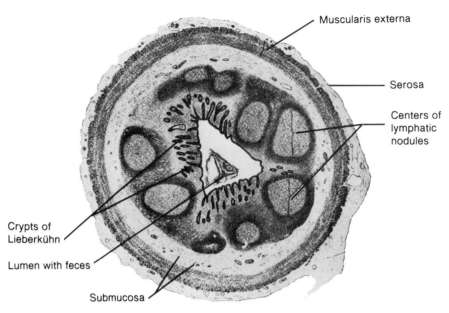

Muscularis externa

Serosa

Centers of lymphatic nodules

Crypts of Lieberkühn

Lumen with feces

Submucosa

## C. The Liver

The liver aids digestion by producing and secreting *bile* which emulsifies fat. Bile leaves the liver in the *common hepatic duct*, which branches to form the *cystic duct* and *common bile duct*. The cystic duct channels bile to the gallbladder where it is stored and concentrated. The common bile duct, together with the opening of the pancreatic duct, empties into the duodenum.

The liver also serves to modify the composition of the blood that drains from the intestine into the **hepatic portal vein.** Before this venous blood can return to the heart, it must pass through *sinusoids* in the liver tissue (figs. 9.8 and 9.9). These sinusoids function as liver capillaries, though they are wider than other types of capillaries and also differ from other capillaries in that they are lined with phagocytic cells (called *Kupffer cells*). Blood from the sinusoids is drained by small *central veins*, which ultimately merge to form the **hepatic vein** (fig. 9.9), which carries blood away from the liver. The sinusoids also receive arterial blood from branches of the **hepatic artery.** Arterial blood mixes with blood from the portal vein as it passes through the sinusoids to the central vein.

**Figure 9.8.** The structure of the liver. This diagram shows the arrangement of the hepatic plates, sinusoids, and blood vessels.

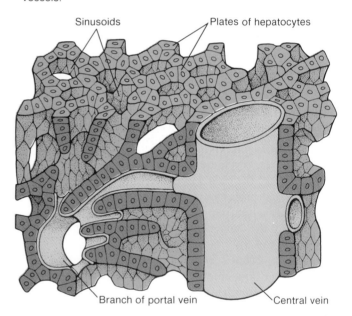

Sinusoids

Plates of hepatocytes

Branch of portal vein

Central vein

**Figure 9.9.** A liver lobule.

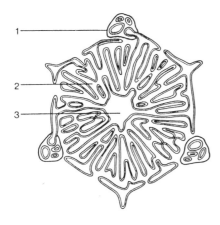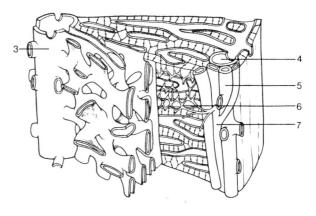

1. Hepatic triad
2. Sinusoid
3. Central vein
4. Hepatic portal vein

5. Hepatic artery
6. Bile capillary
7. Bile duct

Bile is produced and secreted by the liver cells (*hepatocytes*), but it does *not* mix with blood because it is secreted into *bile canaliculi,* located between adjacent hepatocytes and so does not enter the sinusoids (fig. 9.10). Bile is drained from the canaliculi into *bile ducts,* located near the openings of the portal vein and hepatic artery. The grouping of the portal vein, hepatic artery, and bile duct that one sees in a microscopic view of the liver is called a **portal triad.**

## Procedure

1. Examine a slide of the liver under low magnification, and locate a central vein and a portal triad. The central vein appears as a large "hole" into which a number of sinusoids empty. The portal vein may also appear as a large hole, but can easily be distinguished from the central vein by the fact that it is accompanied by openings of the hepatic artery and bile duct.
2. Observe a portal triad under high magnification, and distinguish between the portal vein, hepatic artery, and bile duct. The portal vein is the largest of the three; the hepatic artery can be identified by its layer of smooth muscle and lining of simple squamous endothelium, whereas the hepatic duct lacks smooth muscle and is lined with simple columnar epithelium.

## D. The Pancreas

The pancreas is both an exocrine and an endocrine gland. Most of the pancreas is composed of exocrine tissue, with secretory cells arranged in clusters, or **acini** (fig. 9.11). The pancreatic acini secrete *pancreatic juice* into openings of the *pancreatic duct,* which carries these secretions

to the duodenum. Pancreatic juice contains water, bicarbonate, and a variety of digestive enzymes, including *trypsin, lipase,* and *amylase* (for the digestion of protein, fat, and carbohydrates, respectively).

Scattered among the exocrine acini are islands of endocrine cells. These are the **islets of Langerhans** (fig. 9.11). The islets contain *alpha cells,* which secrete the hormone *glucagon,* and *beta cells,* which secrete the hormone *insulin.* These hormones are secreted into surrounding blood capillaries rather than into the pancreatic duct.

### Clinical Significance

Inflammation of the liver, or *hepatitis,* may result from viral infections, alcohol abuse, allergy, and a variety of drugs. This condition is usually reversible. In *cirrhosis,* large areas of liver tissue are destroyed and replaced with permanent connective tissue and "regenerative nodules" of hepatocytes that lack the platelike structure of normal liver tissue. Since, among its many functions, the liver produces plasma albumin and converts ammonia to urea, liver disease may be accompanied by a decrease in the plasma albumin concentration and in the appearance of ammonia in the blood.

Inflammation of the pancreas, or *pancreatitis,* can result from the action of digestive enzymes on pancreatic tissue. The digestive enzymes produced within the pancreas are normally inactive until they enter the duodenum, but activated enzymes may reflux from the duodenum into the pancreatic duct. When this occurs an inflammation reaction is produced, which is accompanied by a "leakage" of enzymes into the blood. This may be detected clinically by a rise in the plasma concentration of pancreatic amylase activity.

**Figure 9.10.** The flow of blood and bile in a liver lobule. Blood flows within sinusoids from the portal vein to the central vein (from the periphery to the center of a lobule). Bile flows in canaliculi within the hepatic plates in the opposite direction to bile ducts at the periphery of the lobule.

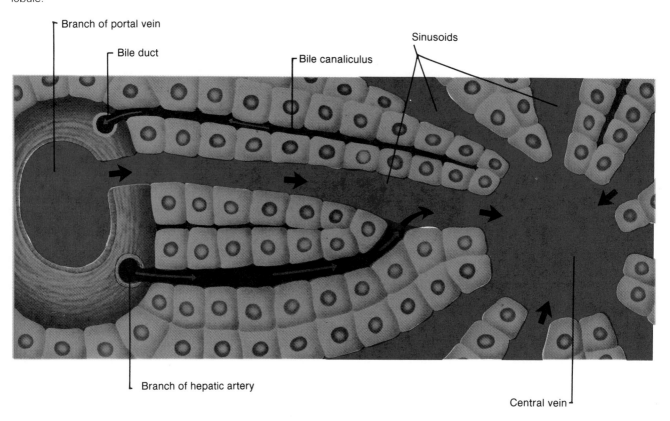

**Figure 9.11.** The histological structure of the pancreas (101×).

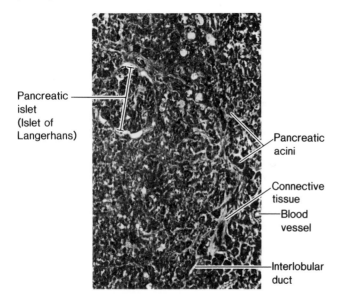

**Procedure**

1. Examine the pancreas under low magnification. The numerous small clusters of cells are the pancreatic acini. Occasional larger groupings of cells that are less intensely stained are islets of Langerhans.

2. Scan the slide for a pancreatic duct in cross section. When one has been found, change to high magnification, and observe its simple columnar epithelium.

Name _____

Date _____

Section _____

1. List the three layers found within the mucosa of the digestive tract:

_____

2. The cells of the gastric mucosa that secrete HCl are the _____ cells; the

   cells that secrete pepsinogen are the _____ cells.

3. Fingerlike projections of the mucosa of the small intestine are called _____ ; large

   folds of submucosa in the small intestine are called _____ .

4. Fingerlike projections of the apical cell membranes of mucosal cells in the small intestine are called _____

   _____ .

5. Blood from the intestine is transported to the liver in a vessel called the _____ ;

   this blood passes through the liver in structures called _____ .

6. The exocrine units of the pancreas are called _____ ; the endocrine structures are known as

   the _____ .

7. Describe the structural adaptations of the small intestine that help increase the rate at which digestion products
   can be absorbed.

8. Describe the location of digestive enzymes produced by the small intestine, and explain the function of the crypts
   of Lieberkühn.

9. Describe the histologic structure of the liver. Explain how this structure (*a*) allows the liver to modify the composition of blood and (*b*) keeps blood separate from bile.

10. Trace the path of pancreatic juice production and secretion. Explain how this path differs from the production and secretion of insulin.

# Digestion of Starch by Salivary Amylase

Saliva contains salivary amylase (ptyalin) that digests starch into sugars. By testing for the disappearance of substrate (starch) and the appearance of product (sugar), the effects of pH and heat denaturation on enzyme activity can be determined.

## Objectives

1. Describe the action of salivary amylase, and explain how its enzymatic activity can be demonstrated.
2. Explain how the activity of salivary amylase is influenced by changes in pH and how high temperature affects enzyme activity.

## Materials

1. Water bath (set at 37° C), Bunsen burners, test tubes, test-tube clamp, graduated cylinders
2. Starch solution: dissolve 1.0 g per 100 ml over heat
3. Iodine (Lugol's) reagent: dissolve 1.0 g iodine and 2.0 g potassium iodide in 300 ml of water
4. Benedict's reagent: dissolve 50.0 g sodium carbonate, 85.0 g sodium citrate, and 8.5 g copper sulfate in 5.0 liters of water

The digestion of starch begins in the mouth, where it is mixed with saliva containing the enzyme salivary amylase, or ptyalin. Starch, which is a long chain of repeating glucose subunits, is hydrolyzed first into shorter polysaccharide chains and eventually into the disaccharide maltose, which consists of two glucose subunits. Maltose, glucose, and other monosaccharides are known as **reducing sugars.**

In this exercise, the effects of pH and temperature on the activity of ptyalin will be tested by checking for the disappearance of substrate (starch) and the appearance of product (maltose) at the end of an incubation period.

The appearance of maltose in the incubation medium will be determined by the **Benedict's test,** where an alkaline solution of cupric ions ($Cu^{++}$) is reduced to cuprous ions ($Cu^+$), forming a yellow-colored precipitate of cuprous oxide ($Cu_2O$).

## Clinical Significance

Starch digestion begins in the mouth with the action of salivary amylase (ptyalin). This is usually of minor importance in digestion (unless one chews excessively), because most of the digestion of polysaccharides and complex sugars to monosaccharides occurs in the small intestine.

The action of salivary amylase may help prevent the accumulation of carbohydrates between the gums (gingiva) and the teeth, thus serving to protect against the growth of harmful bacteria that result in dental cavities (*caries*).

## Procedure (see fig. 9.12)

1. Label four clean test tubes 1–4.
2. Obtain 10 ml of saliva (use a small, graduated cylinder). Salivation can be aided by chewing a piece of paraffin. If only 5 ml of saliva is obtained, dilute the saliva with an equal volume of distilled water.
3. Add 3.0 ml of distilled water to tube 1.
4. Add 3.0 ml of saliva to tubes 2 and 3.
5. Add 3 drops of concentrated HCl to tube 3.
6. Boil the remaining saliva in a pyrex test tube by passing the tube through the flame of a Bunsen burner. (Use a test-tube clamp, and keep the tube at an angle, pointing it away from yourself and other students.) Add 3.0 ml of this boiled saliva to tube 4.
7. Add 5.0 ml of cooked starch (provided by the instructor) to each of the four tubes.

**Figure 9.12.** A chart of the procedure for exercise 9.2.

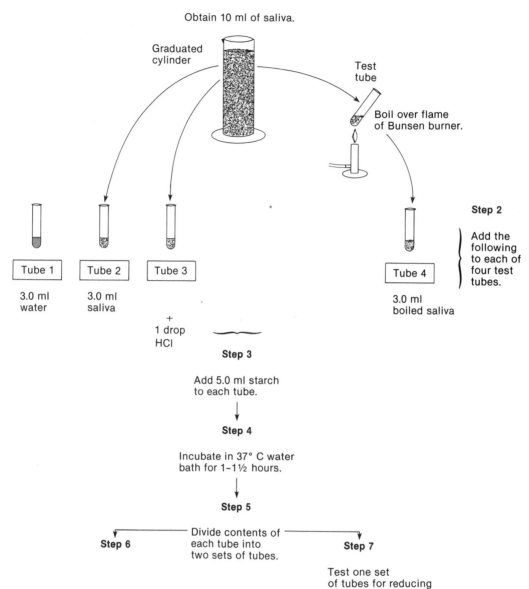

**Step 1**

Obtain 10 ml of saliva.

Graduated cylinder

Test tube

Boil over flame of Bunsen burner.

**Step 2**

Add the following to each of four test tubes.

| Tube 1 | Tube 2 | Tube 3 | Tube 4 |

3.0 ml water

3.0 ml saliva

+
1 drop
HCl

3.0 ml boiled saliva

**Step 3**

Add 5.0 ml starch to each tube.

**Step 4**

Incubate in 37° C water bath for 1–1½ hours.

**Step 5**

Divide contents of each tube into two sets of tubes.

**Step 6**

**Step 7**

Test one set of tubes for reducing sugars with Benedict's reagent.

8. Allow the tubes to incubate for 1–1½ hours in a 37° C water bath.
9. Divide the contents of each sample in half by pouring into four new test tubes.
10. Test one set of solutions for starch by adding a few drops of iodine solution (*Lugol's reagent*). A positive test is indicated by the development of a purplish black color.
11. Test the other set of solutions for reducing sugars in the following way:
   *a*) Add 5.0 ml of Benedict's reagent to each of the four test tubes, and immerse in a rapidly boiling water bath for 2 minutes.

*b*) Remove the tubes from the boiling water with a test-tube clamp, and rate the amount of reducing sugar present according to the following scale:

| | |
|---|---|
| blue | − |
| green | + |
| yellow | + + |
| orange | + + + |
| red | + + + + |

12. Enter your results in the data table in your laboratory report.

# Laboratory Report 9.2

## Data from Exercise 9.2

Enter your data in the table below using the rating method described in the procedure:

| Contents before Incubation | Starch after Incubation | Maltose after Incubation |
|---|---|---|
| 1. Starch + distilled water | | |
| 2. Starch + saliva | | |
| 3. Starch + saliva + HCl | | |
| 4. Starch + boiled saliva | | |

## Questions for Exercise 9.2

1. Which tube(s) contained the most starch following incubation? Which tube(s) contained the most sugar? What conclusions can you draw from these results?

2. What conclusions can you draw if both the test for starch and the test for sugar are positive for a particular tube? What might be the results if you let the tubes incubate for a longer period of time?

3. Reviewing your data, predict what would happen to salivary amylase activity once saliva is swallowed. Explain.

4. What effect does cooking have on enzyme activity? Explain why this effect occurs.

# Digestion of Egg Albumin by Pepsin

Exercise **9.3**

Pepsin hydrolyzes the peptide bonds of proteins and thus digests proteins into smaller polypeptide fragments. Pepsin is maximally active under the acidic conditions found in gastric juice.

## Objectives

1. Describe the action of pepsin, and demonstrate its ability to digest proteins.
2. Demonstrate the pH and temperature requirements of pepsin.
3. Explain why the stomach does not normally digest itself and how peptic ulcers may be formed.

## Materials

1. Water bath (set at 37° C), test tubes, droppers
2. Freezer or ice bath
3. Pepsin (5 g per 100 ml), 2 N HCl, 10 N NaOH
4. White of hard-boiled eggs

Although ptyalin is most active at the pH of saliva (pH 6–7), the enzyme pepsin has a pH optimum that is adapted to the normal pH of the stomach (pH less than 2). The low pH of the stomach is due to the secretion of HCl by parietal cells in the gastric glands. The strong acidity of the stomach coagulates proteins, thus facilitating their digestion by pepsin and the proteolytic enzymes in the small intestine.

Pepsin, which is secreted by the chief cells of the gastric glands, is responsible for the digestion of less than 15% of the protein into amino acids. Removal of the stomach (complete gastrectomy) thus has little effect on protein digestion. The major site of protein digestion is the small intestine, where the enzymes trypsin and chymotrypsin (secreted by the pancreas) and the dipeptidases (in the intestinal mucosa) hydrolyze proteins and smaller polypeptides into absorbable amino acids.

The stomach does not normally digest itself. When regions of the mucosa of the stomach or duodenum are digested by the strongly acidic gastric juice, a **peptic ulcer** (gastric or duodenal) is present. Although the etiology of peptic ulcers is not entirely known, it is believed that ulcers are caused by the influx of acid ($H^+$) from the gastric lumen into the mucosa rather than by digestion of the mucosa by pepsin.

Gastric ulcers are apparently not due to an increase in stomach acidity, but rather to a breakdown in the normal mucosal barriers to digestion. The barriers are believed to be (1) the "tight junctions" between adjacent epithelial cells that prevent $H^+$ ions from entering the mucosa and (2) the rapid renewal of surface epithelial cells. (The stomach sheds half a million cells a minute, completely renewing the gastric mucosa every three days.) The thick layer of mucus that covers the gastric epithelium is not by itself an effective barrier to self-digestion. The weakening of the mucosal barrier to $H^+$ ions is promoted by alcohol and salicylates (e.g., aspirin). Alcohol and salicylates taken in combination have a more than additive effect on the mucosal barrier (beware of taking aspirin to avoid a hangover!). The tight junctions between epithelial cells may also be disrupted by the detergent action of bile, which may be regurgitated from the duodenum and promote the development of gastric ulcers.

When the acidic products of the stomach (*chyme*) enter the duodenum, the intestine is stimulated to release the hormone **secretin,** which inhibits the gastric secretion of acid and stimulates the release of alkaline pancreatic juice. The acidic chyme is diluted and neutralized in the small intestine. These mechanisms, however, may not be sufficient to protect the intestinal mucosa when the stomach produces an excess of acid. Excessive stomach acid may be produced in susceptible individuals as a result of vagus stimulation and aggravate a duodenal ulcer.

**Figure 9.13.** A chart of the procedure for exercise 9.3.

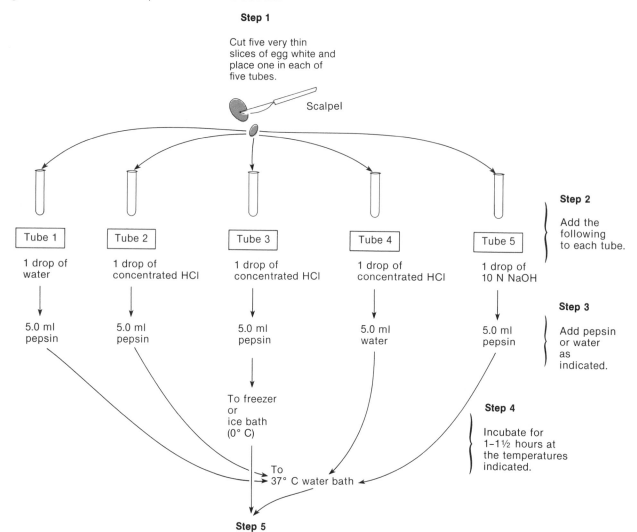

**Step 1**

Cut five very thin slices of egg white and place one in each of five tubes.

Scalpel

| Tube 1 | Tube 2 | Tube 3 | Tube 4 | Tube 5 |

**Step 2**

Add the following to each tube.

1 drop of water / 1 drop of concentrated HCl / 1 drop of concentrated HCl / 1 drop of concentrated HCl / 1 drop of 10 N NaOH

**Step 3**

Add pepsin or water as indicated.

5.0 ml pepsin / 5.0 ml pepsin / 5.0 ml pepsin / 5.0 ml water / 5.0 ml pepsin

To freezer or ice bath (0° C)

**Step 4**

Incubate for 1–1½ hours at the temperatures indicated.

To 37° C water bath

**Step 5**

Observe appearance of egg white.

## Procedure (see fig. 9.13)

1. Label five clean test tubes 1–5.
2. Using a sharp scalpel or razor blade, cut slices of egg white that are about the size of a fingernail and as thin as possible. This is critical; the slices should be very thin and uniform. Place an equally sized slice of egg white in each of the five test tubes.
3. Add one drop of distilled water to tube 1. Add 1 drop of concentrated hydrochloric acid (HCl) to tubes 2, 3, and 4. Add 1 drop of concentrated (10 N) NaOH to tube 5.
4. Add 5.0 ml of pepsin solution to tubes 1, 2, 3, and 5. Add 5.0 ml of distilled water to tube 4.
5. Place tubes 1, 2, 4, and 5 in a 37° C water bath. Place tube 3 in a freezer or ice bath.
6. After 1½–2 hours, remove the tubes (thaw the one that was frozen), and record the appearance of the egg white in the data table in your laboratory report.

## Data from Exercise 9.3

Enter your observations in the data table below:

| Conditions of Incubation | Appearance of Egg White after Incubation |
|---|---|
| 1. Protein + pepsin at 37° C | |
| 2. Protein + pepsin + HCl at 37° C | |
| 3. Protein + pepsin + HCl at 0° C | |
| 4. Protein + HCl at 37° C | |
| 5. Protein + pepsin + NaOH at 37° C | |

## Questions for Exercise 9.3

1. Which test tube showed the most digestion of egg albumin? What can you conclude about the pH optimum of pepsin?

2. Compare the effects of HCl on protein digestion by pepsin with the effects of HCl on starch digestion by salivary amylase (exercise 9.2). Explain the physiological significance of these effects.

3. Using the results of this exercise, explain why food that is frozen keeps longer than food at room temperature.

4. Why doesn't the stomach normally digest itself? Why doesn't gastric juice normally digest the duodenum?

# Digestion of Fat by Pancreatic Juice and Bile

Pancreatic juice contains a lipase enzyme that can hydrolyze the bonds joining fatty acids with glycerol. Maximum lipase activity is produced when fat is emulsified by bile salts.

## Objectives

1. Define the term *emulsification,* and explain how this process aids in the digestion of fat.
2. Demonstrate the action of pancreatic lipase and bile in fat digestion.
3. Describe how fat is digested, absorbed, and transported in the body.

## Materials

1. Water bath (set at 37° C), test tubes, droppers
2. pH meter or short-range pH paper
3. Pancreatin solution (1 g per 100 ml), bile salts
4. Cream or vegetable oil

Although the stomach produces a gastric lipase, the major digestion of fat occurs in the small intestine through the action of pancreatic and intestinal lipase. The digestion of fat in the small intestine is dependent on the presence of bile, produced by the liver and transported to the duodenum via the bile duct. (The gallbladder serves only to store and concentrate the bile.)

Since fat and water are not soluble in each other, the fat entering the duodenum is in the form of large droplets and contains the fat-soluble vitamins A, D, E, and K. The detergent action of bile salts lowers the surface tension of these large droplets, breaking them up into smaller droplets (**emulsification**). In this way, more surface area is presented to the lipase enzymes, allowing the digestion of fat into glycerol and fatty acids and the release of the fat-soluble vitamins.

The absorption of fat is more complicated than that of the water-soluble monomers. The glycerol and fatty acids produced by lipase action aggregate to form spherical structures (*micelles*), which are absorbed by the lining epithelium. Once in the epithelial cells, the monomers are resynthesized to form tiny droplets (*chylomicrons*) of triglycerides (fats), which are then secreted into lymphatic vessels and from there are carried to veins. Unlike the other products of digestion, therefore, lipids enter the blood as polymers rather than monomers. It should be emphasized, however, that all foodstuffs, including fats, must be completely digested into their monomers before they can be absorbed by the digestive epithelium.

In this exercise, we will test the digestion of fat into glycerol and fatty acids by measuring the *decrease in pH,* produced by the liberation of free fatty acids, as the digestion of triglycerides proceeds.

## Clinical Significance

The formation of *gallstones* is believed to be due, in part, to an excessive concentration of cholesterol in the bile. Blockage of the bile duct with a gallstone can result in the inadequate flow of bile to the intestine, producing obstructive jaundice and *steatorrhea* (the appearance of fat in the feces due to the inadequate digestion and absorption of fat). Steatorrhea is associated with a deficiency in the fat-soluble vitamins A, D, E, and K. Since vitamin K is necessary for normal blood clotting, this condition can be serious. *Obstructive jaundice* is an elevation in the blood content of the bile pigment bilirubin due to blockage of the bile duct, resulting in a yellowish discoloration of the skin, of the sclera of the eyes, and of the mucous membranes.

**Procedure**

1. Add the following to the indicated test tubes.

   1—3.0 ml of cream or vegetable oil + 5.0 ml of water + a few grains of bile salts

   2—3.0 ml of cream or vegetable oil + 5.0 ml of pancreatin solution

   3—3.0 ml of cream or vegetable oil + 5.0 ml of pancreatin solution + a few grains of bile salts

2. Incubate the tubes at 37° C for 1 hour, checking the pH of the solutions at 20-minute intervals with a pH meter or with short-range pH paper.

3. Record your data in the table in your laboratory report.

Name _____

Date _____

Section _____

## Data from Exercise 9.4

Record your data in the table below:

| | pH | | |
|---|---|---|---|
| Time | **1.** Cream or oil + bile salts | **2.** Cream or oil + pancreatin | **3.** Cream or oil + bile salts + pancreatin |
| 0 minutes | | | |
| 20 minutes | | | |
| 40 minutes | | | |
| 60 minutes | | | |

## Questions for Exercise 9.4

1. Explain why fat digestion affects the pH of the solution.

2. Does bile digest fat? Explain.

3. In which tube did fat digestion occur most rapidly? Explain why this is true.

4. A person with gallstones is observed to suffer from jaundice and an abnormally long clotting time. Explain the relationships between these observations.

5. How does the absorption of fat differ from the absorption of glucose and amino acids?

# The Endocrine System, Reproduction, and Genetics

Glands are units of secretory cells derived from the invagination of part of an epithelial membrane into the underlying connective tissue. If the invagination remains, it forms a duct leading from the secretory cells to the outside of the epithelial membrane and to the outside of the body (the body surface or the lumen of the digestive, respiratory, urinary, or reproductive tract). These glands are called *exocrine* glands. If the invagination disappears, the product of the gland **(hormone)** is secreted into the blood capillaries—the product is an internal secretion. These ductless glands are called **endocrine glands** (fig. 10.1).

Hormones secreted by endocrine glands regulate the activities of other organs. This regulation complements that of the nervous system and serves to direct the metabolism of the hormone's target cells along paths that benefit the body as a whole. By regulating the enzymatic activity of their target cells, hormones regulate total body metabolism and the function of the reproductive system.

**Figure 10.1.** The formation of exocrine and endocrine glands.

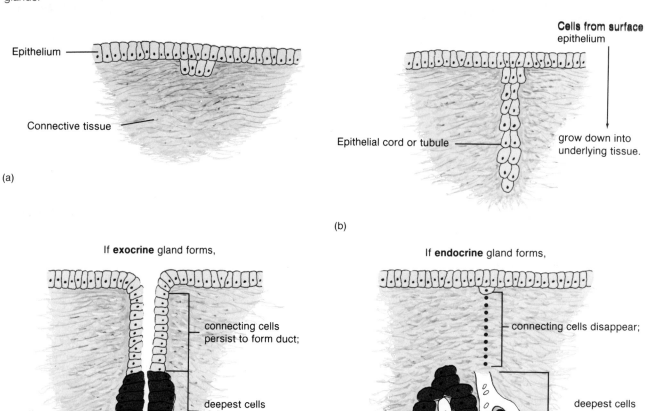

(a)

Epithelium

Connective tissue

Cells from surface epithelium

Epithelial cord or tubule

grow down into underlying tissue.

(b)

If **exocrine** gland forms,

connecting cells persist to form duct;

deepest cells become secretory.

(c)

If **endocrine** gland forms,

connecting cells disappear;

deepest cells remain to secrete into capillaries.

(d)

# Histology of the Endocrine Glands

Endocrine glands vary greatly in structure but share similarities in that all secrete hormones into the blood. The histological structure of the endocrine glands shows how these glands function and how they are related to surrounding nonendocrine structures.

## Objectives

1. Describe the structure of the ovaries and testes and the functions performed by their component parts.
2. Describe the histological structure of the pancreas, and identify its endocrine and exocrine structures.
3. Describe the structure of the thyroid and adrenal glands, and identify the functions of their component parts.
4. Describe the embryological origin and structure of the anterior pituitary and posterior pituitary gland.
5. List the hormones secreted by the anterior pituitary and posterior pituitary gland, and explain how the secretion of these hormones is regulated.

## Materials

1. Microscopes
2. Prepared slides

Endocrine glands may be independent organs (table 10.1), or they may be part of an organ that performs non-endocrine functions as well. Examples of the latter type of endocrine glands include the brain, stomach, pancreas, and liver.

Hormones are carried by the blood to all organs of the body; only certain organs, however, can respond to a given hormone. These are called the *target organs* for the hormone. Hormones affect the metabolism of their target organs and in so doing help regulate growth and development, total body metabolism, and reproduction.

## Clinical Significance

Knowledge of the normal histology of the endocrine glands not only helps in understanding their normal physiology, but also aids in the diagnosis of various pathological states. Endocrine glands may *atrophy* (lose structure) or have hormone-secreting tumors known as *adenomas*.

Various diseases of the testes, such as those resulting from Klinefelter's syndrome (XXY genotype) or mumps, are associated with atrophy of the seminiferous epithelium. In the ovaries, granulosa cell tumors may secrete excessive estrogen. The beta cells of the islets of Langerhans may decrease in number and have decreased granules per beta cell in diabetes mellitus. Pheochromocytoma, a tumor of the adrenal medulla, secretes excess epinephrine. Tumors of the anterior pituitary may result in gigantism and acromegaly (from elevated growth hormone), hyperpigmentation (from excessive adrenocorticotrophic hormone), or persistent lactation (from elevated prolactin secretion). These examples are but a few of many endocrine disorders associated with an abnormal histology of the glands involved.

## A. The Ovary

The ovary is an endocrine gland as well as the producer of female gametes (ova). The ovum can be thought of as an exocrine secretion, since it enters a duct (the uterine tube) after leaving the ovary. The hormones of the ovary—*estrogen* and *progesterone*—are secreted into the blood of the circulatory system.

The **ovarian follicles** are brought to maturity under the influence of the gonadotrophic hormones secreted by the anterior pituitary gland. In every cycle, one of the follicles eventually ruptures through the surface of the ovary, releasing its ovum. The empty follicle is then converted into a new endocrine structure, called the **corpus luteum.** If fertilization does not occur, the corpus luteum regresses, and the cycle is ready to begin again.

**Table 10.1** A partial list of the endocrine glands.

| Endocrine Gland | Major Hormones | Primary Target Organs | Primary Effects |
|---|---|---|---|
| Adrenal cortex | Cortisol<br>Aldosterone | Liver and muscles<br>Kidneys | Glucose metabolism<br>$Na^+$ retention, $K^+$ excretion |
| Adrenal medulla | Epinephrine | Heart, bronchioles, and blood vessels | Adrenergic stimulation |
| Hypothalamus | Releasing and inhibiting hormones | Anterior pituitary | Regulate secretion of anterior pituitary hormones |
| Intestine | Secretin and cholecystokinin | Stomach, liver, and pancreas | Inhibit gastric motility; stimulate bile and pancreatic juice secretion |
| Islets of Langerhans (pancreas) | Insulin | Many organs | Promote cellular uptake of glucose and formation of glycogen and fat |
| | Glucagon | Liver and adipose tissue | Stimulate hydrolysis of glycogen and fat |
| Ovaries | Estradiol–17β and progesterone | Female genital tract and mammary glands | Maintain structure of genital tract; promote secondary sexual characteristics |
| Parathyroids | Parathyroid hormone | Bone, intestine, and kidneys | Increase $Ca^{++}$ concentration in blood |
| Pineal | Melatonin | Hypothalamus and anterior pituitary | Affects secretion of gonadotrophic hormones |
| Pituitary, anterior | Trophic hormones | Endocrine glands and other organs | Stimulate growth and development of target organs; stimulate secretion of other hormones |
| Pituitary, posterior | Vasopressin<br>Oxytocin | Kidneys and blood vessels<br>Uterus and mammary glands | Promotes water retention and vasoconstriction<br>Stimulates contraction of uterus and mammary secretory units |
| Stomach | Gastrin | Stomach | Stimulates acid secretion |
| Testes | Testosterone | Prostate, seminal vesicles, and other organs | Stimulates secondary sexual development |
| Thymus | Thymosin | Lymph nodes | Stimulates white blood cell production |
| Thyroid | Thyroxine ($T_4$) and triiodothyronine ($T_3$) | Most organs | Growth and development; stimulate basal rate of cell respiration (basal metabolic rate, or BMR) |

The microscopic appearance of the ovary is thus continuously changing as the cycle progresses. A single slide of the ovary, furthermore, will reveal many follicles at different stages of maturation. To simplify matters, only the structure of a mature follicle (called a *graafian follicle*) just prior to ovulation will be considered.

## Procedure

Scan the slide of an ovarian follicle using the low-power objective, looking for a circular to elliptical structure that encloses a space filled with fluid and scattered cells. Identify the following parts of the follicle (fig. 10.2).

1. **Ovum.** The ovum is by far the largest cell in the follicle.
2. **Granulosa cells.** Granulosa cells are the numerous small cells found within the follicle.
3. **Antrum.** The antrum is the central, fluid-filled cavity of the follicle.

4. **Cumulus oophorus.** Cumulus oophorus means "egg-bearing hill." This is the mound of granulosa cells that supports the ovum.
5. **Corona radiata.** The corona radiata is the layer of granulosa cells that surrounds the ovum. This layer remains around the ovum after ovulation and presents the first barrier to sperm penetration during fertilization.

## B. The Testis

The testis produces both the male gametes (sperm) and the male sex hormone (testosterone). Sperm are produced within the **seminiferous tubules** and travel through these tubules to the *epididymis,* where the sperm are passed into a single tubule that becomes the *ductus (vas) deferens.* The ductus deferens picks up fluid from the seminal vesicles and the prostate gland and passes its contents, now called semen, to the ejaculatory duct.

**Figure 10.2.** An ovarian follicle with ovum (450×).

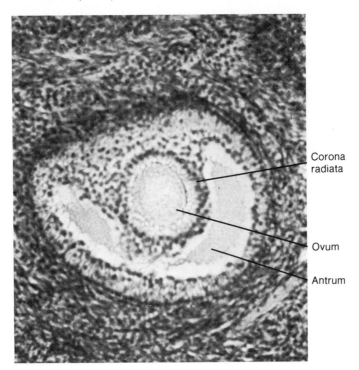

Corona radiata

Ovum

Antrum

The seminiferous tubules are highly convoluted and tightly packed within the testis. The small spaces (interstices) between adjacent convolutions of the tubules are filled with connective tissue known as **interstitial tissue.** Within this connective tissue are endocrine cells known as **Leydig cells,** which produce the *androgens* (male sex steroid hormones). The major androgen secreted by the Leydig cells of sexually mature males is *testosterone.*

Since the seminiferous tubules are highly convoluted, the chances of seeing a longitudinal section of a tubule are remote. Most of the tubules will be cut more or less in cross section, giving a circular to oblong appearance.

### Procedure

Scan the slide of the testis under low power. Since there are only one to four seminiferous tubules per lobule of the testis, most of the tubules you will see are actually sections through the same tubule that has been cut at different places. Using your high-power objective, observe the following structures (fig. 10.3).

1. **Spermatogenic cells.** Spermatogenic cells form a specialized type of epithelium that comprises most of the wall of the tubules. These cells divide by *meiosis* to produce the sperm. The cells in the outer wall are diploid (forty-six

chromosomes), whereas the cells in the inner wall have completed meiotic division and are haploid (twenty-three chromosomes). *Chromosomes* can be seen at various stages of meiosis within the tubular epithelium. Mature *spermatozoa* can be seen within the tubular lumen.

2. **Interstitial Leydig cells.** The interstitial cells can be seen between adjacent convolutions of the tubules.

## C. The Islets of Langerhans

The pancreas has both an exocrine and an endocrine function. The exocrine secretion (*pancreatic juice*) is produced by clusters of pancreatic cells, the pancreatic *acini,* which are arranged in clumps around a central duct. The exocrine secretion drains into *interlobular ducts,* located in bands of connective tissue, and from here drains into the pancreatic duct, which passes this secretion into the duodenum.

The endocrine secretions of the pancreas (*insulin* and *glucagon*) are produced by scattered groups of cells called the *islets of Langerhans.* These hormones do not enter the interlobular ducts but instead leave the pancreas via the vascular system.

**Figure 10.3.** A cross section of seminiferous tubules of testes. (a) A low-power photomicrograph (100×); (b) a high-power photomicrograph (450×) of a single seminiferous tubule.

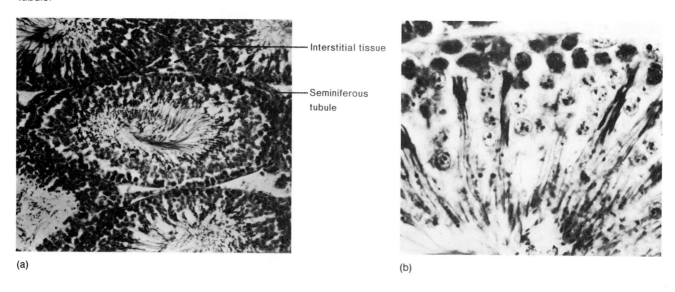

Interstitial tissue

Seminiferous tubule

(a)                                                    (b)

## Procedure

Scan the slide of the pancreas and identify the following structures (fig. 10.4).

1. **Pancreatic acini.** The pancreatic acini are dark-staining clusters of cells that form most of the body of the pancreas.
2. **Interlobular ducts.** The interlobular ducts may be mistaken for veins because of their large size, thin walls, and flattened, irregular shape. Unlike veins, however, their walls are composed of only a single layer of columnar epithelial cells, and no red blood cells will be seen in the lumina.
3. **Islets of Langerhans.** Under low power, the islets will appear as light patches, circular in shape, against the dark background of the acini. Under high power, the *alpha cells* (which secrete glucagon) can easily be distinguished from the *beta cells* (which secrete insulin) because the alpha cells are smaller and contain pink-staining granules, whereas the beta cells are larger and blue staining.

## D. The Adrenal Gland

The adrenal gland is really two different glands located in the same organ. In lower organisms, these glands are separated; but in higher organisms (including humans), they are closely associated as the **adrenal cortex** (outer part) and **adrenal medulla** (inner part).

**Figure 10.4.** Pancreatic tissue with an islet of Langerhans. © Carolina Biological Supply Company

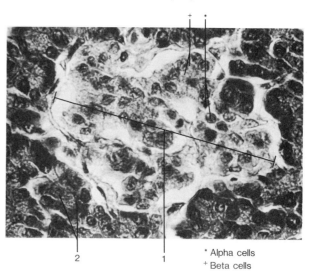

* Alpha cells
+ Beta cells

1. Islet of Langerhans
2. Acinar cells of pancreas

The adrenal cortex secretes steroid hormones. These include hormones that regulate salt balance (the *mineralocorticoids*) and hormones that regulate glucose homeostasis (the *glucocorticoids*). The adrenal medulla secretes two amine hormones, *epinephrine* and *norepinephrine,* which act together with sympathetic nerve stimulation to enhance the response of the cardiovascular system to increased physical demand. The cells of the adrenal medulla are derived from the same embryonic tissue

**Figure 10.5.** The adrenal gland: (a) the z. glomerulosa and the z. fasciculata of adrenal cortex (450×); (b) the z. reticularis of the cortex and adrenal medulla. © Carolina Biological Supply Company

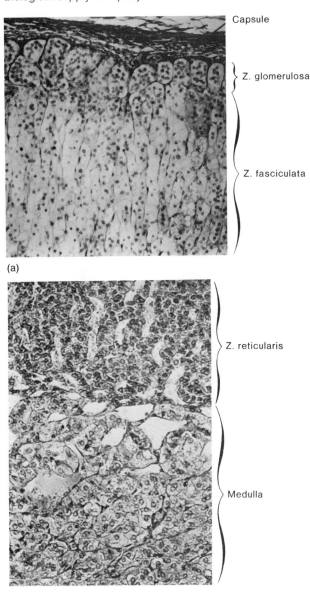

(a)

Capsule

Z. glomerulosa

Z. fasciculata

(b)

Z. reticularis

Medulla

1. **Capsule.** The capsule is a thin, tough layer of connective tissue that surrounds the gland.
2. **Zona glomerulosa.** The zona glomerulosa is the outer layer of the adrenal cortex, where the cells are tightly packed in an irregular arrangement. The z. glomerulosa secretes the mineralocorticoids—mainly *aldosterone* and *deoxycorticosterone.* The secretion of these hormones is largely under the control of angiotensin II.
3. **Zona fasciculata.** The zona fasciculata is located under the z. glomerulosa; this layer is the thickest part of the adrenal cortex. The cells in this layer are arranged in columns, or cords. These cells secrete the glucocorticoids when stimulated by adrenocorticotrophic hormone (ACTH), secreted by the anterior pituitary gland. The most important glucocorticoids are *cortisone* and *hydrocortisone* (*cortisol*).
4. **Zona reticularis.** The epithelial cells in the zona reticularis form interconnections (anastomoses) with one another and stain a darker color than the z. fasciculata. The z. reticularis is the innermost layer of the adrenal cortex and is also involved in the secretion of the glucocorticoids.
5. **Adrenal medulla.** The adrenal medulla is the central region of the gland and stains a lighter color than the surrounding z. reticularis.

## E. The Thyroid

Like the ovary, the functional units of the thyroid are arranged in the form of **follicles.** The thyroid follicles are composed of a single layer of epithelial cells surrounding a homogenous fluid, the *colloid*.

The secretions of the thyroid follicles are *triiodothyronine* ($T_3$) and *tetraiodothyronine* ($T_4$, or thyroxine). These hormones are passed from the epithelial cells of the follicle into the adjacent capillaries and are important regulators of growth and metabolism.

The thyroid gland also contains *parafollicular cells* that secrete the hormone *calcitonin* (also called *thyrocalcitonin*). This hormone is believed to play a relatively minor role in the regulation of blood calcium concentrations.

as postganglionic sympathetic neurons, whereas the adrenal cortex is derived from a different embryonic tissue. These two regions of the adrenal gland are therefore different both physiologically and histologically.

### Procedure

Before observing the slide of the adrenal gland under the microscope, hold it up to the light and observe that the adrenal cortex and medulla can easily be distinguished. Using the low-power objective, focus on the edge of the gland. As you scan from this point inward, identify the following structures (fig. 10.5).

### Procedure

Scan the slide under low power and observe the follicles (fig. 10.6). Note that when the slide was prepared, the colloid pulled away from the surrounding epithelial cells, leaving a clear space. This space is an artifact (produced by manipulation of the tissue) and is not present *in vivo*.

**Figure 10.6.** The histological structure of the thyroid gland. © Carolina Biological Supply Company

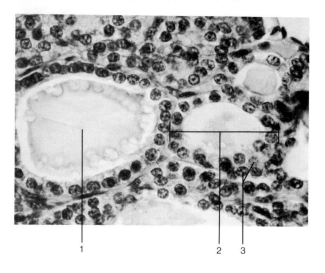

1. Thyroid colloid
2. Thyroid follicle
3. Parafollicular cells

## F. The Pituitary Gland

The pituitary, or *hypophysis* (fig. 10.7), like the adrenal gland, is composed of two distinct embryonic units. The **anterior pituitary,** also known as the **adenohypophysis** (*adeno* means "glandular"), is derived in the embryo from a dorsal outpouching (*Rathke's pouch*) of oral epithelium. Often referred to as the master gland, the anterior pituitary secretes the trophic hormones that control other glands and tissues (such as adrenocorticotrophic hormone, ACTH; thyroid stimulating hormone, TSH, etc.). The **posterior pituitary** (also known as the **neurohypophysis**) is derived in the embryo from a ventral outpouching of the floor of the brain and secretes only two hormones—vasopressin (or antidiuretic hormone) and oxytocin.

The secretion of both the anterior and the posterior pituitary glands is controlled by a part of the brain known as the *hypothalamus.* Since the posterior pituitary is derived from a downgrowth of the brain, there is a direct *neural* connection between this gland and the hypothalamus. Vasopressin and oxytocin are manufactured in the cell bodies of hypothalamic neurons and travel down the axons of these neurons to the posterior pituitary. The cells of this gland store these hormones until stimulated to release them by depolarization of the axons. The posterior pituitary is therefore simply a storage organ.

**Figure 10.7.** The structure of the pituitary gland seen in sagittal view.

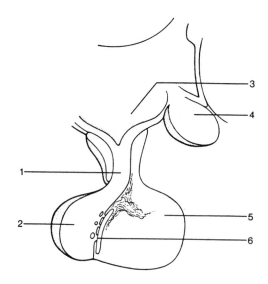

1. Infundibulum
2. Posterior lobe (neurohypophysis)
3. Hypothalamus
4. Optic chiasma
5. Anterior lobe (adenohypophysis)
6. Intermediate lobe

Since the anterior pituitary is derived from oral epithelium, and not from brain tissue, there is no direct neural connection between the hypothalamus and the anterior pituitary. There is, however, a special vascular connection between these two organs. A capillary bed in the hypothalamus is connected to a capillary bed in the anterior pituitary by means of venules that run between them. This vascular connection is known as the **hypothalamo-hypophyseal portal system.**

Unlike the posterior pituitary, the anterior pituitary manufactures its own hormones. The anterior pituitary releases its hormones upon the arrival of specific chemical messengers (called *releasing hormones*) secreted into the hypothalamo-hypophyseal portal system by the hypothalamus. This is illustrated in figure 10.8.

Knowledge of the physiology and embryology of the pituitary will greatly aid in studying its histology.

**Figure 10.8.** The relationship between the hypothalamus, anterior pituitary, and the target organs of the anterior pituitary hormones.

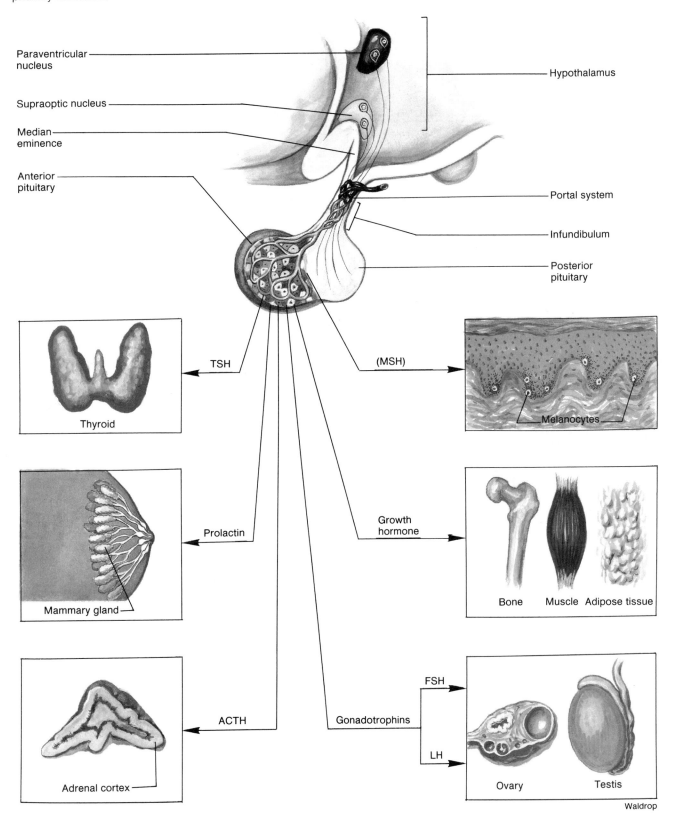

Paraventricular nucleus

Supraoptic nucleus

Median eminence

Anterior pituitary

Hypothalamus

Portal system

Infundibulum

Posterior pituitary

TSH

Thyroid

(MSH)

Melanocytes

Prolactin

Mammary gland

Growth hormone

Bone     Muscle   Adipose tissue

ACTH

Adrenal cortex

Gonadotrophins

FSH

LH

Ovary          Testis

Waldrop

## Procedure

Scan the slide of the pituitary gland under low power (fig. 10.9). You can immediately distinguish the anterior pituitary from the posterior pituitary by observing the distribution of capillaries. After you have distinguished the anterior and posterior pituitary, switch to the high-power objective, and identify the following structures.

1. Anterior pituitary
   a) **Sinusoids.** Sinusoids are a type of capillary that lack an endothelial wall. They can easily be identified by the presence of red blood cells.
   b) **Chromophils.** Chromophils get their name from the fact that the cytoplasm of these cells readily takes up stain. They are divided into two general categories on the basis of their staining properties—*acidophils,* which contain red-staining granules, and *basophils,* which contain blue-staining granules. These two categories of cells produce different hormones.
   c) **Chromophobes.** The cytoplasm of chromophobes does not pick up stain, and hence they appear quite dull next to the chromophils. It is believed that the chromophobes are not involved in hormone production.
2. Posterior pituitary
   a) **Nerve fibers.** Nerve fibers are the axons of hypothalamic neurons and compose most of the mass of the gland.
   b) **Pituicytes.** Pituicytes are randomly distributed among the nerve fibers and lack the bright colors of the cells of the anterior pituitary.

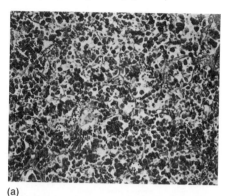

(a)

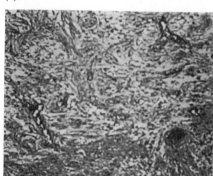

(b)

**Figure 10.9.** The pituitary gland. (a) the anterior pituitary (100×); (b) the posterior pituitary (100×).

Name _____

Date _____

Section _____

Match the gland with the hormone it secretes:

_____ 1. ovarian follicle
_____ 2. interstitial cells of Leydig
_____ 3. alpha cells of islets of Langerhans
_____ 4. beta cells of islets of Langerhans
_____ 5. zona glomerulosa of adrenal cortex
_____ 6. zona fasciculata of adrenal cortex
_____ 7. adrenal medulla
_____ 8. posterior pituitary gland
_____ 9. anterior pituitary gland

(a) growth hormone
(b) glucagon
(c) hydrocortisone
(d) insulin
(e) testosterone
(f) aldosterone
(g) estrogen
(h) oxytocin
(i) epinephrine
(j) thyroxine

10. The fluid-filled central cavity of an ovarian follicle is called a(n) _____ .

11. Most of the mass of the testis is composed of _____ .

12. Another name for tetraiodothyronine is _____ ;

    this hormone is secreted by the _____ .

13. Two glands that are derived from nervous tissue are the _____

    and the _____ .

14. What are the differences between an exocrine gland and an endocrine gland?

15. Would ligation (tying) of the pancreatic duct affect a measurement of blood glucose taken a few hours later? Explain your answer by relating it to your answer to question 14.

16. The anterior pituitary has sometimes been called the "master gland." Why is this term used? Why is this term incorrect?

# Thin-Layer Chromatography of Steroid Hormones

Slight differences in steroid structure produce significant differences in biological effects. Differences in structure and thus solubility can be used to separate a mixture of steroids and to identify unknown molecules.

## Objectives

1. Identify the major classes of steroid hormones and the glands that secrete them.
2. Describe the primary differences between different functional classes of steroid hormones.
3. Demonstrate the technique of thin-layer chromatography, and explain how this procedure works.

## Materials

1. Thin-layer plates (silica gel, F–254), chromatography developing chambers, capillary tubes
2. Driers (chromatography or hair driers), ultraviolet viewing box (short wavelength), rulers or spotting template (optional)
3. Steroid solutions, 1.0 mg/ml in absolute methanol of testosterone, hydrocortisone, cortisone, corticosterone, and deoxycorticosterone; 5 mg/ml of estradiol
4. Unknown steroid solution containing any two of the steroids previously described
5. Developing solvent: 60 ml benzene plus 10 ml ethyl acetate plus 10 ml acetone, or a volume containing a comparable 6:1:1 ratio of solvents

## Steroid Hormones

The steroid hormones, secreted by the adrenal cortex and the gonads, are characterized by a common four-ring structure. The carbon atoms in this structure are numbered as follows:

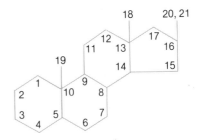

Seemingly slight modifications in chemical structure result in very great differences in biological activity. On the basis of their activity and their structure, the steroid hormones can be grouped into the following functional categories: (1) androgenic hormones; (2) estrogenic hormones; (3) progestational hormones; and (4) corticosteroid hormones, which are further divided into the subcategories of glucocorticoids and mineralocorticoids.

The *androgenic* hormones are characterized structurally by the fact that they are nineteen-carbon steroids and functionally by the fact that they promote the development of secondary male sex characteristics. The most potent androgenic hormone secreted by the testes is **testosterone.**

Testosterone

Although the primary source of androgens is the testes, the adrenal cortex also secretes small amounts. Large amounts of androgens are present in the plasma of persons suffering from tumors of the testes. Adrenal hyperplasia (Cushing's syndrome) and tumors of the adrenal cortex can also cause excessive androgen levels, which can have a masculinizing effect in females.

Testosterone and the other androgens are secreted in the testes by the interstitial Leydig cells. This secretion is stimulated by a gonadotrophic hormone of the anterior pituitary, *interstitial cell–stimulating hormone* (*ICSH*), which is identical to *luteinizing hormone* (*LH*).

Although the structural difference between the androgens and the *estrogens* is seemingly slight—the estrogens are eighteen-carbon steroids with three points of unsaturation (double bonds, see appendix 1) in the A ring—the difference in biological effects is pleasantly pronounced. The chief estrogenic hormone is **estradiol.**

Estradiol

The estrogens are normally secreted in cyclically increasing and decreasing amounts by the ovaries, reaching a peak at about the time of ovulation. The cyclical secretion of estrogens is stimulated by the cyclical secretion of a gonadotrophic hormone of the anterior pituitary, *follicle-stimulating hormone* (*FSH*).

Abnormally high concentrations of circulating estrogenic hormones may be due to tumors of the adrenal cortex or the gonads. This can have a feminizing effect in males.

In the normal female cycle, estrogens stimulate growth and development of the inner lining of the uterus (the *endometrium*). The final maturation of the endometrium is under the control of the hormone **progesterone,** secreted in the phase of the cycle after ovulation (*luteal* phase) by the *corpus luteum* of the ovaries. The cyclical secretion of progesterone is stimulated by the cyclical secretion of *luteinizing hormone* (*LH*) from the anterior pituitary. (LH and ICSH are two names for the same hormone, which has different effects in the two sexes.)

During pregnancy, the *placenta* secretes increasing amounts of progesterone, which is correlated with the development of the fetus. Progesterone is a twenty-one-carbon steroid.

Progesterone

The steroid hormones of the adrenal cortex (*corticosteroids*) also contain twenty-one carbons but differ from progesterone by the presence of three or more oxygen groups. These hormones are divided into two functional classes and are secreted by two functionally distinct regions of the cortex.

The *mineralocorticoids,* secreted by the zona glomerulosa, are involved in the regulation of sodium and potassium balance. The secretion of aldosterone (a mineralocorticoid) is stimulated by angiotensin II and is thus regulated by the secretion of renin from the kidneys. The most potent mineralocorticoids are **aldosterone** and, to a lesser degree, **deoxycorticosterone (DOC).**

Aldosterone

DOC

The *glucocorticoids,* secreted by the zona fasciculata and the zona reticularis, stimulate the breakdown of muscle proteins and the conversion of amino acids into glucose (gluconeogenesis). The secretions of the z. fasciculata and the z. reticularis are stimulated by the anterior pituitary hormone, adrenocorticotrophin (ACTH). The most potent glucocorticoids are **corticosterone, hydrocortisone (cortisol)**, and **cortisone.**

CH_2OH

Corticosterone

Cortisol (hydrocortisone)

Cortisone

An abnormal secretion of the mineralocorticoids is usually associated with hypertension and may be produced by primary aldosteronism or by secondary aldosteronism due to low blood sodium, high blood potassium, hypovolemia, cardiac failure, kidney failure, or cirrhosis of the liver. An increased secretion of the glucocorticoids is found in Cushing's syndrome (adrenal hyperplasia), pregnancy, and stress due to disease, surgery, and burns.

## Thin-layer Chromatography

In this exercise, an attempt will be made to identify two unknown steroids that are present in the same solution. To do this, you must (1) *separate* and (2) *identify* these steroids by comparing their behavior with that of known steroids.

Since each steroid has a different structure, each will have a different *solubility* (ability to be dissolved) in a given solvent. These differences will be used to separate and identify the steroids on a *thin-layer plate.*

The thin-layer plate consists of a thin layer of porous material (in this procedure, silica gel) that is coated on one side of a plastic, glass, or aluminum plate. The solutions of steroids are applied on different spots of the plate (a procedure called "spotting"), and the plate is placed in a solvent bath with the spots above the solvent.

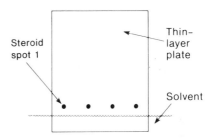

As the solvent creeps up the plate by capillary action, it will wash the steroids off their original spots (the *origin*) and carry them upward toward the other end of the plate. Since the solubility of each steroid is different, it takes longer for the solvent to wash and carry some than to wash and carry others. If the process is halted before all the steroids have been washed off the top of the plate, some will have migrated farther from the origin than others.

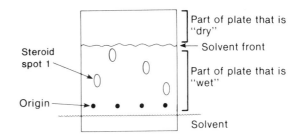

If this chromatography were repeated using the same steroids and the same solvent, the final pattern (*chromatogram*) would be the same as obtained previously. In other words, the distance that a given steroid migrates in a given solvent, relative to the *solvent front,* can be used as an identifying characteristic of that steroid. We can give this identity a numerical value by calculating the distance the steroid traveled relative to the front (the $R_f$ value) as follows.

$$R_f = \frac{\text{distance from origin to steroid spot } (D_s)}{\text{distance from origin to solvent front } (D_f)}$$

We can identify the unknown steroid by comparing its $R_f$ value in a given solvent with the $R_f$ values of known steroids in the same solvent.

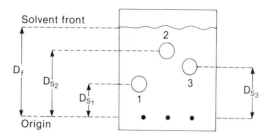

## Clinical Significance

The chromatographic separation and identification of steroid hormones has revealed much about endocrine physiology that is clinically useful. It was learned, for example, that the placenta secretes estrogens that are more polar (water soluble) than the predominant ovarian estrogen, estradiol. These polar placental estrogens—*estriol* and *estetrol*—are now measured clinically during pregnancy to assess the health of the placenta.

Chromatography of androgens recovered from their target tissues (such as the prostate) has revealed that these tissues convert testosterone into other products. Further, these products appear to be more biologically active (more androgenic) than testosterone itself. Testosterone secreted by the testes is thus a *prehormone,* which is enzymatically converted in the target tissue into more active products—*dihydrotestosterone (DHT)*, in many tissues. Males who have a congenital deficiency in 5α-reductase, the enzyme responsible for this conversion, therefore, show many symptoms of androgen deficiency even though their testes secrete large amounts of testosterone.

## Procedure

1. Using a pencil, make a tiny notch on the left margin of the thin-layer plate, approximately 1½ inches from the bottom. The origin of all the spots will lie on an imaginary line extending across the plate from this notch.

2. Using a capillary pipette, carefully spot steroid solution 1 (estradiol) about ½ inch in from the left-hand margin of the plate, along the imaginary line. Repeat this procedure, using the same steroid at the same spot, two more times. Allow the spot to dry between applications.

3. Repeat step 2 with each of the remaining steroid solutions (2, testosterone; 3, hydrocortisone; 4, cortisone; 5, corticosterone; 6, deoxycorticosterone; 7, unknown), spotting each steroid approximately ½ inch to the right of the previous steroid, along the imaginary line.

4. Observe the steroid spots at the origin under an ultraviolet lamp. (**Note:** Do not look directly at the UV light.)

5. Place the thin-layer plates in a developing chamber filled with solvent (benzene/ethyl acetate/acetone, 6:1:1), and allow the chromatogram to develop for 1 hour.

6. Remove the thin-layer plate, dry, and observe it under the UV light. Using a pencil, outline the spots observed under the UV light.

7. In the laboratory report, record the $R_f$ values of the known steroids, and determine the steroids present in the unknown solution.

## Data from Exercise 10.2

Record your data in the table below, and calculate the $R_f$ value of each spot.

| Steroid | Distance to Front | Distance to Spot | $R_f$ |
|---|---|---|---|
| 1. Estradiol | | | |
| 2. Testosterone | same | | |
| 3. Hydrocortisone | ——— | | |
| 4. Cortisone | ——— | | |
| 5. Corticosterone | ——— | | |
| 6. Deoxycorticosterone | ——— | | |
| 7. Unknown 1 | ——— | | |
| Unknown 2 | ——— | | |

## Questions for Exercise 10.2

1. The chief estrogenic hormone is _____ ;

   the most potent androgen is _____ .

2. Name the following steroids:

   (a) eighteen-carbon sex steroid _____

   (b) nineteen-carbon sex steroid _____

   (c) twenty-one-carbon sex steroid _____

3. Progesterone is secreted by the _____ and

   the _____ .

4. The most potent mineralocorticoid is _____ ;

   the major glucocorticoid is _____ .

5. Review the $R_f$ values of the different steroids in this exercise, and by comparing these, describe the relative solubilities of the steroids in the solvent used.

6. Suppose that prostate tissue were incubated with a flask of radioactively labeled testosterone. If the steroids were subsequently extracted from this tissue and chromatographed, which steroids would be radioactive? Explain the physiological and clinical significance of these results.

# Insulin Shock

Insulin stimulates the tissue uptake of blood glucose and thus acts to lower the blood glucose concentration. Excessive insulin can therefore cause hypoglycemia, which because of the brain's reliance on blood glucose, can affect brain function and even produce coma and death.

## Objectives

1. Describe the mechanism by which insulin regulates the blood glucose concentration.
2. Demonstrate the effects of excessive insulin on a small fish, and explain the clinical significance of these effects.

## Materials

1. Large beaker filled with water
2. Guppy, goldfish, or another fish of comparable size
3. Insulin (insulin, zinc—100 I.U.), glucose

Insulin is a polypeptide hormone secreted by the beta cells of the islets of Langerhans. Insulin stimulates the *transport* of glucose from the blood into the muscles, liver, and adipose tissue, thus lowering the blood sugar.

When the islets are incapable of secreting an adequate amount of insulin (a condition known as **diabetes mellitus**), the transport of glucose from the blood into the body tissues is impaired. This results in an increase in the blood sugar level (hyperglycemia) and in the appearance of glucose in the urine.

Under these conditions, the body tissues cannot obtain sufficient glucose for cellular respiration and thus rely increasingly on the metabolism of fat for energy. The intermediate products of fat metabolism (ketone bodies) increase in the blood, resulting in *ketoacidosis*. As a result of these changes, the kidneys excrete excessive amounts of water in the urine, resulting in *dehydration*. The combination of acidosis and dehydration that results from insufficient insulin may produce a *diabetic coma*.

The diabetic patient must be given insulin injections to maintain a homeostatic state. If the diabetic is given too much insulin, however, the blood sugar level will fall below normal (**hypoglycemia**). Since the central nervous system can only metabolize glucose for energy, and since it cannot store glucose in the form of glycogen (unlike the liver and muscles), the lowering of blood sugar essentially starves the brain. This condition is called *insulin shock*.

The blood glucose concentration may rapidly decrease to hypoglycemic levels when a diabetic patient takes an overdose of insulin. This may result in the symptoms of insulin shock, as illustrated by the reaction of the fish to insulin in the present experiment. Hypoglycemia can, however, have other causes and can result in symptoms less severe than those seen in insulin shock.

*Reactive hypoglycemia* may occur following a meal if the beta cells secrete excessive insulin in response to carbohydrates in the food. This type of hypoglycemia sometimes occurs in the beginning stages of diabetes mellitus and can often be treated by dietary restrictions— eating smaller, more frequent meals that are lower in carbohydrates. Hypoglycemia can also occur as a result of alcohol ingestion, for reasons that are not well understood. Other causes of hypoglycemia include tumors of the beta cells (insulinomas), which secrete excessive insulin, and liver diseases in which the ability to produce glucose from glycogen and noncarbohydrate molecules is impaired.

The symptoms of hypoglycemia appear when the blood glucose concentration is about 45 mg/dl, although symptoms can appear at higher glucose concentrations if the cerebral circulation is impaired, as it may be in elderly people as a result of atherosclerosis. These symptoms of glucose deficiency are similar to those seen when the brain lacks sufficient oxygen—faintness, weakness, nervousness, hunger, muscular trembling, and tachycardia. More prolonged hypoglycemia may damage other parts of the brain, resulting in behavior resembling neuroses and psychoses, and severe brain damage may result in coma and death.

Hypoglycemia, like diabetes mellitus, may be detected by means of the oral glucose tolerance test. In this test, a patient ingests a glucose solution, after which blood samples are taken periodically. Hypoglycemia is suggested when the elevated blood glucose concentration returns to the normal level too quickly because of excessive insulin secretion or action.

## Procedure

1. Place a small fish (guppy or goldfish) in a large beaker of water to which a few hundred units of insulin have been added.
2. Observe the effects of insulin overdose. (If no effects are seen in 30 minutes, repeat this step with another fish.)
3. Remove the fish to a second beaker of water containing 5% glucose.

1. A person in a diabetic state may have acetone breath. Explain why this occurs.

2. A person on a strict noncarbohydrate diet may develop symptoms characteristic of diabetes mellitus. These dieters are advised to check their urine for ketone bodies and drink plenty of water. Explain.

3. Hyperglycemia is a symptom, not a cause, of diabetes mellitus. Hypoglycemia, on the other hand, is a direct cause of the symptoms associated with an oversecretion of insulin. Explain.

# Ovarian Cycle as Studied by a Vaginal Smear of the Rat

The cyclic changes in ovarian hormone secretion cause cyclic changes in the epithelium of the female genital tract. The observation of exfoliated cells provides information about the stage of the ovarian cycle and about the level of ovarian hormone secretion.

## Objectives

1. Identify the phases of the ovarian cycle.
2. Describe the changes that occur in the endometrium, and correlate these with the stages of the ovarian cycle.
3. Describe the appearance of a vaginal smear at different stages of the cycle, and explain the clinical usefulness of a vaginal smear.

## Materials

1. Young female rats
2. Ether jar (large, widemouthed jar with close-fitting lid) and ether
3. Isotonic saline and cotton swabs
4. Giemsa's stain (dilute concentrate 1:50) and absolute methyl alcohol in staining jars
5. Microscopes and microscope slides

The amount of gonadotrophic hormones secreted by the anterior pituitary of females increases and decreases in a cyclical fashion. The secretion of estrogen and progesterone by the ovary will thus follow the same cycle. In most mammals, sexual receptivity (heat or estrus) occurs during a specific part of the cycle, and the cycle is called an **estrus cycle.** In human and subhuman primates, sexual receptivity occurs throughout the cycle, and monthly bleeding occurs at the beginning of each cycle. These cycles are called **menstrual cycles** (*menses* means "monthly").

The uterus is one of the target organs of the ovarian hormones. As the secretions of estrogen and progesterone increase during the cycle, the inner lining of the uterus (the endometrium) increases in thickness. The ovary is preparing the uterus for the possible implantation of the developing embryo, should fertilization occur. If fertilization does not occur, the cyclical decrease in estrogen and progesterone causes the necrosis (cellular death) and sloughing off of the upper two-thirds of the endometrium. The cycle is ready to begin anew.

The different stages of an estrus or menstrual cycle may be followed by observing the cyclical changes of the endometrium. However, since these changes are correlated with the types of cells found in the vaginal lumen, the same information can be obtained more conveniently by taking a *vaginal smear.*

The estrus cycle of a rat is usually completed in four to five days. The cycle is roughly divisible into four stages.

1. **Proestrus.** Proestrus is the beginning of a new cycle. The follicles of the ovary start to mature under the influence of the gonadotrophic hormones, and the ovary starts to increase its secretion of estrogen.
   *Vaginal smear.* Nucleated epithelial cells (figs. 10.10*a* and *b*).
2. **Estrus.** The uterus is enlarged and distended because of the accumulation of fluid. Estrogen secretion is at its height.
   *Vaginal smear.* Squamous cornified cells (fig. 10.10*c*).
3. **Metestrus.** Metestrus is the stage after ovulation has occurred. The ovary contains functioning corpora lutea secreting progesterone.
   *Vaginal smear.* Many leukocytes, some cornified epithelial cells.
4. **Diestrus.** The corpora lutea regress, and the declining secretion of estrogen and progesterone causes regression of the uterus.
   *Vaginal smear.* Entirely leukocytes.

**Figure 10.10.** The vaginal smear. (a) and (b) Nucleated epithelial cells and leukocytes; (c) nucleated epithelial cells and cornified cells.

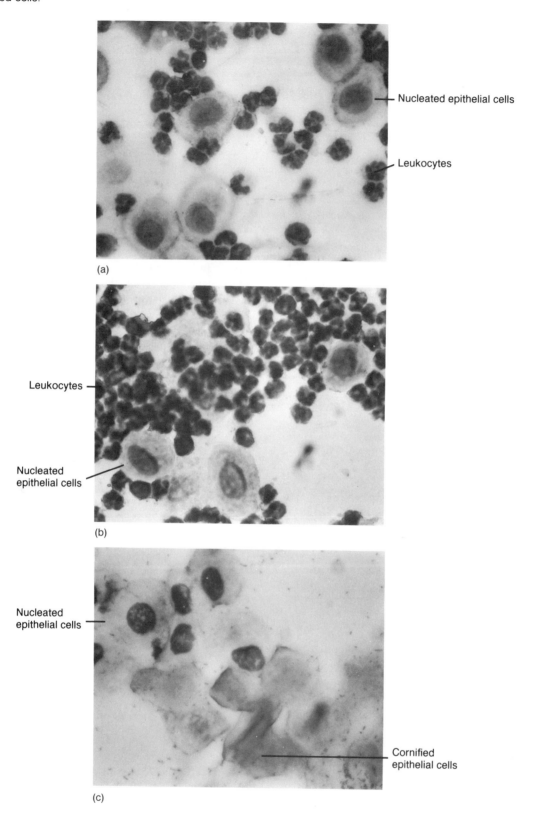

Nucleated epithelial cells

Leukocytes

(a)

Leukocytes

Nucleated
epithelial cells

(b)

Nucleated
epithelial cells

Cornified
epithelial cells

(c)

The stages of the estrus cycle correspond to the phases of the menstrual cycle as follows: proestrus corresponds to the *follicular* phase, estrus to the *ovulatory* phase, metestrus to the *luteal* phase, and diestrus to the *menstrual* phase.

Like the endometrium of the uterus, the vaginal epithelium undergoes cyclic changes during the menstrual cycle. Estrogen stimulates growth and development of the vaginal epithelium, and under conditions of high estrogen, four layers can be distinguished—superficial squamous cells, an intermediate layer, a parabasal layer, and a basal layer. It is always the topmost layer that *exfoliates* (sheds) and is seen in a vaginal smear. A vaginal smear during the *proliferative* phase of the cycle (corresponding to the follicular phase of the ovaries), when the estrogen level is high, consists almost exclusively of superficial squamous cells. Under the influence of progesterone, during the *secretory* phase of the cycle (corresponding to the luteal stage of the ovaries) and during pregnancy, the top layer of cells in the vaginal epithelium is the intermediate layer. These cells are therefore seen in a vaginal smear taken during the second half of the cycle and during pregnancy. In the absence of all sex steroids (for example, prior to puberty or *menarche*), the vaginal epithelium is atrophic, and parabasal cells are seen in a vaginal smear.

## Clinical Significance

It is clear that vaginal smears can be used clinically to determine the stage of the menstrual cycle, the effectiveness of exogenous hormone treatments, and the stage and health of pregnancy. Vaginal smears are also helpful in the diagnosis of pathological states, such as *amenorrhea* (the absence of a menstrual period), inflammation, and cancer. Indeed, since malignant tissue exfoliates to a greater extent than normal tissue, this technique may detect cancers that are too small to detect by other means. The staining technique most often used clinically for vaginal smears was developed by a pioneer in this field named Papanicolaou; since the introduction of this technique in 1942, the **pap smear** has become synonymous with the clinical vaginal smear.

## Procedure

1. Anesthetize the rats with ether.
2. Moisten the cotton tip of a swab with isotonic saline, and insert into the vagina. Smear this on a clean microscope slide. (One swab is sufficient to make approximately six slides.)
3. Stain the slides as follows.
    a) Dry the slide in air.
    b) Immerse the slide in absolute methyl alcohol (5 seconds).
    c) Air-dry the slide.
    d) Place it in Giemsa's stain (1:50) for 30 minutes.
    e) Rinse it in tap water.
    f) Dry the slide, and observe it without a cover slip under the microscope.

1. The stage of the estrus cycle that is characterized by the appearance of cornified epithelial cells and in which estrogen secretion is high, is called the _____ phase. The corresponding phase of the menstrual cycle is the _____ phase.

2. The stage of the estrus cycle in which estrogen and progesterone secretion declines is called the _____ phase. The corresponding phase of the menstrual cycle is the _____ phase.

3. The proliferative phase of the endometrium occurs during the _____ phase of the menstrual cycle.

4. The secretory phase of the endometrium occurs during the _____ phase of the menstrual cycle.

5. What would be the appearance of a vaginal smear performed on an ovariectomized rat (one with its ovaries removed)? Explain.

6. The contraceptive pill is composed of estrogen and progesterone. Suppose your laboratory rat, with an estrus cycle of four days, were to take the pill on a three-days-on-and-one-day-off regimen. What would be the appearance of vaginal smears taken on each of the four days? Explain.

7. Explain how the vaginal smear could be used clinically to determine the minimum effective dose of estrogen in a woman given estrogen after menopause.

# Human Chorionic Gonadotrophin and the Pregnancy Test

Shortly after fertilization occurs cells that are going to become part of the placenta secrete a hormone called human chorionic gonadotrophin (hCG). Pregnancy is commonly tested by an assay for hCG in the urine.

## Objectives

1. Describe the fate of the corpus luteum at the end of a nonfertile cycle.
2. Describe the source of hCG and the physiological role of this hormone in pregnancy.
3. Demonstrate a pregnancy test, and explain how this procedure tests for pregnancy.

## Materials

1. Urine collection cup
2. Pregnancy kit (DAP test kit, Wampole)

After fertilization occurs, the developing embryo implants into the wall of the endometrium. Under these conditions, the cyclical fall in the secretion of ovarian hormones, with the resultant shedding of the upper two-thirds of the endometrium, would result in an abortion. The secretions of the ovary must therefore be freed from their enslavement to the pituitary.

The rule of the pituitary is overthrown by the tiny embryo. Cells of the embryo, which will later become part of the **placenta,** secrete their own gonadotrophic hormone. Under the influence of this hormone (*hCG*), the corpus luteum of the ovary continues to secrete large amounts of estrogen and progesterone for the first ten weeks of pregnancy. After this, the placenta secretes both estrogen and progesterone until birth.

Large amounts of hCG are excreted in the urine of pregnant women, whereas no hCG is present in the urine of nonpregnant women. An assay for the presence of hCG in urine is thus an accurate test for pregnancy.

In this exercise, the presence of hCG will be assayed by means of an antigen-antibody reaction. An *antigen* is a large molecule (usually a foreign protein) that is capable of stimulating lymphocytes to produce antibodies. *Antibodies* are proteins that are capable of bonding to specific antigens. The antigen-antibody reaction in the body is termed the *immune response,* and an assay that makes use of this reaction is termed an **immunoassay.**

In this immunoassay for hCG, antibodies are stuck onto tiny white latex particles. If urine containing hCG (the antigen) is added, chemical bonds form between the antigens and antibodies, causing the latex particles to clump together (*agglutinate*). Since antibodies are relatively specific in their reaction with antigens, no agglutination reaction will occur if hCG is absent from the urine. See figure 10.11 for examples of positive and negative agglutination reactions.

## Clinical Significance

The immunoassay of hCG in urine is a very accurate test for pregnancy, and in one form or another, this is now the most widely used type of pregnancy test. If this test is performed too soon after conception, however, the hCG level may be below the sensitivity of the assay and may produce false negative results. These tests should therefore be performed at least two weeks following a missed period. False positive tests are less common and may be due to tumors that secrete hCG (such as choriocarcinomas).

**Figure 10.11.** A positive pregnancy test. (a) no agglutination when urine is added to a control solution containing latex particles with rabbit gamma globulin (from a rabbit not sensitized to hCG); (b) agglutination of latex particles when urine is added to latex coated with antibodies from a rabbit sensitized to hCG. (Note the appearance of agglutinated latex particles.)

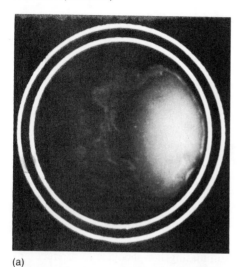

(a)

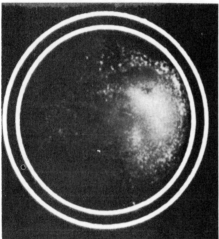

(b)

## Procedure

1. Allow the urine sample to reach room temperature.
2. Fill the plastic reservoir provided in the pregnancy kit with urine, and insert the filtering attachment.
3. Expel the urine onto two circles on the disposable slide provided by squeezing the reservoir.
4. Shake the bottle of reagent (latex particles with antibodies against hCG), and add 1 drop to the first circle. Mix the urine and reagent with an applicator stick by spreading the mixture over the entire circle.
5. Shake the latex control (latex particles with gamma globulin), and add 1 drop to the second circle. Mix as before.
6. Rock the slide gently for 1 minute, and look for agglutination. In a negative test, the solution will remain milky, whereas in a positive test it will appear grainy.

1. The structure that secretes estrogen and progesterone for the first ten weeks of pregnancy is the _____ _____ .

2. Human chorionic gonadotrophin is secreted by the _____ .

3. The action of hCG is similar to that of a hormone secreted by the anterior pituitary gland. This hormone is _____ .

4. Describe the formation, function, and fate of the corpus luteum during the nonfertile menstrual cycle. What happens to the corpus luteum when fertilization occurs?

5. Why are most pregnancy tests not valid unless performed at least a couple of weeks after a missed period?

6. Why is this pregnancy test called an immunoassay? Explain how this test works to detect pregnancy.

# Patterns of Heredity

The inheritance of many aspects of body structure and function follow a pattern that can be understood by applying relatively simple concepts. A knowledge of these patterns of heredity is needed for proper understanding of anatomy and physiology and for clinical purposes, such as the genetic counseling of prospective parents.

## Objectives

1. Define and explain the terms *dominant, recessive, homozygous,* and *heterozygous.*
2. Describe and distinguish between autosomal and sex-linked inheritance.
3. Describe the Rh and ABO blood-typing systems, and explain their physiological significance and clinical applications.
4. Explain the nature and inheritance of sickle-cell anemia.
5. Explain the inheritance of hemophilia and color blindness.

## Materials

1. PTC paper
2. Glass slides, and toothpicks
3. Anti-A, -B, and -Rh sera
4. Sickle-Sol tube test (Dade)
5. Ishihara color blindness charts
6. Lancets and 70% ethyl alcohol
7. Slide warmer

A person inherits two sets of genes controlling every trait, one from the mother and one from the father (if these genes are *autosomal*—that is, not located on the sex chromosomes). If both genes are identical, the person is said to be **homozygous** for that trait. A person who is homozygous for normal hemoglobin, for example, has the genotype *AA*, whereas a person who is homozygous for hemoglobin S has the genotype *SS*.

If a person inherits the gene for hemoglobin A from one parent and the gene for hemoglobin S from the other parent, this person is said to be **heterozygous** for that trait and has the genotype *AS*. This person has the sickle-cell *trait* but does not have sickle-cell *disease*. The phenotype (in this case the absence of sickle-cell disease) is the same for the heterozygote as it is for the person who is homozygous normal. Thus, the gene for hemoglobin A is **dominant** to the gene for hemoglobin S (or the gene for hemoglobin S is **recessive** to the gene for hemoglobin A).

Although the heterozygote does not display the phenotype of sickle-cell disease, this person is a carrier of the sickle-cell trait, since one-half of the gametes will contain the gene for hemoglobin A and one-half will contain the gene for hemoglobin S (in the process of gamete formation, known as *meiosis*, the chromosome number is halved). If this individual mates with one who is homozygous *AA*, half the progeny will be homozygous *AA*, and half will be heterozygous *AS*.

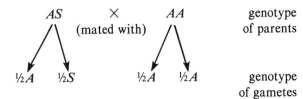

$$\frac{1}{2}A \times \frac{1}{2}A = \frac{1}{4}\ AA$$
$$\frac{1}{2}A \times \frac{1}{2}A = \frac{1}{4}\ AA \quad\Big\}\ 2/4\ AA$$
$$\frac{1}{2}S \times \frac{1}{2}A = \frac{1}{4}\ AS$$
$$\frac{1}{2}S \times \frac{1}{2}A = \frac{1}{4}\ AS \quad\Big\}\ 2/4\ AS$$

If two individuals who are both heterozygous *AS* mate, one-fourth of the progeny will have the genotype *AA*, one-fourth will have the genotype *SS,* and one-half will have the genotype *AS*. Although individuals with the homozygous genotype *AA* and the heterozygous genotype *AS* are healthy, the chances are *one in four* that a child from this mating will have the phenotype of sickle-cell disease (genotype *SS*).

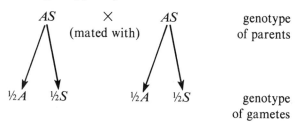

$$\tfrac{1}{2}A \times \tfrac{1}{2}A = \tfrac{1}{4} \ AA$$
$$\tfrac{1}{2}A \times \tfrac{1}{2}S = \tfrac{1}{4} \ AS \quad \Big\} \quad 3/4 \ \text{normal phenotype}$$
$$\tfrac{1}{2}S \times \tfrac{1}{2}A = \tfrac{1}{4} \ AS$$
$$\tfrac{1}{2}S \times \tfrac{1}{2}S = \tfrac{1}{4} \ SS \quad \ \ 1/4 \ \text{sickle-cell disease}$$

## Clinical Significance

Most of the concepts of heredity discussed in this exercise were discovered in the 1860s by an Austrian monk named Gregor Mendel; consequently, these patterns of heredity are often called *simple Mendelian heredity*. A proper knowledge of these patterns is obviously needed for genetic counseling of carriers of genetic diseases. If both parents are carriers of such diseases as sickle-cell anemia, Tay-Sachs disease, phenylketonuria (PKU), and others that are inherited as autosomal recessive traits, it is important that they understand that there is a 25% chance that their children will get the disease. If only one parent is a carrier, they should know that their children will definitely not get the disease. Further, they should be cautioned that, whether they have no children or a dozen, the probability that their next child will get the disease always remains the same.

## A. Inheritance of PTC Taste

The ability to taste PTC paper (phenylthiocarbamide) is inherited as a dominant trait. Therefore, if *T* is taster and *t* is nontaster, then tasters have the genotype *TT* or *Tt*, and nontasters have the genotype *tt*.

### Procedure

Taste the PTC paper by leaving a strip of it on the tongue for a minute or so. If the paper has an unpleasantly bitter taste, you are a taster. Determine the number of tasters and nontasters in the class, and enter this data in your laboratory report.

## B. Inheritance of the Rh Factor

When blood from one person is mixed with plasma from another person, the red blood cells will sometimes clump together (**agglutinate**). This agglutination reaction, which is very important in determining the safety of transfusions (agglutinated cells can block small blood vessels), is due to a mismatch of genetically determined blood types.

On the surface of each red blood cell there are a number of molecules that have antigenic properties, and each antibody in the plasma has two combining sites for antigens. In a positive agglutination test, therefore, the red blood cells clump together because they are combined through antibody bridges.

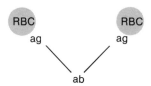

One of the antigens on the surface of red blood cells, the Rh factor (so named because it was first discovered in Rhesus monkeys), is found on the red blood cells of approximately 85% of the people in the United States. The presence of this antigen on the red blood cells (an *Rh positive* phenotype) is inherited as a dominant trait and is produced by both the homozygous (*RR*) and the heterozygous (*Rr*) genotypes. Individuals who have the homozygous recessive genotype (*rr*) do not have this antigen on their red blood cells and are said to have the *Rh negative* phenotype.

Suppose an Rh positive man who is heterozygous (*Rr*) mates with an Rh positive woman who is also heterozygous (*Rr*).

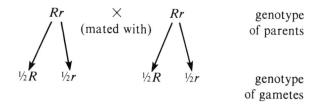

Then:               *Progeny*
$$\tfrac{1}{2}R \times \tfrac{1}{2}R = \tfrac{1}{4} \ RR$$
$$\tfrac{1}{2}R \times \tfrac{1}{2}r = \tfrac{1}{4} \ Rr \quad \Big\} \quad 3/4 \ \text{Rh positive phenotype}$$
$$\tfrac{1}{2}r \times \tfrac{1}{2}R = \tfrac{1}{4}Rr$$
$$\tfrac{1}{2}r \times \tfrac{1}{2}r = \tfrac{1}{4}rr \quad \ \ 1/4 \ \text{Rh negative phenotype}$$

Since the mother is Rh positive in this example, her immune system cannot be stimulated to produce antibodies by the presence of an Rh positive fetus; fortunately for the Rh positive mother, an Rh negative fetus does not yet have an immune response. The development of **immunological competence** occurs shortly after birth.

When an Rh negative mother is carrying an Rh positive fetus, some of the Rh antigens may enter her circulation when the placenta breaks at birth (red blood cells do not normally cross the placenta during pregnancy). Since these red blood cells contain an antigen (the Rh factor) that is foreign to the mother, they will stimulate her immune system to produce antibodies that are capable of destroying the red blood cells of subsequent Rh positive fetuses. Hemolytic disease of the newborn (**erythroblastosis fetalis**) can be prevented by the administration of exogenous Rh antibodies (a drug known as *RhoGAM*) to the mother within seventy-two hours after delivery. These antibodies destroy the fetal red blood cells that have entered the maternal circulation before they can stimulate an immune response.

## Procedure

1. Place 1 drop of anti-Rh serum on a clean glass slide.
2. Add an equal amount of fingertip blood, and mix it with the antiserum (use an applicator stick or a toothpick).
3. Place the slide on a slide warmer (45°–50° C), and rock it back and forth.
4. Examine the slide for agglutination. If no agglutination is observed after a 2-minute period, examine the slide under the low-power objective of the microscope. The presence of grains of agglutinated red blood cells indicates Rh positive blood.
5. Enter your Rh factor type (positive or negative) in the laboratory report.

## C. Inheritance of the ABO Antigen System

Each individual inherits two genes, one from each parent, that control the synthesis of red blood cell antigens of the ABO classification. Each gene contains the information for one of three possible phenotypes—antigen A, antigen B, or no antigen (written O). Thus, an individual may have one of six possible genotypes—AA, AO, BB, BO, AB, OO.

An individual who has the genotype AO will produce type A antigens just like an individual who has the genotype AA, and thus both are said to have *type A* blood. Likewise, an individual with the genotype BO and one with the genotype BB will both have *type B* blood. Since lack of antigen is a recessive trait, an individual with blood *type O* must have the genotype OO.

Unlike the other traits considered, the heterozygous genotype AB has a phenotype that is different from either of the homozygous genotypes (AA or BB). Since there is no dominance (or codominance) between A and B, individuals with the genotype AB produce red blood cells with both the A and B antigens (*type AB* blood).

Also, unlike the other immune responses considered, antibodies against the A and B antigens are not induced by prior exposure to these blood types. A person with type A blood, for example, has antibodies in the plasma against type B blood even though that person may never have been exposed to this antigen. A transfusion with type B blood would therefore be extremely dangerous because the antibodies in the recipient's plasma would agglutinate the red blood cells in the donor's blood. Exactly the same result would occur if the donor were type A and the recipient type B (see plate 2).

| Antigen on RBCs | Antibody in Plasma |
|---|---|
| A | Anti-B |
| B | Anti-A |
| O | Anti-*A* and anti-*B* |
| AB | No antibody |

The most common blood types are type O and type A, whereas type AB is the rarest (table 10.2).

| Table 10.2 | Incidence of blood types. | | |
|---|---|---|---|
| | **Approximate Incidence in U.S. (%)** | | |
| **Blood Types** | **Caucasian** | **Black** | **Oriental** |
| O | 45 | 48 | 36 |
| A | 41 | 27 | 28 |
| B | 10 | 21 | 23 |
| AB | 4 | 4 | 13 |

## Procedure

1. Draw a line down the center of a clean glass slide with a marking pencil, and label one side A and the other B.
2. Place a drop of anti-A serum on the side marked A and a drop of anti-B serum on the side marked B.
3. Add a drop of blood to each antiserum, and mix with a clean applicator stick.
4. Tilt the slide back and forth, and examine for agglutination over a 2-minute period. Do not heat the slide on the slide warmer.
5. Enter your ABO blood type in the laboratory report.

## D. Sickle-Cell Anemia

Sickle-cell anemia is an autosomal recessive disease affecting 8%–11% of the black population of the United States. In this disease, a single base change in the DNA, through the mechanisms of transcription and translation, results in the production of an abnormal hemoglobin (*hemoglobin S*), which differs from the normal hemoglobin (*hemoglobin A*) by the substitution of one amino acid for another (valine for glutamic acid) in one position of the protein.

A rapid test for sickle-cell anemia uses the fact that under conditions of reduced oxygen tension, hemoglobin S is less soluble than hemoglobin A and tends to make a solution turbid, or cloudy (fig. 10.12*a*).

---

### Procedure

1. Fill a calibrated capillary tube with blood up to the line, and blow the blood into a test tube containing 2.0 ml of test reagent (contains sodium dithionite, which produces low oxygen tension).
2. If the solution does not become cloudy within 5 minutes, the test is negative.
3. Record your data in the laboratory report.

## E. Sex-Linked Traits: Inheritance of Color Blindness

The sex of an individual is determined by one of the twenty-three pairs of chromosomes inherited from the parents—these are the sex chromosomes, X and Y. The female has the genotype XX, and the male has the genotype XY. Traits that are determined by genes located on the *X chromosome,* as opposed to the other (autosomal) chromosomes, are called *sex-linked traits* (the Y chromosome apparently carries very few genes).

Unlike the patterns of heredity previously considered, where the genes are carried on autosomal chromosomes, the inheritance of genes carried on the X chromosome follows a different pattern for males than for females. This is because the male inherits only one X chromosome (and thus only one set of sex-linked traits) from his mother, whereas the female inherits an X chromosome from both parents.

The genes for color vision and for some of the blood-clotting factors are carried on the X chromosome, where the phenotypes for color blindness and hemophilia are recessive to the normal phenotypes. A normal female may have either the homozygous dominant or the heterozygous ("carrier") genotypes, whereas a male must have either the normal or the affected phenotypes.

Suppose a normal man mates with a woman who is a carrier for color blindness ($C$ is normal, $c$ is color-blind).

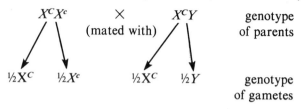

$$\frac{1}{2}X^C \times \frac{1}{2}X^C = \frac{1}{4}X^CX^C$$
$$\frac{1}{2}X^C \times \frac{1}{2}Y = \frac{1}{4}X^CY$$
$$\frac{1}{2}X^c \times \frac{1}{2}X^C = \frac{1}{4}X^CX^c$$
$$\frac{1}{2}X^c \times \frac{1}{2}Y = \frac{1}{4}X^cY$$

genotypes of progeny

The probability that a child formed from this union will be color-blind is one-fourth (25%); and the probability that this child will be male is 100%. All female children formed from this union will of course have the normal phenotype, but the probability that a given female child will be a carrier for color blindness is one-half (50%).

The perception of color is due to the action of certain photoreceptor cells, known as **cones,** in the retina of the eye. According to the Young-Helmholtz theory of color vision, the perception of all the colors of the visible spectrum is due to the stimulation of only three types of cones—blue, green, and red. These three names refer to the regions of the spectrum at which each type of cone is maximally stimulated. When one of these three types of cones is defective owing to the inheritance of a sex-linked recessive trait, the ability to distinguish certain colors is diminished.

---

### Procedure

In the Ishihara test, colored dots are arranged in a series of circles in such a way that a person with normal vision can see a number embedded within each circle, whereas a color-blind person will only see an apparently random array of colored dots (plate 3).

**Plate 2** Results of blood typing. (a) type A blood agglutinating (clumping) with antiserum A (top right), and type B blood agglutinating with antiserum B (bottom left); type O blood would not agglutinate with either antiserum. (b) type AB blood agglutinating with both antiserum B (left) and antiserum A (right).

Anti-B                                                    Anti-A

Type A

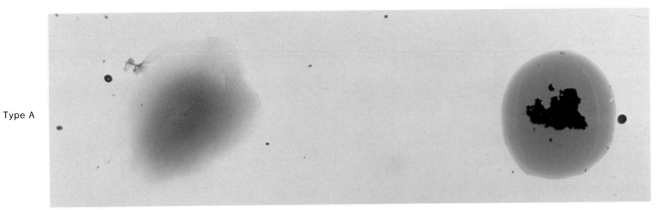

Type B

Type AB

(a)

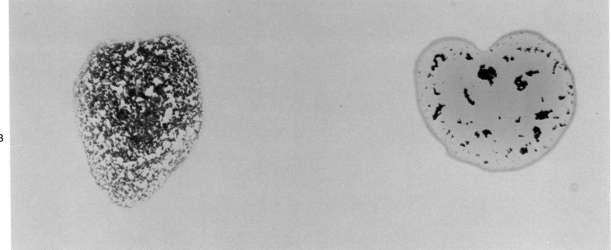

(b)

**Plate 3**   The Ishihara color blindness test.

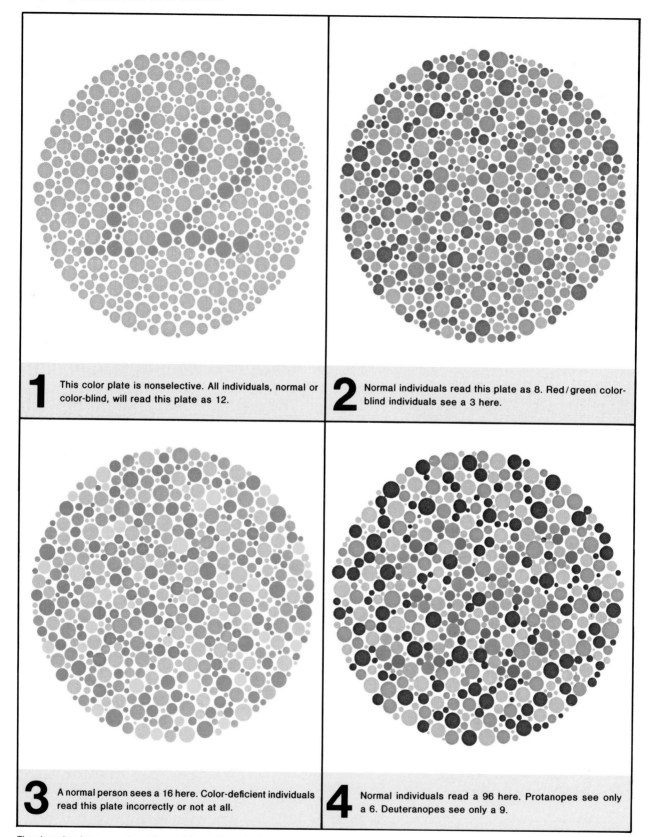

**1** This color plate is nonselective. All individuals, normal or color-blind, will read this plate as 12.

**2** Normal individuals read this plate as 8. Red/green color-blind individuals see a 3 here.

**3** A normal person sees a 16 here. Color-deficient individuals read this plate incorrectly or not at all.

**4** Normal individuals read a 96 here. Protanopes see only a 6. Deuteranopes see only a 9.

The above has been reproduced from *Ishihara's Tests for Colour Blindness* published by Kanehara & Co. Ltd., Tokyo, Japan, but tests for color blindness cannot be conducted with this material. For accurate testing, the original plates should be used.

**Figure 10.12.**   (a) A turbidity test for sickle-cell anemia;
(b) sickled cells under a light microscope; (c) normal red
blood cells under a scanning electron microscope; (d) sickled
red blood cells under a scanning electron microscope.

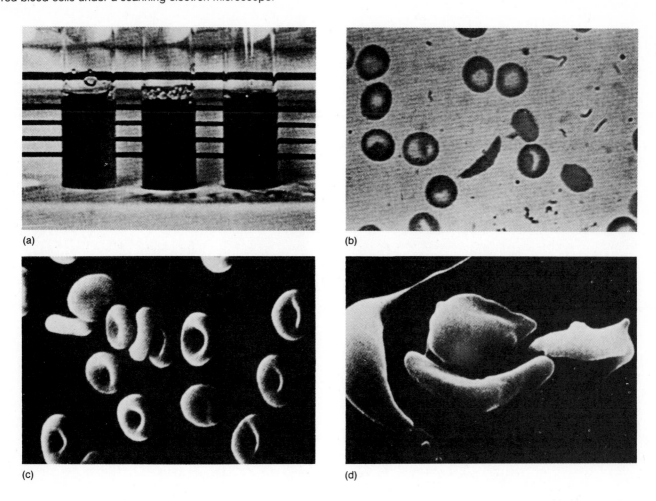

(a)

(b)

(c)

(d)

# Laboratory Report 10.6

Name _____

Date _____

Section _____

## Data from Exercise 10.6

### A. Inheritance of PTC Taste

1. Are you a taster? _____

2. Enter the number of tasters and nontasters in your class in the table below:

|  | Number in Class |
|---|---|
| Tasters |  |
| Nontasters |  |

3. Calculate the proportion of tasters (the number of tasters divided by the total number of students). Enter this value in the space below:

_____

### B. Inheritance of the Rh Factor

Are you Rh positive or negative? _____

### C. Inheritance of the ABO Antigen System

What is your ABO blood type? _____

### D. Sickle-Cell Anemia

Was your test positive or negative? _____

### E. Sex-Linked Traits: Inheritance of Color Blindness

Are you color-blind? If so, what type of color blindness do you have? _____

# Questions for Exercise 10.6

1. A student discovers that he and his mother are PTC tasters and his father is a nontaster. What are the genotypes of these three people?

2. If a man with sickle-cell disease marries a woman with sickle-cell trait, what is the probability that their children will have (*a*) sickle-cell trait and (*b*) sickle-cell disease?

3. Explain why a person who has blood type A negative cannot receive blood that is type B positive.

4. What is the probability that a fetus will be Rh positive if the mother is Rh negative and the father is (*a*) homozygous Rh positive or (*b*) heterozygous Rh positive?

5. Explain how the disease erythroblastosis fetalis is produced, and how this disease can be prevented.

6. In a paternity suit a woman (type O) accuses a man (type A) of being the father of her baby (type O). Will the blood types prove or disprove her claim? Explain.

7. A normal man marries a woman who is a carrier for hemophilia (hemophilia is a sex-linked trait). What is the probability that the first child will have hemophilia? What is the sex of the child? What is the probability that their next child will have hemophilia? Explain.

# Appendix
## Basic Chemistry

## Atoms

All of the matter on earth, living as well as nonliving, is composed of about one hundred different types of atoms. Each atom consists of a cloud of negatively charged *electrons* around a central positively charged *nucleus*. The nucleus, which makes up most of the mass of the atom but only a tiny fraction of its volume, consists of positively charged *protons* and, with one exception ($H^1$), noncharged particles known as *neutrons*.

| $H^1$ | $H^2$ (Deuterium) | $H^3$ (Tritium) |
|---|---|---|
| 1 proton | 1 proton | 1 proton |
| 1 electron | 1 neutron | 2 neutrons |
| | 1 electron | 1 electron |

A given element may exist in different forms *(isotopes)* because of the presence of different numbers of neutrons in the nucleus.

The superscript above the symbol of the element is known as the *mass number* and indicates the total number of protons and neutrons in the isotope. Although some isotopes are stable, others (e.g., $H^3$, or tritium) are unstable and undergo radioactive decomposition, emitting gamma rays (very high-energy light) or beta particles (high-energy electrons).

The *atomic number* of an element refers to the number of its protons. The *atomic weight* of an element refers to its weight relative to that of carbon, which is given as 12, and is approximately equal to the number of protons and neutrons in the element.

| Element | Symbol | Atomic Number | Atom Weight |
|---|---|---|---|
| Hydrogen | H | 1 | 1.01 |
| Carbon | C | 6 | 12.01 |
| Nitrogen | N | 7 | 14.01 |
| Oxygen | O | 8 | 16.00 |
| Sodium | Na | 11 | 23.00 |
| Magnesium | Mg | 12 | 24.31 |
| Phosphorus | P | 15 | 30.97 |
| Sulfur | S | 16 | 32.06 |
| Chlorine | Cl | 17 | 35.45 |
| Potassium | K | 19 | 39.10 |
| Calcium | Ca | 20 | 40.08 |
| Iron | Fe | 26 | 55.85 |
| Copper | Cu | 29 | 63.54 |
| Iodine | I | 53 | 126.90 |

## Chemical Bonds

The chemical properties of an atom are determined by its electron cloud. Electrons of similar energies form shells around the nucleus, and each shell can only accommodate a limited number of electrons. From the inner shell outward, the maximum number of electrons is 2, 8, 18, 32, and so forth. The chemical properties of the atoms are determined by the number of electrons in the outer shell. If this number is less than the maximum, the difference can be made up by sharing electrons with another atom. Bonds formed by the mutual sharing of electrons are very strong and are called *covalent bonds*.

Hydrogen, for example, only has one electron and needs one more electron to complete its outer shell. Oxygen has eight electrons, two in its inner shell and six in its outer shell—it needs two more electrons to complete its outer shell. This requirement can be met by sharing electrons with two hydrogen atoms, forming a *molecule* of water.

$$H \cdot + H \cdot + \cdot \overset{\cdot\cdot}{\underset{\cdot\cdot}{O}} \cdot \longrightarrow H \overset{\cdot\cdot}{\underset{\cdot\cdot}{:}} O : H, \text{ or } H—O—H, \text{ or } H_2O$$

Oxygen gas is composed of oxygen molecules formed by the covalent bonding of two oxygen atoms. In this case, two pairs of electrons are shared by the two atoms, forming a double bond between them.

$$\ddot{\underset{..}{O}} : + : \ddot{\underset{..}{O}} : \longrightarrow : \ddot{O} :: \ddot{O} :, \text{ or } O = O, \text{ or } O_2$$

An atom of nitrogen has seven electrons, two in its inner shell and five in its outer shell. It requires three electrons to complete its outer shell. This requirement may be met by sharing electrons with three hydrogen atoms, forming a molecule of ammonia, or by sharing three pairs of electrons with another atom of nitrogen, forming a molecule of nitrogen gas.

$$: \overset{.}{\underset{.}{N}} \cdot + 3H \cdot \longrightarrow : \overset{..}{N} : H, \text{ or } \underset{H}{\overset{H}{N}} - H, \text{ or } NH_3$$

$$\cdot \overset{.}{N} : + : \overset{.}{N} \cdot \longrightarrow N ::: N, \text{ or } N \equiv N, \text{ or } N_2$$

When the electrons are not shared equally, but instead are held by only one of the two nuclei, the atom that captures the electron has a negative charge and the atom that loses the electron has a positive charge. These charged atoms (called *ions*) may be held together by a weak electronic attraction known as an *ionic bond*.

## Ions and Electrolytes

When a compound that is held together by weak ionic bonds is dissolved in water, it *dissociates* into positively charged ions (*cations*) and negatively charged ions (*anions*). These ions can conduct electricity, and hence the original ionic compound is called an *electrolyte*. The most ubiquitous electrolyte is common table salt (NaCl).

$$\underset{\text{Ionic compound}}{NaCl} \longrightarrow \underset{\text{Cation}}{Na^+} + \underset{\text{Anion}}{Cl^-}$$

Some atoms form ionic bonds as a group with other atoms and remain together as a group when the ionic compound dissociates. These groups are called *radicals*. Examples of radicals include sulfate ($SO_4$), phosphate ($PO_4$), ammonium ($NH_4$), and hydroxyl ($OH$).

$$\underset{\text{Ammonium sulfate}}{(NH_4)_2SO_4} \longrightarrow \underset{\text{Ammonium}}{2\,NH_4^+} + \underset{\text{Sulfate}}{SO_4^=}$$

Notice that the sulfate radical has two negative charges and that two ammonium radicals are needed to retain electrical neutrality.

| Cation | Symbol | Anion | Symbol |
|---|---|---|---|
| Sodium | $Na^+$ | Chloride | $Cl^-$ |
| Potassium | $K^+$ | Sulfate | $SO_4^=$ |
| Calcium | $Ca^{++}$ | Bicarbonate | $HCO_3^-$ |
| Magnesium | $Mg^{++}$ | Phosphate | $PO_4^\equiv$ |
| Hydrogen | $H^+$ | Hydroxyl | $OH^-$ |
| Ammonium | $NH_4^+$ | Carbonate | $CO_3^=$ |

## pH and Buffers

The hydrogen ion concentration of a solution can vary between $10^{-14}$ molar and zero (see exercise 2.6 for discussion of molarity). Pure water, which has a hydrogen ion concentration of $10^{-7}$ molar, is considered neutral.

$$H - O - H \longrightarrow H^+ + OH^-$$

Any substance that increases the $H^+$ concentration is called an *acid,* and any substance that decreases the $H^+$ concentration is called a *base*. Bases decrease the $H^+$ concentration by adding $OH^-$ to the solution, which can combine with free hydrogen ions to form water.

$$\underset{\text{Hydrochloric acid}}{HCl} \longrightarrow H^+ + Cl^-$$

$$\underset{\substack{\text{Sodium hydroxide} \\ \text{(a base)}}}{NaOH} \longrightarrow Na^+ + OH^-$$

When equal amounts of hydrogen cation and hydroxyl anion are added to a solution, the acid and base neutralize each other, forming water and a *salt*.

$$\underset{\text{Acid}}{HCl} + \underset{\text{Base}}{NaOH} \longrightarrow \underset{\text{Salt}}{NaCl} + \underset{\text{Water}}{H_2O}$$

A convenient way of expressing the hydrogen ion concentration of a solution is by the use of the symbol *pH*, which is the negative logarithm of the hydrogen ion concentration.

$$pH = \log \frac{1}{[H^+]}$$

Thus, pure water, with a $H^+$ concentration of $10^{-7}$ molar, has a pH of 7.000. Since the pH is an inverse function of the $H^+$ concentration, an increase in the hydrogen concentration above that of water (i.e., an *acidic solution*) is indicated by a pH of *less than 7.000*, whereas a decrease in the H⁺ concentration (i.e., a *basic solution*) has a pH between 7.000 and 14. A solution with an $H^+$ concentration of $10^{-2}$ molar (pH 2) is acidic, whereas a solution that contains $10^{-12}$ molar $H^+$ (pH 12) is basic.

| Acid | Symbol | Base | Symbol |
|---|---|---|---|
| Hydrochloric acid | $HCl$ | Sodium hydroxide | $NaOH$ |
| Phosphoric acid | $H_3PO_4$ | Potassium hydroxide | $KOH$ |
| Nitric acid | $HNO_3$ | Calcium hydroxide | $Ca(OH)_2$ |
| Sulfuric acid | $H_2So_4$ | Ammonium hydroxide | $NH_4OH$ |

A *buffer* is a compound that serves to prevent drastic pH changes when acids or bases are added to a solution. It does this by replacing a strong acid or base (one that ionizes completely) with a weak acid or base (one that does not completely ionize).

$$NaHCO_3 \quad + \quad HCl \longrightarrow H_2CO_3 \quad + \quad NaCl$$

| Sodium bicarbonate buffer | Hydrochloric acid | Carbonic acid | Sodium chloride |
|---|---|---|---|

Notice that the strong hydrochloric acid was replaced by the weaker carbonic acid, thus minimizing the change in pH that would have been induced had HCl been added to the solution in the absence of buffer. The carbonic acid/bicarbonate *buffer system* also minimizes the effect of added base on the pH of the solution.

$$H_2CO_3 \quad + \quad NaOH \longrightarrow NaHCO_3 \quad + \quad H_2O$$

| Carbonic acid | Sodium hydroxide | Sodium bicarbonate | Water |
|---|---|---|---|

## Organic Chemistry

The chemistry of organic compounds is based on the ability of *carbon* atoms to form chains and rings with other carbon atoms. This ability is due to the fact that carbon, which has six electrons (two in the first shell and four in the second shell), requires four more electrons to complete its outer shell. Carbon is thus said to have four *bonding sites*.

Hydrogen (one bonding site)

$H : H$, or $H—H$, or $H_2$

Oxygen (two bonding sites)

$H : O : H$, or $H—O—H$, or $H_2O$

Nitrogen (three bonding sites)

$H : N : H$, or $H—N—H$, or $NH_3$

Carbon (four bonding sites)

$H : C : H$, or $H—C—H$, or $CH_4$

Carbon atoms can be covalently bonded to each other by sharing one pair of electrons (single bond) or by sharing two pairs of electrons (double bonds). Carbon-carbon double bonds are called sites of *unsaturation*, since they do not have the maximum number of hydrogen atoms.

Carbon atoms can be covalently bonded together to form long chains or rings.

or

$$CH_3 — CH_2 — CH_2 — CH_2 — CH_2 — CH_3$$

or

$C_6H_{14}$ (hexane)

or or $C_6H_{12}$ (cyclohexane)

Notice that in the shorthand structural formulas for cyclic carbon compounds, the carbon atoms are represented by the corners of the figure and hydrogen atoms are not indicated.

Cyclic carbon compounds that are based on the structure of benzene are known as *aromatic* compounds. The common feature of the structural formula of these compounds is the presence of three alternating double bonds in a six-carbon ring. This structural formula is in a sense misleading, since all the carbons in the aromatic ring are equivalent; hence, double bonds can be indicated between any two carbons in the ring.

or or $C_6H_6$ (benzene)

When carbon atoms are bonded together to form chains or rings, the remaining free bonding sites are available to combine with hydrogen atoms or with other compounds known as *functional groups*. These functional groups are generally more chemically reactive than the hydrocarbon backbone.

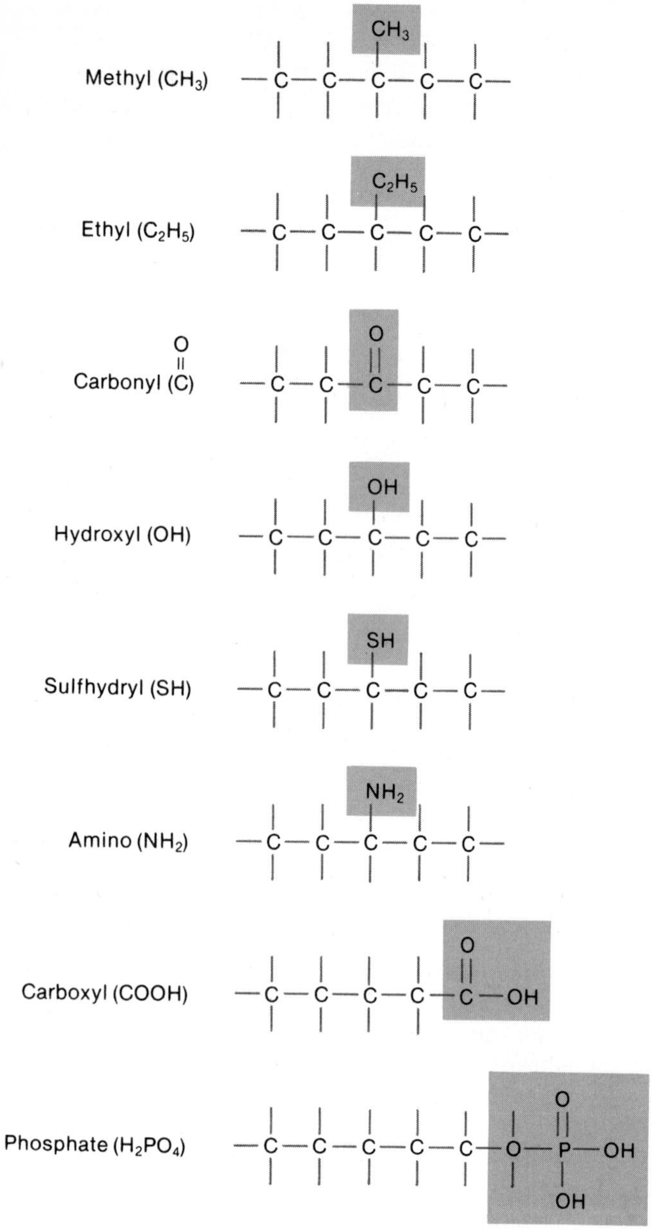

## Functional Groups

Some classes of organic compounds are named according to their functional groups. *Ketones,* for example, have a carbonyl group within the carbon chain, whereas *aldehydes* have a carbonyl group at one end of the chain. *Alcohols* have a hydroxyl group at one end of the chain, whereas acids have a carboxyl group at the end of the carbon chain.

Molecules that are identical in terms of the type and arrangement of their atoms but that differ with respect to the spatial orientation of key functional groups are called *optical isomers.* This name is derived from the fact that these isomers can rotate plane-polarized light to the right or to the left, depending on the orientation of the functional group. The two optical isomers of the simple sugars and the amino acids are named *D* (right-handed) or *L* (left-handed), according to their similarity to the reference molecule glyceraldehyde.

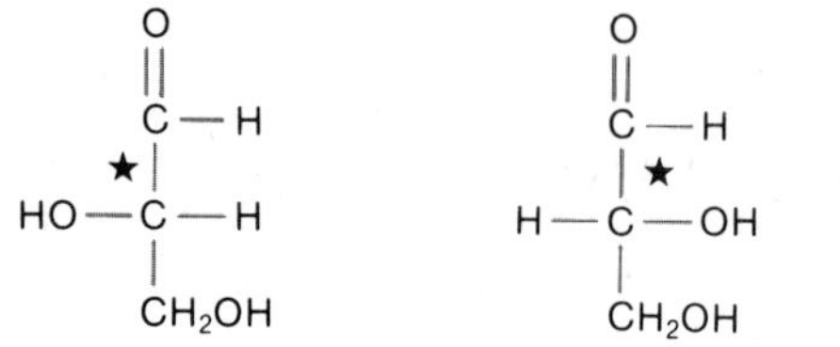

L-glyceraldehyde            D-glyceraldehyde

Even though a synthetic mixture of simple sugars or amino acids would contain equal amounts of both forms, only one of these two optical isomers can be utilized by enzymes in cellular metabolism. Thus, all of the physiologically significant simple sugars are D-isomers, whereas all of the physiologically significant amino acids are L-isomers.

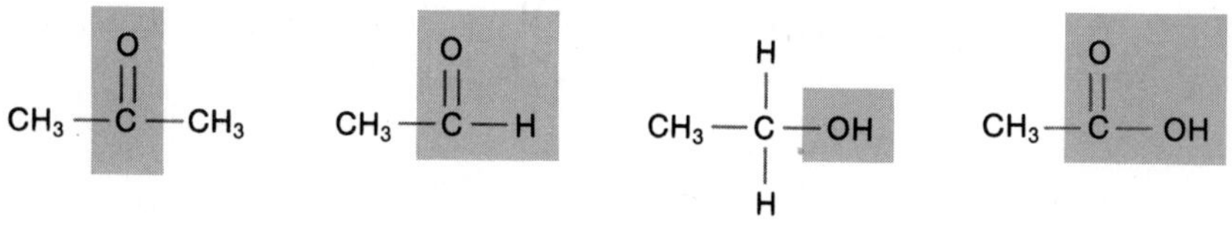

Methyl ($CH_3$)

Ethyl ($C_2H_5$)

Carbonyl (C)

Hydroxyl (OH)

Sulfhydryl (SH)

Amino ($NH_2$)

Carboxyl (COOH)

Phosphate ($H_2PO_4$)

Ketone

Aldehyde

Alcohol

Organic acid

# Appendix
## Sources of Equipment and Solutions

**American Scientific Products, Division of American Hospital Supply Corporation**

**Atlanta**
1750 Stoneridge Drive
Stone Mountain, Georgia 30083
(404)943–4070
(800)232–3550 (GA)
(800)241–6640 (Out of state)

**Boston**
20 Wiggins Avenue
Bedford, Massachusetts 01730
(617)275–1100
(800)842–1208 (MA)
(800)225–1642 (Out of state)

**Charlotte**
8350 Arrowridge Blvd.
Charlotte, North Carolina 28210
(704)525–1021
(800)432–6997 (NC)
(800)438–1234 (Out of state)

**Chicago**
1210 Waukegan Road
McGaw Park, Illinois 60085
(312)689–8410
(800)942–4591 (IL)
(800)323–4515 (Out of state)

**Cleveland**
3201 East Royalton Road
Broadview Heights, Ohio 44147
(216)526–2430
(800)362–9111 (OH)

**Columbus**
2340 McGaw Road
Obetz, Ohio 43207
(614)491–0050
(800)848–9670 (OH)
(800)282–9640 (Out of state)

**Dallas**
210 Great Southwest Parkway
Grand Prairie, Texas 75050
(214)647–2000
(800)492–4820 (TX)
(800)527–6230 (Out of state)

**Denver**
4910 Moline Street
Denver, Colorado 80239
(303)371–0565
(800)332–1241 (CO)
(800)525–1251 (Out of state)

**Detroit**
30500 Cypress
Romulus, Michigan 48174
(313)729–6000
(800)482–3740 (MI)
(800)521–0757 (Out of state)

**Honolulu**
274 Puuhale Road
Honolulu, Hawaii 98619
(808)847–1585

**Houston**
4660 Pine Timbers
Houston, Texas 77041
(713)462–8000
(800)392–2054 (TX)

**Kansas City**
1118 Clay Street
North Kansas City, Missouri 64116
(816)221–2533
(800)892–2433 (MO)
(800)821–2006 (Out of state)

**Los Angeles**
17111 Red Hill Avenue
P.O. Box C19505
Irvine, California 92713
(714)540–5320
(800)432–7141 (CA)

**Miami**
1900 N.W. 97th Avenue
Miami, Florida 33152
(305)592–4620

**Minneapolis**
13505 Industrial Park Boulevard
Minneapolis, Minnesota 55441
(612)553–1171
(800)642–3220 (MN)
(800)328–7195 (Out of state)

**New Orleans**
155 Brookhollow Esplanade
P.O. Box 23628
Harahan, Louisiana 70183
(504)733–7571
(800)452–8738 (LA)
(800)535–7333 (Out of state)

**New York**
100 Raritan Center Parkway
Edison, New Jersey 08817
(201)494–4000
(212)964–3500 (New York City)
(215)925–3983 (Philadelphia)
(800)526–7510 (Out of state)

**Ocala**
601 S.W. 33rd Avenue
Ocala, Florida 32670
(904)732–3480
(800)342–0191 (FL)

**Philadelphia**
2550 Boulevard of Generals
Valley Forge, Pennsylvania 19482
(215)631–9300

**Phoenix**
602 West 22nd Street
Tempe, Arizona 85282
(602)968–3151
(800)352–1431 (AZ)
(800)528–4471 (Out of state)

**Puerto Rico**
G.P.O. 2796
San Juan, Puerto Rico 00936
(809)788–1200

**Rochester**
2 Town Line Circle
Rochester, New York 14623
(716)475–1470
(716)856–0114 (Buffalo)
(315)242–0747 (Syracuse)
(800)462–5673 (NY state)

**St. Louis**
10888 Metro Court
Maryland Heights, Missouri 63043
(314)569–2960
(800)392–4234 (MO)
(800)325–4520 (Out of state)

**Salt Lake City**
P.O. Box 27568
Salt Lake City, Utah 84125
(801)972–3032
(800)453–4690, 4691

**San Francisco**
255 Caspian Drive
Sunnyvale, California 94086
(408)743–3100
(800)538–1670 (N.CA)
(800)672–8610 (S.CA)

**Seattle (Office Handling Alaska)**
3660 148th Avenue, N.E.
Redmond, Washington 98052
(206)885–4131
(800)562–8060 (WA)
(800)426–2950 (ID, MT, OR)
(800)426–6360 (AK)

**Washington, D.C.**
8855 McGaw Road
Columbia, Maryland 21045
(301)992-0800
(800)638-2813

## Curtin Matheson Scientific, Inc., a Coulter Subsidiary Company

**Atlanta**
2140 Newmarket Parkway
Marietta, Georgia 30067
(404)424-0500

**Boston**
110A Commerce Way
Woburn, Massachusetts 01888
(617)935-8888

**Chicago**
1850 Greenleaf Avenue
Elk Grove Village, Illinois 60007
(312)439-5880

**Cincinnati**
12101 Centron Place
Cincinnati, Ohio 45246
(513)671-1200

**Cleveland**
4540 Willow Parkway
Cleveland, Ohio 44125
(216)883-2424

**Dallas**
1103-07 Slocum Street
Dallas, Texas 75207
(214)747-2503

**Denver**
12950 E. 38th Avenue
Denver, Colorado 80239
(303)371-5713

**Detroit**
1600 Howard Street
Detroit, Michigan 48216
(313)964-0310

**Honolulu (Sales Office)**
99-1169 Iwaena Street
Aiea, Hawaii 96701
(808)487-7220

**Houston**
4220 Jefferson Avenue
Houston, Texas 77023
(713)923-1661

**Indianapolis (Sales Office)**
2511 East 46th, Suite V-1
Indianapolis, Indiana 46205
(317)546-5401

**Kansas City**
6111 Deramus Rd.
Kansas City, Missouri 64120
(816)241-5000

**Los Angeles**
2750 Saturn Street
Brea, California 92621
(714)996-1310

**Miami (Sales Office)**
795 West 83rd Street
Hialeah, Florida 33014
(305)558-0851

**Minneapolis**
2218 University Avenue, S.E.
Minneapolis, Minnesota 55414
(612)378-1110

**New Orleans**
627 Distributors Row
Harahan, Louisiana 70123
(504)733-7763

**New York**
357 Hamburg Turnpike
Wayne, New Jersey 07470

**Orlando**
7524 Currency Drive
Orlando Central Park
Orlando, Florida 32809
(305)859-8281

**St. Louis**
11526 Adie Road
Maryland Heights, Missouri 63043
(314)872-8100

**San Francisco**
470 Valley Drive
Brisbane, California 94005
(415)467-1040

**Seattle**
1177 Andover Park West
Tukwila, Washington 98188
(206)575-0575

**Tulsa**
6550 East 42nd Street
Tulsa, Oklahoma 74145
(918)622-1700

**Washington**
10727 Tucker Street
Beltsville, Maryland 20705
(301)937-5950

## Fisher Scientific Company

**Atlanta**
2775 Pacific Drive
P.O. Box 829
Norcross, Georgia 30091
(404)449-5050

**Baton Rouge**
4334 S. Sherwood Forest Blvd.
Baton Rouge, Louisiana 70816
(504)293-8801

**Boston**
461 Riverside Avenue
P.O. Box 379
Medford, Massachusetts 02155
(617)391-6110

**Chicago**
1600 W. Glenlake Avenue
Itasca, Illinois 60143
(312)773-3050

**Cincinnati**
5418 Creek Road
Cincinnati, Ohio 45242
(513)793-5100

**Cleveland**
Building A
3355 Richmond Road
Beachwood, Ohio 44122
(216)292-7900

**Dallas**
4301 Alpha Road
Dallas, Texas 75234
(214)387-0850

**Denver**
14 Inverness Drive East
P.O. Box 3129
Englewood, Colorado 80155
(303)741-3440

**Detroit**
34401 Industrial Road
Livonia, Michigan 48150
(313)261-3320

**Ft. Lauderdale**
1815 E. Commercial Blvd.
Ft. Lauderdale, Florida 33308
(305)491-7360

**Houston**
10700 Rockley Road
P.O. Box 1307
Houston, Texas 77001
(713)495-6060

**Los Angeles**
2761 Walnut Avenue
Tustin, California 92680
(714)832-9800

**Louisville**
1900 Plantside Drive
Louisville, Kentucky 40299
(502)491-7384

**Memphis**
4403 Delp Street
P.O. Box 181150
Memphis, Tennessee 38118
(901)362-3444

**New York**
52 Fadem Road
Springfield, New Jersey 07081
(201)379-1400

**Orlando**
7464 Chancellor Drive
P.O. Box 13430
Orlando, Florida 32809
(305)857-3600

**Parkersburg**
703 Rayon Drive
P.O. Box 3322
Parkersburg, West Virginia 26101
(304)485-1751

**Philadelphia**
191 South Gulph Road
King of Prussia, Pennsylvania 19406
(215)265-0300

**Pittsburgh**
585 Alpha Drive
Pittsburgh, Pennsylvania 15238
(412)781–3400

**Raleigh**
3315 Winton Road
P.O. Box 11666
Raleigh, North Carolina 27604
(919)876–2351

**Richmond**
Seaboard Bldg., Room 434
3600 W. Broad St.
Richmond, Virginia 23230
(804)359–1301

**Rochester**
15 Jet View Drive
P.O. Box 8740
Rochester, New York 14624
(716)464–8900

**St. Louis**
1241 Ambassador Blvd.
P.O. Box 12405

St. Louis, Missouri 63132
(314)587–7000

**San Francisco**
2170 Martin Avenue
Santa Clara, California 95050
(408)727–0660

**Washington**
7722 Fenton St.
Silver Spring, Maryland 20910
(301)587–7000

## Carolina Biological Supply Company

*Main Office*
Burlington, North Carolina 27215
(800)334–5551
*West Coast Customers*
Powell Laboratory Division
Gladstone, Oregon 97027
(800)547–1733

## VWR Scientific Inc., Subsidiary of Univar

### Southern Region

**Houston**
P.O. Box 33348
Houston, Texas 77033
(713)641–0681

**Dallas**
P.O. Box 35106
Dallas, Texas 75235
(214)631–0261

**New Orleans**
5717 Salmen St.
Harahan, Louisiana 70123
(504)733–4181

**Nashville**
1100 Elm Hill Pike
Nashville, Tennessee 37210
(615)327–1327

**Atlanta**
P.O. Box 1307 Sta. K
Atlanta, Georgia 30324
(404)262–3141

**Miami**
P.O. Box 520127
Miami, Florida 33152
(305)625–7181

### Eastern Region

**Rochester**
P.O. Box 1050
Rochester, New York 14603
(716)247–0610

**Pittsburgh**
147 Delta Drive
Pittsburgh, Pennsylvania 15238
(412)782–4230

**Baltimore**
6601 Amberton Drive
Baltimore, Maryland 21227
(301)796–8500

**Philadelphia**
P.O. Box 8188
Philadelphia, Pennsylvania 19101
(609)467–3333

**Boston**
P.O. Box 232
Boston, Massachusetts 02101
(617)964–0900

**New York City**
P.O. Box 999
South Plainfield, New Jersey 07080
(201)756–8030

**Columbus**
P.O. Box 855
Columbus, Ohio 43216
(614)445–8281

**Detroit**
3140 Grand River Avenue
Detroit, Michigan 48208
(313)833–7800

**Midland**
P.O. Box 2210
Midland, Michigan 48640
(517)496–3930

### Western Region

**Seattle**
P.O. Box 3551
Seattle, Washington 98124
(206)575–5100

**Anchorage**
1301 East First Avenue
Anchorage, Alaska 99501
(907)272–9507

**Portland**
P.O. Box 14070
Portland, Oregon 97214
(503)234–9272

**San Francisco**
P.O. Box 3200
San Francisco, California 94119
(416)468–7150

**Honolulu**
P.O. Box 29697
Honolulu, Hawaii 96820
(808)833–9544

**Denver**
P.O. Box 39398
Denver, Colorado 80239
(303)371–0970

**Salt Lake City**
P.O. Box 1678
Salt Lake City, Utah 84110
(801)486–4851

**Los Angeles**
P.O. Box 1004
Norwalk, California 90650
(213)921–0821

**San Diego**
P.O. Box 80962
San Diego, California 92138
(714)297–4851

**Phoenix**
P.O. Box 29027
Phoenix, Arizona 85038
(602)269–7511

### Central Region

**Chicago**
2619 Congress Street
Bellwood, Illinois 60104
(312)647–3900

**Davenport**
P.O. Box 2827
Davenport, Iowa 52809
(319)322–6223

**Milwaukee**
16675 West Glendale Drive
New Berlin, Wisconsin 53151
(414)786–9400

**St. Louis**
P.O. Box 13320
St. Louis, Missouri 63157
(314)231–9770

**Kansas City**
P.O. Box 23037
Kansas City, Missouri 64161
(816)842–9536

**Minneapolis**
1124 Stinson Blvd.
Minneapolis, Minnesota 55413
(612)331–4850

# Visual Credits

## PHOTOGRAPHS

### Section 1

**1.1:** Courtesy of Reichert Scientific Instruments; **1.10 a–n:** © Edwin Reschke.

### Section 2

**2.2:** Courtesy of Bausch & Lomb, Analytical Systems Division; **2.7 a–h:** Courtesy of Gelman Instrument Company; **2.14:** Kessel and Kardon/ © W. H. Freeman and Company.

### Section 3

**3.9:** Courtesy of Phipps & Bird, Inc.; **3.11:** © Dr. Sheril D. Burton, assisted by Dr. Douglas W. Hacking; **3.17 (right):** Vaughn, D. and Asbury, T.: *General Ophthalmology,* 7th ed., © Lange Medical Publications, Los Altos, CA, 1974.

### Section 4

**4.1 (top):** © H. E. Huxley; **4.2, 4.3:** Courtesy of Narco Bio-Systems.

### Section 6

**6.1:** Courtesy of Warren E. Collins, Braintree, MA.

### Section 8

**8.3 a–h:** Courtesy of Abbott Laboratories.

### Section 9

**9.3:** F. E. Templeton and W. B. Saunders Company; **9.4:** © Edwin Reschke; **9.6:** DiFiore, M.S.H.: *Atlas of Human Histology.* © Lea & Febiger, 1981; **9.7:** After Sobotta, from Bloom, William and Fawcett, D. W.: *A Textbook of Histology,* 10th ed. © W. B. Saunders Company, 1975; **9.11:** © Dr. Kerry L. Openshaw.

### Section 10

**10.12 a–d:** From McCurdy, P. R.: *Sickle Cell Disease.* © Medcom, Inc., 1973. Reprinted with permission.

## LINE ART AND TABLES

### Section 1

**1.2, 1.4, 1.5, 1.6, 1.7, 1.8, 1.9, 1.11:** From Van De Graaff, Kent M., *Human Anatomy Laboratory Textbook,* 2nd ed. © 1981, 1984 Wm. C. Brown Publishers, Dubuque, Iowa. All Rights Reserved. Reprinted by permission. **Table 1.3, Table 1.4:** From Van De Graaff, Kent M., *Human Anatomy.* © 1984 Wm. C. Brown Publishers, Dubuque, Iowa. All Rights Reserved. Reprinted by permission. **1.3:** From Hole, John W., Jr., *Human Anatomy and Physiology,* 3rd ed. © 1978, 1981, 1984 Wm. C. Brown Publishers, Dubuque, Iowa. All Rights Reserved. Reprinted by permission.

### Section 2

**2.4:** From Fox, Stuart I., *Human Physiology.* © 1984 Wm. C. Brown Publishers, Dubuque, Iowa All Rights Reserved. Reprinted by permission. **2.6:** Courtesy of Gelman Instrument Company.

### Section 3

**3.1:** From Hole, John W., Jr., *Human Anatomy and Physiology,* 3rd ed. © 1978, 1981, 1984 Wm. C. Brown Publishers, Dubuque, Iowa. All Rights Reserved. Reprinted by permission. **3.3:** From *Laboratory Guide to Physiology.* © Thornton Associates, Inc., Waltham, MA. Reprinted by permission. **3.4, 3.7, 3.10:** From Fox, Stuart I., *Human Physiology.* © 1984 Wm. C. Brown Publishers, Dubuque, Iowa. All Rights Reserved. Reprinted by permission. **3.8, 3.13:** From Van De Graaff, Kent M., *Human Anatomy.* © 1984 Wm. C. Brown Publishers, Dubuque, Iowa. All Rights Reserved. Reprinted by permission. **3.12, Table 3.2:** From Van De Graaff, Kent M., *Human Anatomy Laboratory Textbook,* 2nd ed. © 1981, 1984 Wm. C. Brown Publishers, Dubuque, Iowa. All Rights Reserved. Reprinted by permission. **3.16:** From Chaffee, E. E., and E. M. Greisheimer, *Basic Physiology and Anatomy,* 3rd ed. © 1974 J. B. Lippencott Company, Philadelphia. **3.17:** From Vaughn, P., and T. Asbury, *General Ophthalmology.* © Lange Medical Publications, Los Altos, CA. **3.21:** From McClintoc, J. Robert, *Basic Anatomy and Physiology.* © John Wiley and Sons, Inc., New York. **3.25:** Adapted from Macmillan Publishing Company from *The Human Body: Its Structure and Physiology* by Sigmund Grollman. Copyright © 1974, Sigmund Grollman.

### Section 4

**4.1:** From Fox, Stuart I., *Human Physiology.* © 1984 Wm. C. Brown Publishers, Dubuque, Iowa. All Rights Reserved. Reprinted by permission.

### Section 5

**5.6, 5.16:** From Fox, Stuart I., and Kent M. Van De Graaff, *Laboratory Guide to Human Anatomy and Physiology: Concepts and Clinical Applications.* © 1986 Wm. C. Brown Publishers, Dubuque, Iowa. All Rights Reserved. Reprinted by permission. **5.11, 5.12:** From Fox, Stuart I., *Human Physiology.* © 1984 Wm. C. Brown Publishers, Dubuque, Iowa. All Rights Reserved. Reprinted by permission. **5.15, illustration on p. 185:** From Hewlett-Packard Company, Palo Alto, CA. **5.20:** Modified from Geddes, L. A., *The Direct and Indirect Measurement of Blood Pressure.* Copyright © 1970 by Year Book Medical Publishers, Inc., Chicago.

### Section 6

**6.3:** From Van De Graaff, Kent M., *Human Anatomy Laboratory Textbook,* 2nd ed. © 1981, 1984 Wm. C. Brown Publishers, Dubuque, Iowa. All Rights Reserved. Reprinted by permission. **6.10:** Reprinted from Warren E. Collins, Inc., Braintree, MA. **Illustrations on p. 224:** From Fox, Stuart I., and Kent M. Van De Graaff, *Laboratory Guide to Human Anatomy and Physiology: Concepts and Clinical Applications.* © 1986 Wm. C. Brown Publishers, Dubuque, Iowa. All Rights Reserved. Reprinted by permission.

### Section 7

**7.1:** From Fox, Stuart I., *Human Physiology.* © 1984 Wm. C. Brown Publishers, Dubuque, Iowa. All Rights Reserved. Reprinted by permission. **7.10:** From Instrumentation Lab, Inc. **Plate 1:** From Benson, Harold J., et. al., *Anatomy and Physiology Laboratory Textbook,* 3rd ed. © 1970, 1976, 1983 Wm. C. Brown Publishers, Dubuque, Iowa. All Rights Reserved. Reprinted by permission.

### Section 8

**8.1:** From Fox, Stuart I., *Human Physiology.* © 1984 Wm. C. Brown Publishers, Dubuque, Iowa. All Rights Reserved. Reprinted by permission. **8.4:** From Benson, Harold J., et. al., *Physiological Applications.* © 1982 Wm. C. Brown Publishers, Dubuque, Iowa. All Rights Reserved. Reprinted by permission.

### Section 9

**9.1:** From Mader, Sylvia S., *Inquiry Into Life,* 4th ed. © 1976, 1979, 1982, 1985 Wm. C. Brown Publishers, Dubuque, Iowa. All Rights Reserved. Reprinted by permission. **Table 9.1:** Modified from R. S. Shepard, *Human Physiology* (Philadelphia: J. B. Lippencott Company, 1971). **9.2, 9.10:** From Fox, Stuart I., *Human Physiology.* © 1984 Wm. C. Brown Publishers, Dubuque, Iowa. All Rights Reserved. Reprinted by permission. **9.5:** From Hole, John W., Jr., *Human Anatomy and Physiology,* 3rd ed. © 1978, 1981, 1984 Wm. C. Brown Publishers, Dubuque, Iowa. All Rights Reserved. Reprinted by permission. **9.8:** From Fox, Stuart I., and Kent M. Van De Graaff, *Laboratory Guide to Human Anatomy and Physiology: Concepts and Clinical Applications.* © 1986 Wm. C. Brown Publishers, Dubuque, Iowa. All Rights Reserved. Reprinted by permission. **9.9:** From Van De Graaff, Kent M., *Human Anatomy Laboratory Textbook,* 2nd ed. © 1981, 1984 Wm. C. Brown Publishers, Dubuque, Iowa. All Rights Reserved. Reprinted by permission.

### Section 10

**10.1:** From Ham, A. W., *Histology.* J. B. Lippencott Company, Philadelphia, 1974. **10.7:** From Van De Graaff, Kent M., *Human Anatomy Laboratory Textbook,* 2nd ed. © 1981, 1984 Wm. C. Brown Publishers, Dubuque, Iowa. All Rights Reserved. Reprinted by permission. **10.8:** From Fox, Stuart I., and Kent M. Van De Graaff, *Laboratory Guide to Human Anatomy and Physiology: Concepts and Clinical Applications.* © 1986 Wm. C. Brown Publishers, Dubuque, Iowa. All Rights Reserved. Reprinted by permission.

# Index

Absorbance in colorimetry, 29
Absorption of food, 299
Acid-base balance, 231–33
Action potentials
    muscles, 137
    nerves, 82–84
Active transport, 71
Adenosine triphosphate (ATP), 203
Adrenal gland, 328–29
Adrenocorticotrophic hormone (ACTH), 330,
    331
Aerobic capacity, 199
Afterimage, 119
Agglutination, 351, 356
Air trapping in lungs, 211
Albinism, 66
Aldosterone, 279, 336
Alkalosis, 231–33
Alkaptonuria, 66
Allergy, 267
All-or-none law, 85
Alpha rhythm of EEG, 91
Amino acids
    chemistry of, 34, 47
    essential, 57
    thin-layer chromatography, 43
Anabolism, 203
Anemia, 246
Antibodies, 263
Antidiuretic hormone, 279
Antigens, 256
Arthritis, 267
Astigmatism, 114
Atherosclerosis, 178
Atrial fibrillation and flutter, 172
Atrioventricular node, 169
Atropine, 162
Autoimmunity, 267–68

Babinski reflex, 100
Basal metabolic rate, 225
Beer's law, 29
Benedict's test, 313
Bicarbonate, 232
Bile, 321
Bilirubin, 242, 254
Binaural localization of sound, 125
Biofeedback, 153
Blind spot, 118–19
Blood pressure, 193–96
Blood types, 298–99
Bone, 13
Boyle's law, 204
Brush border enzymes, 304
Buffers, 232
Bundle of His, 169

Caffeine, 163
Calcium
    and blood clotting, 272
    effect of, on the heart, 161
    role of, in muscle contraction, 137
Carbohydrates, 31
Carbonic acid, 232
Carboxyhemoglobin, 245, 249
Catabolism, 203
Catalysts, 53
Cell-mediated immunity, 256

Cell respiration, 203
Chemoreceptors and respiration, 226
Cholesterol, 33
Chromatography, thin-layer
    of amino acids, 43–45
    of steroids, 335–38
Chylomicrons, 319
Clotting system, 271–72
Colloid osmotic (oncotic) pressure, 34
Color blindness, 358
Colorimeter, 29–31
Color vision, 119
Concentration gradient, 71
Condensation reaction, 29
Connective tissue, 12
Convergence of eyes, 116
Coomb's test, 263
Corpus luteum, 325
Corticosteroids, 336
Crenation of red blood cells, 74
Cutaneous receptors, 103–6
Cystinuria, 67

Deafness, 123
Deciliter, 32
Deoxyribonucleic acid (DNA), 65–66
Detergents, 72
Diabetes mellitus, 292, 341–42
Dialysis, 73
Diapedesis, 255
Diffusion, 71
Digestion
    of fat, 321
    of protein, 317
    of starch, 313
Digestive system, 299–308
Digitalis, 161
Dihydrotestosterone (DHT), 338
Dimensional analysis, 4–5
Diopters, 113
Disaccharides, 31

Ears, structure and function, 123–25
Edema, 35
Electrocardiogram (ECG), 169–75
Electroencephalogram (EEG), 91–93
Electromyogram (EMG), 151–53
Electrophoresis, 47–50
Emphysema, 211
Emulsification of fat, 319
Endocrine glands, 325–33
Enzymes
    chemical properties of, 53–54
    in digestive tract, 300
    in plasma, 54–58
Epinephrine, 162
Epithelial tissue, 11–12
Equivalent weight, 279–80
Erythroblastosis fetalis, 357
Erythropoietin, 241
Estradiol, 336
Estrus cycle, 345
Excitatory postsynaptic potential (EPSP), 91
Exercise
    effect on cardiovascular system, 199–201
    effect on ECG, 177–78
    effect on respiration, 225–26
Expiratory reserve volume, 204, 208

Extrinsic eye muscles, 116–17
Eyes, structure and function, 113–20

Fat, 33
Fatigue, muscle, 147
Feedback, negative, 21–22
Fibrillation, 172
Forced expiratory volume (FEV), 211–14
Fovea centralis, 117
Functional groups, 34
Functional residual capacity, 204

Gallstones, 319
Gamma globulin, 48, 263
Genetics
    gene function, 65–66
    inheritance of traits, 355–58
Glands, development of, 323
Glomerular filtrate, 277
Glomerular filtration rate (GFR), 285
Glomerulonephritis, 292
Glucagon, 327, 328
Glucocorticoids, 337
Gluconeogenesis, 285
Glucose, 31
Glycogen, 31
Glycosuria, 292
Gram, 4

Heart
    automaticity and rhythmicity, 169
    cardiac cycle, 187
    conduction system, 169–70
    effect of drugs on, 161–63
    and heart sounds, 187–89
    histology, 14
    pathological conditions, 170–73
Hematocrit, 244
Hemoglobin
    absorption spectrum of, 249–51
    measurement of, 244–45
    and oxygen transport, 241
Hemophilia, 272
Hemostasis, 271
Homeostasis, 21–22
Hormones, 323
Human chorionic gonadotrophin (hCG), 351
Hydrocortisone (cortisol), 337
Hyperkalemia, 162
Hyperopia, 114
Hyperpnea, 226
Hypertension, 195
Hyperventilation and hypoventilation, 232
Hypoglycemia, 341
Hypothalamus
    control of pituitary, 330
    role in osmoregulation, 279

Immune system, 255–56
Immunoassay, 351
Immunological competence, 356
Inborn errors of metabolism, 66
Inflammation, 255
Inhibitory postsynaptic potential (IPSP), 91
Inspiratory capacity, 204, 208
Insulin, 341–42
Intercalated discs, 14

Interstitial cell stimulating hormone (ICSH), 336
Intestine, 304–5
Inulin clearance rate, 286
Inverted image
    in microscope, 2
    on retina, 114
Ischemia, myocardial, 178
Islets of Langerhans, 307, 327–28

Jaundice
    and bilirubinuria, 242, 293
    due to gallstones, 319

Ketone bodies, 292
Kidneys, functions of, 277
Kleinfelter's syndrome, 325
Kluver-Bucy syndrome, 120
Knee-jerk reflex, 97–98

Law of specific nerve energies, 81
Leukocytes, 255–57
Leukocytosis and leukopenia, 257
Lipids, 33
Liver, 306, 308
Lungs
    pulmonary disorders, 211
    pulmonary function testing, 204–15
    role of, in gas exchange, 225

Macula lutea, 117
Maltose, 31
Maximum breathing capacity, 211–15
Mean corpuscular volume and hemoglobin
        concentration, 246
Meiosis, 355
Membrane potential, 82–87
Menstrual cycle, 345
Metabolic pathways, 65
Metabolic rate, 225
Metabolism, 65
Methemoglobin, 245
Metric system, 4–5
Micelles, 319
Microscope, 1–3
Milliliter, 4
Mineralocorticoids
    chemical structure of, 336
    secretion by adrenal cortex, 328
Mole, 74
Monomers and polymers, 29
Monosaccharides, 31
Motor cortex, 104
Muscle, skeletal
    fatigue, 147
    graded contraction, 147
    histology, 13–14
    mechanism of contraction, 137–38
    tetanus, 147
Muscle spindles, 97–98
Muscular dystrophy, 148
Myasthenia gravis, 143
Myopia, 114

Nephron, 277–78
Nerve
    impulses, 82–87
    recordings from, 85–86
Nervous system, 81
Neural integration, 91
Neuron, 82–83
Nicotine, 163
Nystagmus, 116–17, 129

Ophthalmoscope, 117–18
Organ of Corti, 123–24
Osmolality, 74
Osmoreceptors, 79
Osmosis, 72–73
Osteocytes, 13
Ovary, 325–26
Oxygen debt, 226
Oxygen transport, 241

Pacemaker of the heart, 169
Pancreas, 307
Papilledema, 118
Pap smear, 347
Para-aminohippuric acid (PAH), 286
Parasympathomimetic drugs, 162
Passive transport, 71
Pepsin, 315
Peptic ulcers, 315
Peptide bond, 34
Percent saturation of hemoglobin, 249
Percent transmittance, 30
Peristalsis, 299
Permeability of cell membrane, 71–72
Phenotype, 65
Phenylketonuria (PKU), 66
Pheochromocytoma, 325
Phonocardiogram, 188
Phospholipids, 33
Physical fitness, 199–200
Physiograph, 139–41
Pilocarpine, 162
Pithing of frog, 141–42
Pituitary gland, 330–32
Placenta, 351
Plasma
    alkaline phosphatase assay, 54–57
    cholesterol concentration, 33–34
    colloid osmotic pressure, 35
    glucose concentration, 31–33
    protein concentration, 34–35
    transaminase activity, 57–59
    urea concentration, 285–87
Plasma cells, 256
Platelets, 271
Polar and nonpolar solvents, 72
Polysaccharides, 31
Portal vein, 306
Potassium, effect on the heart, 162
Potential difference, 82
Pregnancy test, 351–52
Premature ventricular contraction (PVC), 173
Presbyopia, 115
Primary tissues, 11
Progesterone, 336
Protein synthesis, 66
Proteinuria, 292
Pupillary reflex, 117
Purkinje fibers, 169

Red blood cell count, 242–44
Referred pain, 109–10
Reflex arc, 97–100
Refraction of light, 113–15
Refractory period, 84
Releasing hormones, 330
Renal clearance rate, 285–86
Renal plasma threshold, 292
Renin-angiotensin system, 329, 336
Residual volume, 204
Reticuloendothelial system, 242
Retina, 118–19
Retinal disparity, 116
$R_f$ in thin-layer chromatography, 44

Rheumatoid factor, 267–68
Rh factor, 356–57
Rhodopsin, 119
Ribonucleic acid (RNA), 66

Salivary amylase (ptyalin), 311–12
Sarcomere, 137–38
Secretin, 301
Sensory adaptation, 105–6
Sensory cortex, 104
Serum, 48
Sex-linked traits, 358
Sickle-cell anemia, 357–58
Sinoatrial (S-A) node, 169
Sodium-potassium pump, 82
Sound localization, 125
Sounds of Korotkoff, 194–95
Specific gravity of urine, 280
Spirometry, 204–5
Standard curve, 30
Steatorrhea, 319
Steroids, 33, 335–37
Stomach, 302–4
Strabismus, 120
Stretch reflexes, 97–99
Sucrose, 31
Summation of muscle twitches, 147
Sympathomimetic drugs, 162
Synapse, 91

Tachycardia, 173
Target organs, 323
Taste, 133–34
Tay-Sach's disease, 66
Testes, 326–27
Testosterone, 335
Tetanus, 147
Threshold stimulus, 86, 142
Thyroid, 329
Tidal volume, 204
Tonicity, 73–75
Total minute volume, 225
Triglycerides, 33
Trypsin, 300
Two-point touch threshold, 104

Units of activity of enzymes, 54
Urea, 285–87
Urine
    appearance, 291
    chemical examination, 292–93
    sediment, 293–94

Vaginal smear, 345–47
Ventilation
    measurements, 204–5
    regulation of, 225–26
Vertigo, 129
Vestibular apparatus, 129–30
Villi and microvilli, 304
Visual acuity, 113
Vital capacity, 204, 208
Vitamins
    as cofactors for enzymes, 54
    fat soluble, 319
    vitamin A and vision, 119
    vitamin K and clotting, 272

White blood cell count
    differential, 255–57
    total, 256

Young-Helmholtz theory, 119

Zwitterion, 47